D1107263

THE A. S. W. ROSENBA

IN BIBLIOGI

THE A. S. W. ROSENBACH FELLOWSHIP
IN BIBLIOGRAPHY

PUBLICATIONS

The Rosenbach Fellowship in Bibliography

PROPOSALS RELATING TO THE EDUCATION OF YOUTH
IN PENNSYLVANIA
by Benjamin Franklin

EX LIBRIS CARISSIMIS
by Christopher Morley

AN AMERICAN BOOKSHELF, 1755
by Lawrence C. Wroth

THE SCRIPT OF JONATHAN SWIFT AND OTHER ESSAYS
by Shane Leslie

BIBLIOGRAPHY AND PSEUDO-BIBLIOGRAPHY
by A. Edward Newton

THREE AMERICANISTS
by Randolph G. Adams

PRINTING IN THE FIFTEENTH CENTURY
by George Parker Winship

THE CAMBRIDGE PRESS, 1638-1692
by George Parker Winship

STANDARDS OF BIBLIOGRAPHICAL DESCRIPTION
by Curt F. Buhler, James G. McManaway, and
Lawrence C. Wroth

THE VOICE OF THE OLD FRONTIER
by R. W. G. Vail

THE GREAT MEDICAL BIBLIOGRAPHERS
by John F. Fulton

BARTOLOMÉ DE LAS CASAS
by Lewis Hanke

PAPERMAKING IN PIONEER AMERICA
by Dard Hunter

THE APPRECIATION OF ANCIENT AND MEDIEVAL SCIENCE
DURING THE RENAISSANCE (1450-1600)
by George Sarton

THE APPRECIATION OF

ANCIENT AND MEDIEVAL SCIENCE DURING THE RENAISSANCE

(1450-1600)

By

GEORGE SARTON

Rosenbach Fellow in Bibliography

1953

Philadelphia

UNIVERSITY OF PENNSYLVANIA PRESS

This book is dedicated to the memory of Aldo Mieli, Founder in 1929 and First Permanent Secretary of the International Academy of the History of Science,

and to the memory of his successor, Petre Sergescu, the Second Permanent Secretary.

Aldo Mieli was born in Livorno, Italy, in 1879, and died at Florida, Buenos Aires, in 1950.* Petre Sergescu was born in Turnu-Severin, Romania, in 1893, and died in Paris, in 1954.

---

* For Mieli, see *Isis 41*, 57; for Sergescu, see *Isis 46*, 53; for the Academy, see *Horus*, 253.

PREFACE

THIS BOOK CONTAINS THE WRITTEN TEXT CORRESPONDING TO MY spoken lectures delivered, the first three as a Rosenbach Fellow, in Houston Hall at the University of Pennsylvania, on January 16, 23, 30, 1953, and the fourth at the American Philosophical Society in Philadelphia on March 24. It is much longer than the spoken lectures, because the author must explain many details and give references which the reader needs but which the listener could not possibly catch on the wing. The difference between a spoken lecture and a written one is as great as that obtaining between a fresco to be seen by a crowd from a distance and a miniature the beauty of which cannot be appreciated except when one is standing very close to it.

The first three lectures were delivered to relatively large audiences; the book is published to satisfy the needs of individual scholars, one at a time.

The invitation extended to me by the University of Pennsylvania to be Rosenbach Fellow in.1952-53 was welcomed, because it gave me a new opportunity to explain my views on the history of science before a select and thoughtful group of scholars. It has been argued by old-fashioned humanists that the history of science is of less interest than other kinds of history, because the main values of life are in the fields of art, philosophy, literature, not in the fields of science and technology. This misunderstanding is caused by the following facts. Firstly, the teachers of science have to deal each of them with such enormous amounts of knowledge that they have no time to explain its historical development. Now, if one neglects the humanities of a field, then *ipso facto* that field lacks humanity. Secondly, the history of any subject is interesting in proportion to our knowledge of it. If you do not care for science and do not bother to know it, then obviously the history of science cannot be of any concern to you. The history of music interests me deeply, because I love music, but would have no appeal for a deaf man.

Too many people make a distinction between science and technology on the left and the humanities on the right. That distinction is false. The true distinction is not vertical but horizontal, grammar versus the humanities.[1] Whatever we study, whether it be Greek, music, or chemistry, we must begin with grammar or its equivalent. As long as one has to learn the grammar, one can hardly speak of humanities. Unfortunately, our scientific education halts but too often at the grammatical (or technical) stage; it stops at the very level where it would become supremely interesting.

I said that if you do not love and know science, one cannot expect you to be interested in its history; on the other hand, the teaching of the humanities of science would create the love of science as well as a deeper understanding of it. Too many of our scientists (even the most distinguished ones) are technicians and nothing more. Our aim is to humanize science and the best way of doing that is to tell and discuss the history of science. If we succeed, men of science will cease to be mere technicians, and will become educated men.

My own interest in the history of science goes back to my student days in Ghent, before 1911, but it was kindled to a greater heat a few years later (in 1916) by the study of the MSS of Leonardo da Vinci. When I realized that Leonardo's knowledge was very largely of medieval origin, I decided to make a full survey of science from Homer's time to 1900. The task was enormously larger than I had imagined and I was finally obliged to stop my *Introduction,* not at 1900 but at 1400, being five centuries behind schedule[2] and half a century short of Leonardo's own time. Though my attention during the last thirty years has been devoted chiefly to medieval science, it does not follow that I have ever abandoned the other periods. In particular, much of my energy has always been devoted to the study of ancient times and of the Renaissance.

In the summer of 1952, my interest in the Renaissance was rekindled by attendance at the two congresses held in Paris and in Touraine to celebrate the fifth century of Leonardo's birth. During our delightful peregrinations along the Loire valley, and even more so on our way back across the Vendômois, Ronsard's country, I was obliged to think more and more in terms of the Renaissance. In the first place, I realized more clearly than ever before that if Leonardo is the climax of the Italian Renaissance, he is also the herald of the French one. Instead of approaching him from the past, from the left, as I had done hitherto, I was now readying myself to approach him from the right, from his own immediate future.

At Amboise, where Leonardo was the honored guest of François Premier, and at the little château of Cloux nearby, where he died on May 2, 1519, I determined the purpose and character of these lectures. Life was too short to enable me to describe the Renaissance as fully as I had described the Middle Ages, but I might at least try to deal with one aspect of it: How did the scholars of the Renaissance understand ancient and medieval science and react to it? That is a big question, much bigger than I was aware of at first, and I do not flatter myself that I have given a complete answer. My survey deals chiefly with ancient science, and with medieval science only indirectly, that is, only in so far as the medieval transmission of ancient science is concerned.

The main event separating the period we call Renaissance from the Middle Ages was the invention of printing. That was a double invention, typography for the text and engraving for the images. It was fructified by the genius of many scholars and men of science but also by the zeal and devotion of the printers and publishers. The latter were not simply businessmen, as are their colleagues of today; many were scholars in their own right, and in any case they loved scholarship and science. They were in business, of course, and had to deal with business matters. The setting up of printing presses required capital: the master printers and their apprentices had to be paid; paper and ink had to be bought; the proofreaders, draughtsmen, engravers, bookbinders had to be given their wages; and the books when printed and bound had to be sold. Yet, these early printers remained scholars and friends of scholars: their greed was moderate; they were anxious to sell their books but not at the cost of any compromise; they did not inflate their selling prices by saddling each book with a fraction of enormous overhead expenditures. Their purpose with regard to money was very much like the purpose of any honest scholar. Money was necessary and therefore desirable but only in second place; the main thing was good scholarship. When an honest scholar (not a businessman in disguise) publishes a book, he welcomes its commercial success and the royalties consequent to it, but he would not rewrite a single page for the sake of increasing those royalties.

That was the spirit of the Renaissance printers and they fully deserve to be honored or, at the very least, to be remembered. Therefore, I have taken pains to mention the names of the printers (or publishers) of Renaissance books whenever I knew them. Occasional failures to mention them are sometimes due to my own ignorance, or sometimes to general ignorance, for many books were printed anonymously. In some instances, I have added to the text or to the footnotes miniature biographies of these early printers; lack of space prevented me from doing that more thoroughly, as I would have loved. My selection of the main printers may be somewhat arbitrary, because I did not know all of them well enough. The number of short biographies is sufficient, however, to give the reader some idea of the whole genus.

It may be said that this book was written to the glory of Renaissance scholars and scientists but also to the glory of their faithful collaborators, the printers and publishers.

I am not a bibliographer *stricto sensu,* or to put it otherwise, bibliography for me is a means rather than an end. I am not even a bibliophile in the narrow sense, for I am interested in ideas rather than in books. May the spirit of Dr. Rosenbach forgive me, but I am just as happy with a facsimile edition or with a photostatic copy of a book as with the original.

My bibliographical descriptions are very far from complete; it satisfies me in general to mention the author, title, place, and date. If the book is a Renaissance edition, I try to name the printer. The reader is given some idea of the length of each book, the number of pages being quoted, *grosso modo* (e.g., 310 pp., instead of xxxv+275) ; if the book is leaved, not paginated, the number of leaves is indicated in the same way.

I have almost always seen and handled one edition of each book, preferably the first, but I have seldom seen more than one. When many editions of a single work have been mentioned, there may be errors of omission or commission, though I have taken pains to avoid them. One could hardly expect me to see every edition as if I had been preparing a special monograph on that very work.

Short statements being much clearer than longer ones, I have generally preferred to say that book A was published by Oporinus, Basel,

1571, rather than by Oporinus, in Basel, in 1571. Grammar is not repudiated but made implicit.

It is highly desirable to use standard forms for proper names of places or persons. The place names are always difficult, because one must decide whether to use the local form or the English one. Should we write Milano or Milan, Venezia or Venice? If a Spanish book was printed in Antwerp, shall we call the place Antwerp, Englishwise; Antwerpen, Flemishwise; or Amberes, Spanishwise? Every one of these forms would be justified in that context. During the Renaissance, many places had various common names plus one or more in Latin.

The names of persons introduce so many difficulties that consistency is impossible or, if carried too far, would become unbearable. Many names were Latinized or Hellenized and, however artificial that might have been at the beginning, general acceptance would often establish that usage. When a form is established, it would be pedantic to reject it. We must write now Melanchthon, instead of Schwarzert, and Erasmus instead of Geert Geerts. Sometimes, a particular form did not obtain general acceptance and then what shall we do? There is no rule, or each rule has so many exceptions that one cannot follow it too closely without pedantry.

Some scholars would claim that the name used on the title page of a book is the correct name, but the same author might spell his own name in different ways in different books. For example, consider the Italian mathematician, Prosdocimo de' Beldomandi (d. 1428). He is always called Beldomandi, but in his *Algorismi tractatus* (1483) his name is spelled Beldamandi and, therefore, D. E. Smith felt authorized to call him Beldamandi. The form Beldomandi is justified by all other documents and is therefore preferable.[3]

The confusion is increased by the fact that when a name was Latinized on a title page, it had to be modified to satisfy Latin usage or euphony, and the Latin modification was eventually introduced into the vernacular. For example, the name of the Englishman, Cuthbert Tunstall, was Latinized Tonstallius to preserve the original pronunciation of the first vowel (if written Tunstallius, the two *u*'s would have been pronounced in the same way as the *u* in *use*), and then some scholars argued that the original English form was Tonstall! In the Latin forms, it was often found necessary to duplicate consonants in order to keep preceding vowels short—e.g., Ruellius for Ruel, Bellonius for Belon, Snellius for Snel, Hamellius for Hamel—and then some scholars believed wrongly that the original names were Ruelle, Bellon, Snell, Hamelle. Or a consonant was changed, as in Vernerius for Werner.

A little knowledge is often a dangerous thing. I have shown the danger of accepting blindly the information given in printed books. One might claim, for example, that the date printed on the title page or the colophon of a book is its correct date of publication; yet, I have proved that many incunabula bear wrong dates, and similar errors have occurred ever since.[4] One must always check on the original documents, yet remember that the original documents may be erroneous.

In general, Christian names are given in full, because the same Christian name may be represented by different initials. If you write Hieronymus, Geronimo, or Jerome, there is no confusion; while the initials H, G, J might be enigmatic.[5] Is the same person meant or not? In some languages, chiefly in Italian, Christian names may be amalgamated, say, Guidobaldo for Guido Ubaldo, Marcantonio for Marco Antonio, Giambattista for Giovanni Battista, Pierandrea for Pietro Andrea. I have tried to avoid the amalgamation for the sake of the index, wherein the amalgamated form would be represented by a single letter instead of two, G. instead of G. U., M. instead of M. A., etc., and that might be deceptive.

In general, specific names should be preferred to more common names. Therefore, I write Charlemagne, Charles Quint, Regiomontanus, Tabernaemontanus, Tragus instead of Charles the Great, Charles the Fifth, Müller, Dietrich, or Bock. The names of the first group are unambiguous, while those of the second group require explanations.

The Latin name is not only the best-known name in many cases, but it is easier to classify alphabetically. For example, Faber instead of Lefèvre, or le Febvre, Clusius instead of de l'Ecluse (under d, l, or e?), Lobelius instead of de L'Obel (under d, l, or o?), Dalecampius instead of Dalechamps or d'Aléchamps, Ramus instead of de la Ramée. Everybody knew Ramus, while Pierre de la Ramée was hardly known under that name even to his students or his neighbors. In some cases, the Latin vernacular forms are so close that it is hardly possible to choose between them (Viète, Vieta).

The names of the printers or publishers are spelled differently in different books: e.g., Italian, Giunti, Giunta; Spanish, Junta; Venetian, Zonta; Latin, apud Juntas (I have tried to use always the name Juntae and the adjective Juntine). I beseech the reader's patience and tolerance. In spite of good will and carefulness, the handling of so many inconsistent documents may have occasionally tripped me up.

The transcription of Greek names into the Roman alphabet is a perennial cause of trouble. My method is as follows. The diphthongs are written as in Greek with the same vowels (e.g., *ai*, not *ae; ei*, not *i; oi*, not *oe*), except *ou* which is written *u* to conform with English pronunciation (by the way, the Greek *ou* is not a real diphthong but a single vowel sound). *Upsilon* is represented by *y;* the diphthong *eu* is left as it is except when followed by another vowel, when the *u* is written *v* (evergetēs, evornis, evydros). The *omicron* is always replaced by an *o*, and hence Greek names are not Latinized but preserve their Greek look and sound. There is really no reason for giving a Latin ending to a Greek name when one is writing not in Latin but in English. Hence, we write Epicuros not Epicurus (the two *u*'s of the Latin word represent different Greek vowels). For more details, see my *History of science,* p. xvii.

Special thanks are owed and warmly given to Dr. Charles Wendell David, Director of Libraries, University of Pennsylvania, to the University of Pennsylvania Press, to the American Philosophical Society, and to its Executive Officer, Dr. Luther Pfahler Eisenhart. Not only did the American Philosophical Society award me a grant in aid, but it kindly permitted me to use my address as an Epilogue to this book.

GEORGE SARTON

April 26, 1953

Contents

ABOUT THE NOTES

The notes will be found on pages 182-221. In the note section, at the upper right-hand corner of each recto page and the upper left-hand corner of each verso page, will be found boldface numbers indicating the pages of the text to which the notes on these two pages refer.

INTRODUCTION

A T THE BEGINNING OF THESE LECTURES, I MUST INVITE YOU TO PAY
tribute with me to the memory of Dr. Abraham S. Wolf Rosenbach
(1876-1952), who established this foundation. Many of you knew him
better than I did, and the Republic of Letters is familiar with him because of his many learned publications, the kind services which he rendered to private and public collectors, and the beautiful *Festschrift* which
was dedicated to him at the time of his seventieth birthday.[1] The Rosenbach Fellowship was founded by him in 1929, and I consider it a great
honor and privilege to have obtained it. I hope that my lectures will
justify the confidence which was thus placed in me, in spite of the fact
that I am not a bibliographer in the technical sense and have never
practised the gentle art of describing ancient books as Dr. Rosenbach
and his peers would like it.

Let me explain briefly what I shall try to do: to give you a picture
of one of the fundamental aspects of scientific research during the Renaissance. The term Renaissance is, unfortunately, a vague one, because that
period, however you may define it (and there are various conflicting defi-
nitions), did not begin and end at the same time in different countries.
Hence, the term should never be used without qualification, such as the
Medical Renaissance in France, or the Mathematical Renaissance in
Northern Italy. The best qualification, however, and the simplest, is the
use of dates, as I am doing in the title of these lectures: "The Renaissance
(1450-1600)."

That is unambiguous. It is like our definition of incunabula (books
printed before 1501); we know very well that many books printed
in 1501 and later are as ancient looking as the incunabula, if not more

1

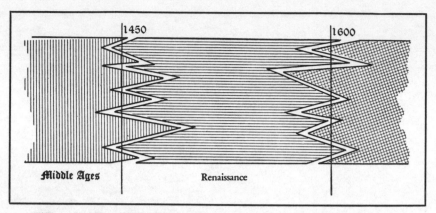

Figure 1. Historical periods, however you may define them, never begin or end abruptly. The dates 1450 and 1600, which we selected arbitrarily, are only averages. The periods dovetail as indicated in this figure.

so, yet it is easier to define them as we do. The definition is arbitrary but far more convenient than any other could be.

The dates which I have chosen can be justified as follows: 1450 marks roughly the beginning of printing (a new age), and I shall deal with printed books rather than with MSS;[2] 1600 is more arbitrary, but it is convenient to end with a century. Thus, our field may be defined as the second half of the fifteenth century and the whole of the sixteenth. That is easy.

One might prefer other limits, however. Let me mention two possibilities. The year 1616, death year of Shakespeare and Cervantes. The year 1632 when Galileo published his dialogue on the two systems of the world, a book which defended the new astronomy yet was chock-full of Renaissance conceits. Each of these limits could be justified; yet, I prefer 1600 for the sake of ease and simplicity. I do not promise, however, to respect it always; on the contrary, I shall transgress whenever this will seem wise or attractive.

The Renaissance, however you may define it, was a rebirth in two very different ways: it was a revival of Antiquity, that was one way; but it was also in some cases a discovery of something more completely new, or which seemed to be so. Novelty we should remember is always relative. There is no absolute novelty, there is no complete imitation. Every novelty has ancient roots, and it is hardly possible to imitate anything without improving or worsening it. For good or evil, the imitator is always somewhat of a deviator and creator. Bearing these restrictions in mind, we may divide the Renaissance activities into two groups: the Imitative and the Nonimitative, the first group including the work of architects like Andrea Palladio who restore the ancient orders, of sculptors who imitate classical models, of scholars who discover and edit the old books written in Greek

2

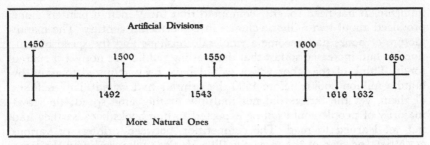

Figure 2. Instead of our arbitrary limits for the Renaissance, 1450 and 1600, one might choose various others, e.g., 1492, discovery of the New World; 1543, publication date of the main works of Vesalius and Copernicus; 1616, death year of Shakespeare and Cervantes; 1632, publication date of Galileo's *Dialogo dei due massimi sistemi del mondo, tolemaico e copernico.*

or in classical Latin. Generally speaking, the men of science of the first group were archaeologists and philologists, who read and wrote Latin with ease and who might have had some knowledge of Greek; those men were truly fashionable, they were the arbiters of taste and culture. The men of the second group were generally innocent of Latin, not to mention Greek; their rivals called them illiterate and barbarian; they were rebels; yet, some of them had genius, and whatever they managed to create was more original than the creations of their learned contemporaries.

In these lectures devoted to the survival or revival of ancient authors we shall deal naturally with the first group—those whom I called the Imitators. That is all right, but we should always remember that their ignorant contemporaries, the Rebels, were doing work which, from the point of view of the historian of science, was equally important, and sometimes far more so. Think of men like Leonardo da Vinci, Paracelsus, Palissy, and Paré.

For the Renaissance imitators the distinction between science and the humanities, which is now in danger of becoming an unbridgeable abyss, hardly existed. Their scientific interests were dovetailed with philosophical ones, and it was an essential part of their reaction against the Middle Ages that they wanted to write as well as possible. The great majority of them in the West wrote Latin, and their ambition was to write it, not like Bacon or St. Thomas, but like Cicero or at least like Petrarca.

Our taking 1450 as the beginning of our investigation is natural enough, because we are interested primarily in the printed texts and printing began about the middle of the fifteenth century. Its early development was slow, but it was gradually accelerated (as the years went by, there were more and more printers and each of them issued more copies of more books) and by the end of the century the number of printed books, as compared with the number of available MSS, was already immense. It has been roughly computed that the Venetian printers alone produced about two million volumes in the fifteenth century. The manufacture of books had become a wholesale business and the speed of production had increased so fast that the reading public was not yet prepared for it. Think of the labor which would have been required to write by hand a million books; before 1500 the printers had issued many millions of them, yet the buyers did not multiply at the same speed; the great majority of people could not be expected to buy books because they had not yet learned to read. The competition between printers of various countries (or even of the same city, like Venice) who reprinted the same books was so intense that they glutted the market and that their own shelves were overcrowded (I have been told that the same thing happens sometimes to the publishers of our own day).

The commercial situation was made more difficult because the printed-book trade did not immediately displace the MS trade, but was simply added to it. MSS continued to be used (in the same way that printed books were used) throughout the sixteenth century and even somewhat later.[3] The average library, whether public or private, contained MSS as well as printed books—e.g., a doctor might have one treatise of Aristotle in printed form and another in MS form. Gradually the number of MSS diminished and the number of printed books increased.[4] Middle-aged people of today have no trouble in understanding that situation, because they experienced a similar one concerning the disks of recorded music. At the beginning, musicians tended to despise them (and not without reason, for the recordings were very unsatisfactory) and to kick them out of their collections; at the present time, it is probable that the library of the average musician contains as many records as sheets of printed music, and perhaps more.

The main point is that the Renaissance editions of ancient scientific treatises were never produced for the sake of curiosity or disinterested scholarship (as happens today), but for practical use. The discovery of a new text was hailed with admiration and with joy, not as we hail today the resurrection of an Egyptian or Babylonian treatise, but rather as if that text contained new knowledge of immediate value. The best of ancient science had been so good and the average of medieval science so poor that those expectations were sometimes fulfilled. The discovery of a new text was not simply of archaeological importance; it was (or might be, at least) a positive addition to the workable knowledge of contemporary men of science or physicians.

Thus, hunting for medical MSS was a form of medical research. Humanists and scientists were often walking along the same trails. We shall witness many examples of their emulation.

Their collaboration was made easy because, instead of repelling one another as they do today, they were the subjects of mutual attractions and their trajectories tended to converge. The scientific editors were so sure of the intrinsic value of the ancient texts that their concern was to edit them as exactly as possible from the philological point of view;[5] with few exceptions, such as Leoniceno's with regard to Pliny,[6] they did not bother about the *realia;* they devoted their energy to the criticism of the words rather than of the facts, of the form rather than of the contents.

This illustrates the relative weakness of the typical Renaissance approach to science proper. It was a literary and wordy approach instead of being experimental and matter of fact. It took scholars an astonishingly long time to discover that science could not be investigated profitably in any book except the great Book of Nature. The few who realized this were more likely to be rebels like Bernard Palissy (*c.*1510-89) and the curious Danish humanist, Peder Sörensen (*c.*1541-1602). It is hardly necessary to introduce to our readers the former of these, the French potter and geologist, but Sörensen may be unknown to them even under his literary Latin name, Petrus Severinus. He was a physician of the Danish kings for thirty years and a teacher of Latin poetry at the University of Copenhagen; he had drunk deep the Paracelsian effusions and been intoxicated by them (much to the disgust of Francis Bacon). Severinus was not a rebel like Palissy, Paré, and others, for he was a very good Latin scholar; the other humanists would have called him, not a rebel, but a betrayer. At any rate, his great book *Idea medicinae philosophicae* (Basel, 1571) includes such extraordinary utterances as this one:

> Go, my sons, sell your lands, your houses, your garments and your jewelry; burn up your books. On the other hand, buy yourselves stout shoes, get away to the mountains, search the valleys, the deserts, the shores of the sea, and the deepest recesses of the earth; mark well the distinctions between animals, the differences of plants, the various kinds of minerals, the properties and mode of origin of everything that exists. Be not ashamed to learn by heart the astronomy and terrestrial philosophy of the peasantry. Lastly, purchase coal, build furnaces, watch and experiment without wearying. In this way and no other, you will arrive at a knowledge of things and of their properties.[7]

We may remark in passing that Paracelsism, in spite of much irrationality and craziness, was often a ferment of rebellion and freedom, a catalyzer of true research in the midst of academic complacency. The Paracelsists were in the West somewhat like the Taoists in China—crazy liberators from inertia and from stupid conformity. A history of Paracelsism is long overdue; it is badly needed for the understanding of medicine, chemistry, and philosophy not only in the late Renaissance but also throughout the seventeenth and eighteenth centuries.[8]

The survey which I am now preparing for you is essentially different from the one to which I have devoted twenty-five years of my life. In my *Introduction,* I tried to determine as carefully as possible the achievements of each half-century; but those achievements were, many of them, of the "imitative" kind—editions or translation of earlier writings, commentaries upon them, supercommentaries, summaries, elaborations, plagiarisms, and so forth. If one examines the contents of vol. 3, dealing with the fourteenth century, one finds that a great part of it is devoted to personalities who died before 1300, some of them many centuries older. The greatest physicians of the fourteenth century were Hippocrates, Galen, and Avicenna; it is they who were quoted most often and whose influence was predominant. These three men, one might say, were very much alive in the fourteenth century. And so it always was. The dominant voice is not always the voice of living men—of men whose flesh is alive— it is very often a voice from beyond the grave. If one were to write a full biography of Hippocrates, one would have to entitle it *The life of Hippocrates from his own time until now*. He is still alive today (see Appendix).

Our problem is thus to consider more closely Renaissance awareness and knowledge of the old scientific classics as revealed by the incunabula and the sixteenth-century books. We must never forget, however, that this was only a part of the scientific literature, and not the most pregnant. Take medicine, for example. Renaissance knowledge was represented by all the books dealing directly or indirectly with Hippocrates, Soranos, Galen, etc. It was represented also by other books on anatomy, surgery, gynecology, obstetrics which were derived from experience or from unwritten tradition. The new medicine, which was gradually developed in the seventeenth century and later, emerged out of the classical learning (Greco-Latin-Arabic) after a long medieval incubation; it was the old learning fertilized and rejuvenated by folkloric ideas and gradually enriched by clinical experience. The great initiatives (e.g., in the proper use of new drugs) were often of folkloric origin, but the new ideas had to be inserted in the old tradition in order to obtain their full value. New science is never entirely new; it is always somewhat like a graft upon an old stem.

Instead of trying to tell the complete story, which would be very long, repetitive, and tedious, my three lectures will investigate three parts of the immense subject—medicine, natural history, and mathematics. I begin with medicine, because it is the easiest to explain and the medical aspect is one that is natural to all men. Only a few of us are physicians, but we are all patients and we should try to be good patients. This does not mean simply that we should obey the doctor and be courageous and coöperative in times of crisis; it means also that we should try to appreciate and understand medical achievements.

There is no better road to such understanding than the study of medical history. Let us interrogate Renaissance physicians. How well did they know and use their scientific inheritance?

LECTURE 1

MEDICINE

1. HIPPOCRATES OF COS (V B.C.)

A COMPLETE STUDY OF THE HIPPOCRATIC TRADITION WOULD INCLUDE each and every one of the books of the Hippocratic canon, each of them taken separately and in its various combinations with others.[9] Such a study would take enormous time and fill a whole volume. In this essay, we shall discuss only the Hippocratic works as a whole, the various "opera" published during our period, and for the sake of brevity we must disregard the fact that the contents of the opera did not always remain the same. The editors of each opera might add items to previous collections or omit others.

The incunabula oblige us, however, to say a few words about special books. The first Hippocratic items to be printed were not by any means the most significant ones and many of them were apocryphal; there are altogether twenty-three Hippocratic or pseudo-Hippocratic titles among the incunabula, but many of them were simply attached to other works such as the *Liber Almansoris* of Rhazes (Milano, 1481, etc.) or included in the *Articella* (Padua, 1476, etc.).[10] All these editions were in Latin, none in Greek, and it is probable that most of them were derived from Arabic translations. The most important of the incunabula items are the *Aphorismi* (1476 ff.), *De natura hominis* (1481 ff.), *De insomniis,* i.e., *Regimen IV* (1481 f.), *De aere et aqua et regionibus* (1481 f.), the *Prognostica* (1476 f.), *De regimine acutorum morborum* (1476 f.). (The date 1476 refers to the first edition of the Articella.) The only part of *Epidemics* printed early was Book VI (one of the least satisfactory); it was included in the *Articella,* but only in the second and following editions (1481 to 1500).

7

In short, the fifteenth-century readers who had to depend only on printed texts (but such readers, we repeat, must have been the exception until the very end of the century) could not have had a very good knowledge of the Father of Medicine.

The first "complete" edition (of course, it was neither complete nor free from irrelevant items; it contained too little and too much) was the Latin translation by Fabio Calvi of Ravenna, dedicated to Clement VII (pope, 1523-34), published by Fr. Minutius in Rome, 1525. This Latin translation anticipated the Greek princeps; we may say that, because it was made on the basis of the Greek text and did not represent the Arabic tradition as did the incunabula, or, at any rate, most of them. According to its elaborate title, it includes eighty works of Hippocrates.

This (Marco) Fabio Calvi was a singular individual, whom it is worth while to get better acquainted with. In order to do that, we must consider one of the greatest artistic events of the Renaissance, the rebuilding of St. Peter's in Rome. This had been begun under Nicholas V in 1450; the building was intrusted to various architects the most famous being Bramante, Raphael, and Michelangelo; it was many times interrupted and almost abandoned but always restarted by half a dozen popes: Paul II, Julius II, Leon X, Pius V, Clement VIII, Paul V. It was completed under the last-named in 1614. Completed, that is, as much as such an immense building can ever be completed. We now know how much was gradually added by Bernini (1598-1680), but this takes us definitely out of the Renaissance into the Baroque Age.

There were endless disputes between the architects, the followers of each, the papal treasurers, and other familiars. Raphael wanted to understand the ancient arrangement of the Neronian gardens and circus upon the site of which the first basilica had been built by Constantine the Great (in 326) and that made necessary the study of Vitruvius. His first friend and adviser, Fra Giocondo, had died in 1515. Who could help him now?

He found an antiquary named Fabius Calvo, who lived the life of a hermit and fed on herbs and lettuces in a den described as little larger or more comfortable than the kennel of Diogenes. He took Calvo into his palace in the Borgo, and kept him there in a state of ease, "that he might profit by his advice and experience." Calvo had already translated the works of Hippocrates. He now turned Vitruvius into Italian, and Raphael mastered the text with care and minuteness, so that he was soon able to lecture on it, and censure or defend the rules of the ancients with facility and grace.

This passage is quoted from Crowe and Cavalcaselle's life of Raphael.[11] It refers to the period 1515-20, after Fra Giocondo's death and before Raphael's own; therefore, I wonder whether the authors are right in saying that Calvi had already completed the gigantic work which was printed in 1525. Be that as it may, there is no doubt that its publication by Franciscus Minutius in that year was a noteworthy event, the beginning of a new era in the history of Hippocratic scholarship.

That is true in spite of the fact that Calvi's work was not of the best kind. He had used Greek MSS, and that was very praiseworthy; but he lacked thoroughness and when he failed to understand the text, he smoothed out the difficulties in his translation; in many cases the translation is barely intelligible; where it is intelligible, it may be deceptive. We should not judge him too severely, however. Editors are often too pleased with what they fancy to be their superiority over their predecessors and one cannot help wondering whether they would have been able to do the work of these at the beginning. It is a good deal easier to revise an edition or translation than to make a new one. Let us rather say Glory to the pioneers[12] and be very thankful to them.

As soon as the Roman edition fell into the hands of rival printers and was scanned by jealous scholars, they found it necessary to correct it and to improve it. Within a year, a new edition was published by Andreas Cratander in Basel (1526), Calvus' translations being corrected (or replaced by other translations) by William Cop, Nicholas Leoniceno, and Andreas Brentius.[13] Think of the size of that work and the shortness of the interval! The mainspring of that improved edition was William Cop of Basel, who had studied in Germany and in Paris, where he communed with Lascaris and Erasmus; he obtained his M.D. in 1495 and became archiater to Louis XII (king of France, 1498-1515) ; and later to François I. He devoted a good part of his life to the translation of Greek medical writings into Latin, first printed in the period 1510-28; he died on 2 December 1532.[14] Cop was one of the many doctors of his time, well acquainted with Arabic medicine, but anxious to recover the Greek sources and devoting all his strength to that great purpose.

We may assume that the Latin *Opera omnia* of 1526, because of the collaboration of four scholars, was definitely superior to the edition of the preceding year, which was the work of but one of them. It was very difficult, if not impossible, for the average doctor, however learned he might be, to appreciate the fidelity of any Latin translation, because he had no easy access to the Greek text. Even if he had a Greek MS, that MS would not be likely to contain more than one treatise or at best a few. That situation was remedied in the same year, 1526, by the appearance of the Greek princeps.

We owe this to the learned printers, the Aldine firm of Venice. The *Omnia opera Hippocratis* were published by them—*in aedibus Aldi et Andreae Asulani soceri,*[15] in May 1526 (233 fol.). It contains a short preface by Andreas' son Franciscus Asulanus,[16] wherein he reproaches Calvi for some of his errors. He remarks that Calvi had used MSS in some cases where printed editions were already available, but were those printed editions more trustworthy than the MSS? Not necessarily.[17] One could not even suggest that the printed text would be easier to handle than the MS, because the early printers reproduced the MSS very closely, if not critically. The Aldine edition of 1526 has the same practical defects: it is printed in a solid block without paragraphs and without notes. It is almost as difficult to read as the MSS themselves and is unreadable without some paleographic training, if only for the interpretation of ligatures and abbreviations.[18] Such as it is, the princeps is still valuable, because it was based partly on MSS which were not available to later editors.

There was a healthy emulation between the Venetian printers of classical texts and the Basel ones. Thus, we are not surprised that the Aldine edition of the Greek text was followed twelve years later by new editions, based on other MSS, published by the house of Froben.[19] The editor, Janus Cornarius, paid tribute to the scientific zeal of his scholarly employers, Jerome Froben and Nicolas Episcopius, who had spared no expense and had caused him to collate three very ancient MSS and to make full use of the Galenic commentaries. Cornarius claimed in his preface to have corrected or reëstablished more than four thousand passages which had been omitted or adulterated in the previous edition; whenever he was in doubt, he followed the reading accepted by Galen. This was a good method, for Galen was so deeply imbued with the old medical tradition that he was more likely to understand an ancient text correctly than a man who appeared fourteen centuries later.

Who was this Janus Cornarius? He was born in Zwickau, Saxony, in 1500; his original name was Johann Hagenblut, a name which could not be used any longer without obscurity and pedantry. His career is so typical that it is worth while to describe it. He was trained (or trained himself) largely as a Hellenist, and by 1521 was professor of philology in Wittenberg. We do not know when he began the study of medicine; his interest in Hippocrates was probably aroused and certainly excited by the Aldine edition of 1526. He traveled considerably in England, Holland, France and spent a year with Erasmus in Basel. It is said that it was Erasmus who encouraged him to undertake a new Hippocratic edition. Yet, he continued his medical practice, was Physicus in Nordhausen, then Stadtphysicus in Frankfurt a.M.[20] For five years (1542-46) he was professor of medicine in Zwickau; then he spent eleven in his native city and finally accepted a call from the University of Jena. His professorship there was interrupted by his sudden death on 16 March 1558. He wrote three medical treatises[21] and edited many Greek medical writings, but his fame is largely based on his edition of Hippocrates (Basel: Froben, 1538). Eight years later, the same printer published his Latin translation of the Hippocratic corpus (folio, 693 pp.; Basel, 1546); that translation was often reprinted.

To complete the account of Renaissance effort for the resurrection of the Hippocratic corpus, I must still introduce two very distinguished scholars, the Italian Geronimo Mercuriali (1530-1606) and the Lorrain Anuce Foes (1528-95), who were almost perfect contemporaries. To the first we owe the first Greco-Latin edition, a large Juntine folio (Venice, 1588)[22] including much additional material (such as ancient glossaries), and a discussion of the writings (*Censura operum Hippocratis*) which were edited in a new order and divided into four classes of diminishing authenticity.[23] Mercuriali introduced new variants derived from MSS unknown to his predecessors and he added many notes.

Geronimo Mercuriali was born at Forli in the Romagna in 1530, obtained his M.D. in Padova, and then returned to practise in his native city. In 1562, his countrymen sent him on a mission to Pope Pius IV, and he remained in Rome studying the classics and practising medicine; he was the first to teach gynecology in the Archigymnasium. In 1569, he was called to Vienna by the Emperor Maximilian II, who created him a count palatine; yet, he did not stay there very long, for he accepted a professorship in Padova in the same year. He was professor in that faculty for eighteen years, then moved to Bologna, Pisa, and finally to his native city where he died on 13 November 1603. His Greco-Latin edition was the most important of his Hippocratic contributions but not by any means the only one. It would take too much space to enumerate them. In spite of his elaborate studies of Greek medicine, he managed to devote much time to medicine itself. He wrote on gynecology, pediatrics, dermatology, melancholy, veneral diseases. The most original of these writings was perhaps his treatise on gymnastics, *Artis gymnasticae apud antiquos libri VI* (Venice: Juntae, 1569); though the sources were Greek, it is considered the first modern book on gymnastics written from the medical point of view. His *De morbis cutaneis* (Venezia, 1572), often reprinted in Venice and Basel, was one of the first independent treatises on skin diseases; his *De morbis puerorum* (Venezia: P. Mejetus, 1583) was also a famous book.[24] Though Mercuriali was a medical humanist and philologist, he was also a genuine physician, keenly aware of the medical problems which living patients and living diseases were all the time suggesting.

His contemporary, Anuce Foes of Metz (1528-90), was a greater philologist but of no medical importance. His family came from Trier (Treves) on the Moselle, but he was educated chiefly in Paris. Like other learned physicians of his time he studied philology first and began his medical initiation later (such a procedure would be well-nigh impossible in our time). Thanks to Fernel's[25] protection, he was permitted to copy or collate three old MSS of Hippocrates at the royal library in Fontainebleau and he also obtained a Vatican MS. After a while (how long?) he returned to Metz, where he was appointed town physician. He loved his native city, and brilliant offers from elsewhere could not determine him to leave it. His life was devoted to his practice and to Hippocrates. He was sustained by his belief that the best way to advance medical knowledge was to reëstablish the Hippocratic text in its purity, to obtain as much of the Hippocratic wisdom as was at all possible, and to apply it faithfully to the medical problems of the day.

We owe to him a Greek-Latin edition of the Hippocratic collection, decidedly superior to all the previous ones. This was published by the heirs of Andreas Wechel in Frankfurt a.M. in the year 1595, and contains an abundance of critical notes. According to Littré, who made full use of it, his translations and annotations were richer than the Greek text would suggest. He was often too timid to modify the text printed by Froben, though his translation proves that he had sufficient authority to do so. This great edition had been preceded by another work entitled *Oeconomia Hippocratis* (Frankfurt a.M.: same printer, 1588)[26], a kind of Hippocratic encyclopedia, or we might call it an encyclopedia of Greek medicine, of almost unbelievable wealth. When we handle such a book as this, we cannot help wondering: How could he carry it through? Would any scholar of today be able to repeat such a performance, and if he did, would he find a publisher? Would any institution be rich and generous enough to patronize its publication?

These two great folios bearing Foes' name represent the climax of the Renaissance Hippocratic tradition. The edition was gradually replaced by others,[27] but no scholar ever had the courage to write an encylopedia more elaborate than his *Oeconomia Hippocratis*. It is still a valuable book, one which every student of Greek medicine should keep near at hand.

2. Celsus (I-1)

A NCIENT MEDICINE WAS ESSENTIALLY GREEK, NOT LATIN; AND YET the procession of the great masters was interrupted at the beginning of our era by one Roman, writing in Latin, Celsus (I-1). This is the more astonishing when one remembers that Latin literature was still very young, and that the learned language of the Roman empire was not Latin, but Greek. Educated Romans of that time were supposed to know Greek pretty well, even as an educated Frenchman or Englishman of the Renaissance was supposed to know Latin and read it fluently.

Though Celsus wrote in Latin and in very good Latin, his medical knowledge was derived exclusively from Greek sources. His treatise *De medicina* belongs to Latin literature in the same secondary sense as a translation does; it is even possible that it was a translation from a lost original, but such a hypothesis is hardly necessary. What does it matter whether Celsus translated a single work or many, or whether he translated the very words or edited Greek thought in the Latin language? At any rate, the great book which he produced, probably under Tiberius (emperor from 14 to 37), was an excellent compendium of medicine, the best available in the long period extending between Hippocrates and Galen. Celsus' *prooemium* (or preface) is a historical introduction from the mythical beginnings to his own day; it includes a good account of Alexandrian medicine, which was a medical renaissance preparing the advance of Soranos and Galen. He discussed the points of view of the rival medical schools—Dogmatic, Methodic, and Empiric—with fairness and moderation.

A. Cornelius Celsus' personality is almost unknown; it is probable that he flourished in Provence; we are not even sure whether he was a professional physician. The medical treatise which is his sole legacy was a part of an encyclopedia divided into six parts: agriculture, medicine, military arts, rhetoric, philosophy, and law.[28] Quintilian (I-2) spoke rather disparagingly when he called him *vir mediocri ingenio*. But was not that, I wonder, the judgment passed on a scientific writer by a man of letters—a kind of judgment with which we are familiar enough in our own day?

The *De medicina* had not been completely unknown in the Middle Ages[29] and three of the chief MSS extant date back to the ninth and tenth centuries; yet, the attention of Renaissance scholars was drawn very strongly to him when Guarino of Verona (1374-1460) discovered a new MS at Bologna in 1426, and his friend, Giovanni Lamola, found another one at Milan in the following year. The Celsian style, pure and elegant, was ingratiating to them. It thus happened that Celsus was printed very early; he was available to the readers of print before Hippocrates or Galen.

The princeps was edited by Bartholomaeus Fontius and printed by Nicolaus Laurentii Alemanus in Florence, 1478. The text was reprinted in Milano, 1481; Venice, 1493 and 1497 (Klebs 260); Lyons, 1516; Venice, 1524. These six early editions contained simply the text without interpolations of any kind. A new kind of edition including variants, notes, commentaries was started by Joannes Baptista Egnatius[30] (Venice: Aldus, 1528). There were at least fifteen editions in the sixteenth century; and more than fifty altogether.[31]

The editor of the princeps, Bartolommeo Fonti (or Fonzio, della Fonte, 1445-1513), was a Florentine humanist of minor importance. Being a friend of Francesco Sassetti, who obtained some MSS for the king of Hungary,[32] and of Taddeo Ugoletto of Parma, who was the king's librarian, Bartolommeo hoped to share the king's favor and went to Buda at the beginning of 1489. Apparently he was not taken into the royal service, for we find him back in Florence in September of the same year. Matthias Corvinus was eagerly building up one of the greatest libraries of the early Renaissance;[33] he employed some thirty copyists and limners and had agents abroad, notably in Florence, for the acquisition of MSS. He it was who introduced printing in Buda and reëstablished the university of that city.[34] Unfortunately, the Bibliotheca Corvina was scattered soon after the king's death; some of its beautiful MSS can be admired in the main libraries of Europe. The Hungarian Renaissance was discouraged by the death of Matthias Corvinus and completely stopped by the Turkish invasions which followed their victory at Mohacs in 1526.

We said that Celsus appeared in print before Hippocrates and Galen. This must not be taken too literally. The first edition of the *Articella* was anterior to the princeps of Celsus (1478), for it appeared in Padova in 1476 (Klebs 116.1) and that edition contained the *Aphorisms,* the

Prognostica, and *De regimine acutorum* of Hippocrates as well as the *Tegni libri III* of Galen. Moreover, the commentaries of Jacopo da Forli (d. 1413) upon the *Aphorisms* were printed twice before 1478—in Venice, 1473, and Padova, 1477 (Klebs 546.1-2)—and upon the *Tegni libri III* once, in Padova, 1475 (Klebs 547.1). Thus, the readers of printed books (not to mention the very numerous readers of MSS) had obtained some knowledge of Hippocrates and Galen before Celsus was available to them. Yet, the *De medicina* was the first medical encyclopedia of Antiquity to appear in print and its influence was the greater because it was felt at the right time, when the physicians were becoming more scholarly and were anxious to know more about the medicine of the wise men of Antiquity. In this particular case, the tradition was relatively simple and easy; it sufficed to print the MS, no translation was needed. The Latin text required no explanation, for every physician of Western Europe—that is, every M.D.—knew Latin (he had been taught and passed his examinations in that language and was acquainted with the technical terms only in Latin; if he were a Frenchman, for example, he would be unable to give their French equivalents). That situation, which was in some respects very favorable to communications at a high level (one scientific language for the whole of Catholic and Protestant Europe), continued until the eighteenth century and this explains why vernacular versions of the *De medicina* were not printed until very late; an Italian version appeared in Venice, 1747, and the English one by Dr. James Greive[35] only in London, 1756. There is perhaps another reason why vernacular translations were not published during the Renaissance. Celsus was first, but Hippocrates and Galen followed closely on his heels, and their own influence grew by leaps and bounds; learned physicians were keener than ever to drink at the pure Hellenic sources, if possible in Greek, if not in Latin, and Celsus became a second choice. Celsus was always considered a very distinguished medical author, but he never enjoyed the fame, the superstitious fame (every great fame is somewhat irrational) which was granted to Hippocrates, Galen, or Avicenna.

3. SORANOS OF EPHESOS (II-1)

LET US NOW RETURN TO THE GREEK PHYSICIANS, OF WHOM SORANOS was perhaps[36] the greatest in the six centuries separating Galen from Hippocrates. It should not be supposed that that half-millennium was medically empty—that would be absurd. Not only were many physicians active, but an abundance of research work was carried on in almost every branch of medicine. Facts were collected and theories invented; the facts were not always well observed (it was impossible to observe most of them well) and were too few in number; none of the theories was satisfactory and hence there were many of them and keen rivalry between them.

Many schools of medicine had grown and struggled in Alexandria, but a new one, the Methodist, was initiated in the last century B.C. by

14

LECTURE I: MEDICINE

Greek doctors established in Rome: Asclepiades of Bithynia (I-1 B.C.), Themison of Laodiceia (I-1 B.C.), Thessalos of Tralleis (I-2 B.C.). The greatest of them was Soranos of Ephesos (II-1), *methodicorum princeps*.

Our knowledge of Methodism is largely derived from Soranos' writings. It was an attempt to explain medical facts in a systematic way, but its dogmatism was moderate. They (the Methodists) were willing to take experiments into account, and the best of them, Rufus and Soranos, were making innumerable observations. Asclepiades had accepted the atomic ideas of the Epicureans and the central theory of Methodism was the doctrine of communities (general states), derived from atomism.

According to this doctrine, the basic types of disease are (1) an excessively dry, tense, and stringent state; (2) an excessively fluid, relaxed, atonic state; and (3) a condition which involves both types of abnormality. Since observable manifestations gave the clue to the "general state" underlying a particular case, it is not surprising that the Methodists developed symptomatology and differential diagnosis to a high degree of perfection. And they distinguished more sharply than did their predecessors between acute and chronic diseases. Their treatment of disease is essentially the use of relaxing measures to counteract excessive tension and the use of astringent measures to counteract excessive looseness.[37]

One would expect Soranos' writings to be eagerly sought for and well known during the Renaissance, but such was not the case. There are no incunabula editions and only a part of his work has been preserved in the Greek original. He has been called the greatest gynecologist of Antiquity, but his gynecological treatise was not printed during the Renaissance, except for a small fragment, a description of the womb and the female pudenda published in 1554 in an anonymous Greek edition of the works of Rufus of Ephesos (II-1)[38] and for the Moschion tradition. Moschion (VI-1) was a Latin physician who flourished in North Africa in the fifth or sixth century and wrote a catechism on women's diseases and midwifery largely derived from Soranos and from an unknown undatable woman, Cleopatra. That catechism obtained so much popularity that in the fifteenth century it was translated into Greek.[39] Later that Greek text was retranslated into Latin. All of which suggests that the Greek text of Soranos was temporarily lost.

Let us sum up rapidly the post-Renaissance tradition of Soranos' obstetrics and gynecology. The Greek princeps was edited by Friedrich Reinhold Dietz (Königsberg i.P., 1838); Greek-Latin edition by Franciscus Zacharios Ermerins (Utrecht, 1869); finally Joannes Ilberg (1860-1930) gave us a critical edition of all the texts existing in Greek in the *Corpus medicorum graecorum* (Leipzig: Teubner, 1927), vol. 4.[40]

To return to the sixteenth century, two great works of Soranos dealing respectively with chronic and acute diseases had been translated in the fifth or sixth century by a Numidian doctor, Caelius Aurelianus (V-1). We know almost nothing about that early translator and yet his Latin text superseded the Greek original (which was lost) and his own name replaced that of the author! This is an almost unique case of

15

perverted tradition.[41] The *Tardarum passionum libri quinque* were edited by Joannes Sichardt and printed by H. Petrus in Basel, 1529, and the *Celerum passionum libri tres,* edited by Johann Günther of Andernach, were printed by Colinaeus in Paris, 1533. Sichardt's translation was reprinted in the Aldine series *Medici antiqui omnes* (Venice, 1547). Both treatises were reëdited anonymously together in Lyon, 1567, and reprinted, 1569; later editions do not concern us except the last one, with an English translation, by I. E. Drabkin.[42] The Drabkin edition must be mentioned not only because of its excellence but also because it continues the old perversion ascribing those treatises not to Soranos but to Caelius Aurelianus! That error is anchored deep in people's minds, because the Renaissance editors, Sichardt and Günther, did not mention Soranos in their title pages; neither did Drabkin. That is almost incredible but is, unfortunately, true. Let us repeat aloud, very loud, that those great medical treatises were written in Greek by Soranos of Ephesos; Caelius was only the translator of them into Latin; he took liberties with the original, abridging it and even making a few additions, but no matter how many liberties he took, these texts did not become his own. It so happens that the Latin translation drove out the Greek original; that incident worsened the tragedy; it ought to sharpen our sense of justice instead of blunting it. Drabkin's excellent translation could not have been made from the lost original; it was made from the early Latin version; no matter how many intermediary translations had been made and lost, the author remains the same—Soranos—and for heaven's sake, let us try to remember it.

This is a unique case in medical tradition, unless we consider Celsus' book as a translation from a lost Greek original and that claim is not patient of proof. It occurred because the Latin version was made, and on the whole well made, relatively early, before another tradition could be established and Soranos' name enshrined in the hearts of men. The Greek scientific classics were generally transmitted to us via two sets of translations—Greek-Arabic and Arabic-Latin; the Soranos tradition was simplified because two of his treatises were Latinized very early before the establishment of the Arabic detour.[43]

The neglect of Soranos was probably caused and certainly aggravated by the greater fame of his younger contemporary Galen. This was not the younger man's fault. Galen mentioned Soranos many times, but the bulk and prestige of his own writings eclipsed those of earlier physicians. After a thousand years the perspective was completely falsified and many medieval and Renaissance scholars thought of Galen as following Hippocrates rather closely.

The only Renaissance scholars who deserve to be remembered because of Soranos are Sichardt, Günther, and, to a smaller extent, Turnèbe. The last-named published only a fragment but, at least, he ascribed it to the real author and even added a biography of the latter (very short, five Greek lines).

Sichardt was primarily a jurist and philologist. He was born at Tauberbischofsheim in N. Baden, *c*.1499, became eventually professor of law in Tübingen, and died there in 1552. He explored a dozen German libraries searching for MSS and found the MS of *Caeli Aureliani Siccensis tardarum passionum libri* in the old abbey of Lorsch (S. Hesse).[44]

Guinterius is sometimes called Johannes Winter, which is rather misleading. He has already too many names without that superfluous one. His original name was Johann Guenther, and for greater precision he was generally called Johann Guenther von Andernach, where he was born in 1505.[45] At the age of twelve he went to Utrecht, where he studied Greek; he was professor of Greek in Louvain, Vesalius being one of his pupils. Many of his contemporaries passed from medicine to philology; Guenther's evolution seems to have been different or, more exactly, medicine and Hellenism dominated his life by turns. In 1525, he went from Louvain to Paris, and obtained his M.D. there in 1530. Soon afterwards, he was appointed physician to François I (king, 1515-47); his appointment must have been due to his prestige as a Hellenist. Being a Lutheran he was obliged to leave Paris, and to move to Metz and later Strasbourg, where he resumed his Greek teaching. He traveled to Germany and Italy but always returned to his new home town, Strasbourg, where he died on 4 October 1574. He was a distinguished anatomist, but his *Institutiones anatomicae* (Paris, 1536) were eclipsed by Vesalius' *Fabrica*. He wrote treatises on the plague and on balneology and translated many medical treatises from Greek into Latin (e.g., some fifty Galenic ones). The scholar in him did not destroy the physician and his medical mind remained alert until the end. The best proof of this is given by his interest in Paracelsus. In Basel, 1571, he published, and dedicated to Maximilian II (emperor, 1564-76), a treatise, *De medicina veteri et nova,* wherein he tried to reconcile Galenic with Paracelsian medicine. This shows that he was not only alert but also open-minded; Paracelsus hated the humanists and they requited his animosity with bitterness. Guenther's fame is illustrated by the early publication of many biographies.[46]

4. GALEN OF PERGAMON (II-2)

IT IS HARDLY NECESSARY TO INTRODUCE GALEN TO ANY MEDICAL AUDIence. There is no name more illustrious in the whole history of medicine, except perhaps that of Hippocrates. If you want to place him in the scale of time, it will suffice to remember that being born in Pergamon in 129 under the rule of Hadrian, it was his great privilege to spend the greatest part of his life during the government of the best emperors, Antoninus Pius (138-61) and Marcus Aurelius (161-80), but then, unfortunately, to end it under brutes like Commodus. You may remember also that he was a contemporary of the best Greek author of the Roman empire, Lucian of Samosata, and of the archaeologist Pausanias. He was educated in Pergamon, which was one of the leading cities of Asia Minor, a center of art, religion, philosophy, and medicine; traveled extensively in the Roman world, spending months or years in the main centers, most of these years in Rome, which was then the capital of the Western world. He was equally diligent in every place, conducting medical investigations, meeting colleagues, reading and writing books, discussing and lecturing. In spite of the diversity and quantity of his duties, he managed to write a large number of books dealing not only with every branch of medicine, but also with philosophy, literature, and the history of science and philosophy. His immense fame was due to a strange combination of qualities, for he was a man of science and a man of letters, a physician and a philosopher. His experience and learning and his very dogmatism established his authority for centuries.

The number and mass of his writings is so large that we must deal with him as we did with Hippocrates. Each of the some 120 treatises bearing his name[47] had a tradition of its own, the description of which would require considerable space; then various groups of treatises (two or more), being copied in the same MSS and later printed in the same editions, had a common tradition; finally, there was a tradition of the whole corpus, the detailed account of which is very complex, because the successive *Opera omnia* did not include exactly the same collections. Each collection might omit treatises included in the preceding one and vice versa.

We shall restrict ourselves to the Renaissance editions of the *Opera omnia,* but before doing so, we must explain briefly how Galen's fame was built up. Galen was exceedingly lucky in that he became the outstanding physician of the Roman empire, which was bilingual, and hence he enjoyed from the beginning a double tradition in Latin and Greek. The latter was at first predominant, while the Latin tradition remained for a few centuries purely oral. In the fifth century, Galen was translated into Latin by Cassius Felix (V-1), even as Soranos was translated by Caelius Aurelianus (V-1). That Latin tradition remained secondary for centuries, and we may say that Galen's fame was built almost exclusively on a Greek foundation. His abundant writings were copied by Greek scribes and then elaborated and commented upon by the early Byzantine physicians, especially the four great ones who flourished from the fourth to the seventh century (we shall get better acquainted with them presently). The Greek world accepted without restriction Galen's authority, and the Galenic writings became its medical bible. Under the pressure of nationalism and of religion, the Greek writings were translated into Syriac by Sergios of Resaina (VI-1) and later into Arabic. In both cases the early translators were unorthodox Christians; a few, Monophysites like Sergios; most of them, Nestorians.[48] A large number of translators were engaged in the task of decanting Greek experience and wisdom into Arabic vessels. It must suffice to name one, one of the greatest scientific dragomans of all ages, Ḥunain ibn Isḥāq (IX-2), who flourished in Jundīshāpūr, then in Baghdād. The whole Galenic corpus was translated by him, or older translations were revised under his direction. We know exactly what he did because he compiled in 856 a list of 129 Galenic treatises known to him, indicating for each item the Syriac and Arabic translations, saying who made or revised each and criticizing briefly their accuracy. That list is one of the most impressive documents of medieval learning.[49] Thanks to Ḥunain and his school the whole Galenic corpus was available in Arabic before the end of the ninth century.

In the course of time Galen was translated from Arabic into Latin, and that constituted for many centuries the main Galenic tradition in the West. The early Latin tradition of Cassius Felix and others was relatively insignificant. The task of decanting Galenism from Arabic into Latin was again such a big one that many hands were needed. It was begun by Constantine the African (XI-2), but the bulk of it was done under the direction of Gerard of Cremona (XII-2) in the "academy" of Toledo patronized by the archbishops Raymond I (1126-51) and his successors, notably D. Sancho II de Aragón (1266-75) and D. Gonzalo II Garcia Gudiel (1280-99).[50]

The majority of medieval Latin MSS of Galen's treatises are derived from the Arabic. A few translators, however, began to investigate the Greek MSS and to translate them into Latin; we may assume that they were helped in each case by the existence of earlier versions from the Arabic. The most distinguished of these men are the Italian Burgundio of Pisa (XII-2), who had studied Greek in Constantinople; the Flemish Dominican Willem of Moerbeke (XIII-2), who had learned the language in Greece, for he had been Archbishop of Corinth from 1278 to his death (1286?); Pietro d'Abano (XIV-1) of Padova; and Niccolò da Reggio (XIV-1). By the beginning of the fourteenth century, Galen was firmly entrenched in the Western universities where the majority of his works could be read in Latin translation from the Arabic or from the Greek and they could be read easily, for there was an abundance of MSS. One of the results of the creation of universities in many countries had been the building up of a MS trade; students as well as teachers needed many MS copies of the same text, and there were gradually established near the schools bookshops which produced MSS wholesale. The numbers of MSS involved were not very large, certainly much smaller than the numbers of copies provided by the early printers, yet they involved methods of manufacture different from those employed by the old-fashioned scribes.[51] The need of multiple copies is illustrated by early university regulations. For example, we have documents of Montpellier dated 1309 and 1340 ordering the students to con a number of Galenic treatises. Thus, did the Galenic influence grow throughout the fourteenth century, and almost every Latin medical treatise was permeated with it. The illustrious Guy de Chauliac (XIV-2), who was a practical surgeon rather than a scholar, cited Galen 890 times in his *Chirurgia magna* (Ibn Sīnā came second with 661 quotations). By the end of the century, Galen's canonization was almost completed, and the Florentine, Niccolò Falcucci,[52] in his *Sermones medicinales* proclaimed the master's infallibility. This is the more remarkable, because Falcucci was very familiar with the Arabic medical literature available in Latin.

This brings us close to the age of printing. Falcucci's *Sermones* were printed five times before 1500 (1484 to 1495?; Klebs 389). Not only were many Galenic texts among the incunabula, but the first edition of his (Latin) *Opera* was published in Venice, by Philippo Pinzio de Caneto, on 27 August 1490.

Before dealing with the other Renaissance editions of the Galenic *Opera*, let us consider rapidly the incunabula of separate treatises. Thirteen treatises were represented, one in Greek, twelve in Latin. Half of these were included in the collection edited by Giorgio Valla (c. 1430-99) and published by Bevilaqua in Venice, 1498. Valla was a mathematician, as well as a physician, a man of letters and an encyclopedist. Two more treatises were published in the *Articella*, the *Tegni libri III* in the six incunabula editions of it (1476 to 1500) and the *De divisione librorum Galeni*—in all incunabula editions, except the first (1483 to 1500).[53] This particular treatise concerns historians of science, as it is one of the two which Galen devoted to his own bibliography; the earliest autobibliographies to be written and the earliest to be printed (Venice, 1483). The four other treatises were appended to editions of Aristotle, al-Rāzī (IX-2), Ibn Sarābī (XII-1), and Francesco Filelfo (1398-1481).

The only treatise printed in Greek before the sixteenth century was the *Therapeutica* composed by Zacharias Callierges for Nicolaus Blastus, Venice, 5 October 1500. This folio of 112 leaves contains the *De methodo medendi* in fourteen books plus the summary *ad Glauconem* in two books.

The first Latin edition of the *Opera* is a Gothic impression of 471 double-columned leaves printed by Pincius (Venice, 1490). There is a copy of it in the Army Medical Library which belonged to Nicolaus Pol.[54] The text of it was prepared by Diomedes Bonardus, physician in Brescia, aided by another doctor, L. Malatenus, both of whom are otherwise unknown to me. That edition was reprinted in Venice, 1502, and again, 1511 (?). Choulant lists many other Latin editions of the sixteenth century, some twenty in all, printed most of them in Italy, but a few in Basel and Lyon.

The Greek editions of all the works were two: the princeps, Venice, 1525, and another in Basel, 1538. We recognize the old competition between the house of Aldus and the learned printers of Basel.

The princeps is made of five volumes folio *ex aedibus Aldi et Andreae Asuloni soceri*. The editor was Giov. Bat. Opizo, patrician and physician in Pavia.

Asulanus dedicated the first part to Clement VII, the second, third, and fourth to other patrons, and the fifth to the editor "Jo. Bpt. Opizoni, patricio papiensi et medico." In his preface to that fifth volume, he praises Opizo's work. My impression is that the Greek princeps must be ascribed to Opizonus and Asulanus. The Basilean edition (also 5 vols., folio; Andreas Cratandrus) was prepared by three scholars—Joachim Camerarius, Leonhard Fuchs, and Hieronymus Gemusaeus—who had the inestimable advantage of being able to use the preceding edition plus a few additional MSS. It included the same treatises as the Aldine, with the simple addition of *De ossibus ad tirones* in Latin.[55] It is easy enough to prepare a better edition twenty-five years after the first one with the help of new MSS and of a new team of scholars. The three scholars who were mainly responsible for the Basel Greek Galen were distinguished men, especially the first two.

Joachim Camerarius, senior, of Bamberg (1500-74)[56] held classical professorships at Nuremberg, Tübingen, Leipzig. He edited a number of Greek and Latin classics, was a great friend of Melanchthon, and a polyhistor. For example, he is one of the many authors of books on comets.[57] Leonhart Fuchs was perhaps less known than Camerarius, but he was a greater man, more original. Born in Wemding, Bavaria, in 1501, he lived until 1566. He obtained at the University of Ingolstadt his medical and Lutheran initiations. He is recognized as one of the "Fathers of Botany" and his name is immortalized in that of a lovely American flower, the fuchsia. His profession was medicine; he was professor of medicine in Ingolstadt and Tübingen, and acquired some fame at the time of an epidemic in 1529. Sudhoff drew attention in 1926 to Fuchs' table of eye diseases and his work in ophthalmology[58]. His main achievement, however, was the publication of a new herbal *De historia stirpium* (Basel, 1542), admirably illustrated with many woodcuts of exceptional quality. Fuchs appreciated the collaboration of two pictores (draughtsmen) and of a sculptor (wood engraver) who prepared the illustrations and he graciously included their portraits in his book, one of the greatest books in the whole history of botany.[59] The third man is less famous. Hieronymus Gemusaeus was an Alsatian (born in Mühlhausen, 1505) who was educated in Basel, then in Torino where he got his M.D. in 1533; he returned to Basel in the following year as professor of physics and died on 29 January 1543. Gemusaeus was the "local" member of the board of editors, at a time when the difficulty of communications made it more necessary even than now to have a man close to the printing shop. He was the editor of the Basel Latin edition of Plutarch's *Opera moralia*

21

(folio; Basel: M. Isingrinius, 1541), simply the editor and the author of a preface, the translators being the same as in the Paris edition of 1521.

The most convenient edition of Galen to this day is the Greek-Latin edition by C. G. Kühn (22 vols.; Leipzig, 1821-33), the last volume of which is a very serviceable index. When one wants to check rapidly a Galenic text, the easiest way is to use Kühn, but one should be ready to check him at every step, for he reproduced uncritically early editions such as the first Basel Greek edition of 1538 or the second Greek-Latin edition by René Chartier (1679). The text given by Kühn can often be checked by reference to a modern edition, but a list of all the critical editions of separate treatises would take considerable space. It must suffice to mention three collections: (1) French edition of eleven works by Charles Daremberg (2 vols.; Paris, 1854-56); (2) the *Opera minora* edited in Greek by Joh. Marquardt, Iw. Mueller, and Georg Helmreich (3 vols.; Leipzig: Teubner, 1884-93); (3) the Greek editions of the *Corpus medicorum graecorum* begun in 1914 (Leipzig: Teubner). When we use Kühn alone, having no time for further exploration, we place ourselves in the hands of Renaissance editors.

We must now give our attention to some of these in addition to those with whom we have already become acquainted. Let us take—roughly in the chronological order of their main Galenic contributions—two Frenchmen, Champier and Rabelais; two Italians, Leoniceno and Manardi; and two Englishmen, Linacre and Caius.[60]

The first of these, Champier, is a remarkable specimen of the early French Renaissance. Not so much a scholar as a man of letters who plays with Greek, because it is the learned fashion, and writes in Latin; yet, is already French to the marrow. Haller said of him in his own queer and barbaric language, "Non indoctus homo, polygraphus et collector, semi-barbarus tamen."[61] Symphorien Champier was born near Lyon in 1472, studied the arts in Paris and medicine in Montpellier, and established himself as a physician in Lyon at the end of the century. In 1506, he traveled to Metz and became eventually archiater to Antoine, duke of Lorraine, whom he accompanied in Italy and attended in the battles of Agnadello (1509) and Marignano[62] (1515). After that second battle, in which François I defeated the Swiss troops of the duke of Milano, the king was knighted by Bayard "le chevalier sans peur et sans reproche," and Champier by his lord, the duke of Lorraine. Note this curious fact, the king being knighted! Champier, as vain as a peacock, was immensely proud of his knighthood and of the circumstances thereof; he married one of Bayard's cousins, dug out for himself a noble ancestry, and combined in his armorial bearings the achievements of both families. Marignano was the heroic climax of his life. We remember that with ease and pleasure, because Marignano is immortalized for music lovers by the delightful chorus which Jannequin wrote to celebrate that victory,[63] "La bataille de Marignan." What a master, this Jannequin!—the first French flower of the illustrious school which had begun in Flanders and Hainaut in the preceding century: Guillaume Dufay, Okeghem, Josquin des Prés.[64] We are now moving in the early French Renaissance and realize its complexity: François I reminds us of Leonardo da Vinci and Italy; Symphorien Champier, of the fine group of Lyonnais humanists and printers; Jannequin, of Flanders and northern France. The Renaissance was blowing in from every direction, south, east, north, and all the trees of art and knowledge were beginning to rustle. The symptoms of a profound change appear first in music, poetry, painting, and sculpture, but they can be perceived also in the field of learning.

After Marignano, Champier spent his time partly in Nancy, partly in Lyon, where he had a prominent share in the foundation of the College of the Trinity and of the medical school. In his childish conceit he called himself *aggregator lugdunensis*. He was one of the consuls of Lyon (i.e., one of the city magistrates) and made the tactical blunder of introducing a tax on wine. A tax on Beaujolais, think of that! His house was plundered by the infuriated populace and for a time the air of Lyon was a little too hot for him. He came back, however, was reëlected consul, and died in 1538 or 1539.[65]

Most of his writings were in Latin; yet, he prepared one of the forty-three French editions of the *Grande Chirurgie* of Guy de Chauliac (XIV-2). The first edition was the one by Nicolas Panis (Lyon, 1478; reprinted in 1485 and 1498). The edition prepared by Champier was the fourth, *Le guidon en françoys* (Lyon, 1503). This was a revision of Panis' edition with additions and a new chapter "universel et très singulier"; it was not reprinted.[66] Other books were published by Champier in French, such as, *La nef des princes et des batailles de noblesse* (Lyon, 1502), *La nef des dames virtueuses* (Lyon, 1503), *Recueil ou chroniques des histoires des royaulmes d'Austrasie ou France orientale dite à présent Lorrayne* .... (Lyon, 1505), *Les grans croniques* .... *des princes de Savoye et de Piémont* (Paris, 1516), *La vie et les gestes du preux chevalier Bayard* (Paris, 1525), *Le myrouel des appothiquaires, Item les lunectes des cyrurgiens* (Lyon[?]; Paris, 1532), etc. Note the titles of these books (I must confess that my knowledge is restricted to them) which have a definite Renaissance flavor. His medical books with the exception of the mirror of apothecaries were naturally written in Latin. Many of these were devoted to Galenic commentaries and controversies, and to the defense of Greek against Arabic medicine. Let us single out two of his Latin works. The first is the *De medicinae claris scriptoribus* (Lyon: J. de Campis, 1506), a medical bibliography, rudimentary, but one of the earliest, and perhaps the best history of medicine then available. The other is the *Symphonia* [67] which was printed by Josse Bade in Paris, 1516. As can be seen from the title page, the book contains other writings, but the main treatise is Champier's attempt to reconcile Plato with Aristotle, and Galen with Hippocrates. It was necessary to reconcile all the Greeks against the Arabic barbarians.

The relations between Italy and France were close in the sixteenth century, much more so than those between Italy and England. It was a good deal easier to reach Florence, Milano, Venice, or even Rome from the Lyonnais or from Touraine than from Canterbury or Oxford. Yet, some English scholars had already explored Italy, e.g., John Free (or Phreas?; d. 1465) who brought back MSS from Italy to his college, Balliol, and to the Bodleian, while Greek MSS in Canterbury were imported from the same country by William de Selling. In the year 1485, or 1488, this William was sent by Henry VII on an embassy to Pope Innocent VIII and he took in his train a young scholar, Thomas Linacre (1460-1524) of Canterbury.

Thomas was educated in Canterbury and Oxford and was already conversant with Greek before his Italian journey; he stopped in Florence to study with two famous teachers of Greek, Demetrios Chalcondyles (1424-1511) and Angelo Poliziano (1454-94), and a little later (c.1490), he worked in Rome with Ermolao Barbaro (1454-93). His attention was drawn to Greek medicine by Barbaro's study of Dioscorides. He also visited Niccolò Leoniceno (1428-1524) in Ferrara. The best proof of his proficiency as a Greek scholar was given by the fact that Aldus befriended and employed him. Aldus[68] had not yet founded his "new academy" of Hellenists (he did that only in 1501); yet, he was already surrounding himself with competent men whose help he would need. It was Linacre who translated for Aldus the treatise of Proclos (V-2) on the sphere in the folio *Astronomici veteres* (1499).[69] Linacre was also one of the first Englishmen to study medicine in Padova. After having obtained his M.D., he traveled in Italy and France, returned home and taught Greek in Oxford. He was tutor and physician to Prince Arthur, to whom he dedicated his Proclos, and later to the little Princess Mary[70] and wrote for her a Latin grammar;[71] he was one of the ordinary physicians to King Henry VIII. His medical importance is great not only because of his practice but also because the foundation of the Royal College of Physicians (1518) was largely due to his efforts; he was the first president of it and remained so until his death. We think of him mainly as a Greek scholar, one of international reputation, and especially as an editor of Galen. He belonged to a magnificent group of English classical scholars: William Grocyn, William Latimer, John Colet, William Lily (all of whom traveled in Italy, Grocyn being Linacre's companion), to whom we may add St. Thomas More and Erasmus.

During his Italian Wanderjahre he collated a number of Galenic MSS and prepared Latin translations: *De sanitate tuenda,* dedicated to

Henry VIII (Paris: G. Rubeus, 1517); *Methodus medendi,* dedicated to the same (Paris: Maheu, 1519); *De temperamentis et de inaequali intemperie* (Cambridge: Siberch, 1521), dedicated to Pope Leo X, one of the first English books with Greek type[72] and the first in England with a copperplate title; *De naturalibus facultatibus,* dedicated to Archbishop Warham (London: Pynson, 1523?); *De pulsum usu,* dedicated to Cardinal Wolsey (London: Pynson, 1523?)—these last two treatises published in a single volume together with the *De motu musculorum,* translated by Niccolò Leoniceno (1428-1524) but edited by his friend Linacre; *De symptomatum differentiis et causis* (London: Pynson, 1524), printed soon after Linacre's death. According to Erasmus, Linacre had translated many other Galenic texts which remained unprinted, and he had been thinking with his friends, Grocyn and Latimer, of preparing a complete Latin translation of Aristotle. The Galenic texts of his which were printed were often reprinted, either separately or in collections. Thus, his part in the shaping of the Galenic thought of the Renaissance was considerable. His influence in England must have been great, as a doctor moving in courtly circles, as an Oxford teacher, as a rector or priest, as the president of the College of Physicians, as a defender of the new medical learning. He was aware of it and arranged to perpetuate it by the foundation of three lectures in medicine (the Linacre's Lectures) two of them in his own alma mater—Oxford (he was a fellow of All Souls)—and *mirabile dictu,* one in Cambridge! His Galenic influence, however, was not only English but international. His first two translations had been first published in Paris, and all of them were reprinted in France and Italy, and perhaps in other countries. Every literate doctor in Western Christendom knew of him.

His character is difficult to appreciate across the false light of conventional eulogies. We may note, however, that Erasmus honored him and that he had many friends whose names have already been listed. One story told by Sir John Cheke is revealing. When Linacre was old, as he was reading the Sermon on the Mount (Matthew 7), he exclaimed, "Either this is not the Gospel or we are not Christians!"[73]

Linacre was a distinguished physician, a great scholar, and a good man.[74]

The two Italians are a remarkable pair, Leoniceno and Manardi, both of whom taught medicine in Ferrara from 1464 to 1536, a stretch of seventy-two years, Leoniceno doing the lion's share of that, no less than sixty years![75]

Niccolò[76] was born in 1428 at Lonigo near Vicenza (hence the name

Leoniceno); he studied in Vicenza and Padova and traveled much, going as far as England. He was a teacher at Padova and Bologna, finally settling down in his native city where he taught from 1464 to his death in 1524. Toward the end of his life when he was asked to explain how he had reached such an old age (he was almost a centenarian) in relatively good health, he used to ascribe his longevity to his guilelessness, equanimity, and frugality. He was thus a forerunner of his younger contemporary, the Venetian, Luigi (Lodovico) Cornaro (1475?-1566), author of the first treatise on macrobiotics, *Trattato della vita sobria* (Padova: G. Perchacino, 1558).[77] Though he was one of the most famous physicians of his age, he was primarily a humanist, a classical scholar, and spent a good part of his time translating into Latin the works of Hippocrates and of Galen; he translated the *Aphorisms* of the former and the *Ars medica* of the latter. Two of his most discussed writings date from his old age. At the age of sixty-four, he published his criticism of Pliny, *Plinii et aliorum auctorum qui de simplicibus medicaminibus scripserunt errores notati* (Ferrara: L. Rubeis and A. Grassis, 1492; reprinted at least thrice in the sixteenth century); five years later, the *Libellus de epidemia quem vulgo morbum gallicum vocant* (Venice: Aldus, 1497; reprinted twice in the fifteenth century, and at least four times in the sixteenth).[78] The first of these books was forward looking, for it contained a criticism of Pliny and other ancients from the point of view of *realia* not of *verba,* and that kind of criticism was very much needed; it did not fully develop until much later, and there are even today a multitude of learned idiots who waste their time discussing words or symbols instead of the realities which these represent. His criticism of Pliny prepared the way for the so-called German "Fathers of Botany." The second was the opposite; in the case of syphilis, the humanist had the best of the physician. Leoniceno would not hear of the disease as a new one; according to him, it was already characterized in the *Aphorisms* of Hippocrates (Book III, 21). He proved himself more enlightened in another respect, for he attacked the astrological prejudices which were dominant in his day; this attitude was emphasized by his dedication of the book to Ioannes Franciscus Mirandulensis, i.e., Giovanni Francesco della Mirandola (murdered in 1533), nephew of the more famous Giovanni Pico della Mirandola (1463-94) who had been a leader in the fight against astrology.

Leoniceno's humanism was evidenced by his contention that one's knowledge of medicine would remain incomplete and imperfect without a sufficient familiarity with philosophy and belles-lettres; this opinion was hardly personal to him, it was the general opinion of all the well-educated physicians, as against surgeons, druggists, and other barbarians. He himself was a leader of the Galenic revival, which implied at this stage a good deal of classical philology; it also implied hostility to Avicenna. This will become clearer when we deal with the latter presently.

Leoniceno may be considered a man of Ferrara, because he spent in that city the best part of his life. Giovanni Manardi was actually born in Ferrara (in 1462); he there received his education and medical training under such men as Francesco Benzi[79] and Leoniceno, and began to teach medicine (*c*.1482-85). From the latter and from Gianfrancesco Pico della Mirandola he imbibed a healthy contempt of astrology. In 1513, he entered the medical service of Laszlo II (king of Hungary, 1490-1516) and was physician also to Laszlo's successor, Lajos II (king, 1516-26), but he left Buda in 1518 and returned to Ferrara. It was during this Hungarian interlude that he wrote a commentary on the *Grabadin* of Mesuë the Younger (XI-1), which was often published with his medical letters. In 1524, he succeeded Leoniceno and continued to teach medicine in Ferrara until his death in 1536. We are not concerned with a treatise of his on syphilis nor on his medical letters of which many collections were published[80] (one would like an analysis of them to understand their popularity), but only with his edition of the *Ars medicinalis* of Galen (Rome, 1525), which was reprinted at least six times in the sixteenth century, four times in Basel, and twice in Padova.[81]

The University of Ferrara founded by the illustrious Este family in 1391[82] had not been successful at first, but it was reorganized in 1430 and owed a modicum of popularity and influence to the coöperation of the humanist, Guarino of Verona,[83] and later of the two doctors, Leoniceno and Manardi, the second of whom continued the crusade of the former against the Arabs and astrology, and for Galen. These two men were not simply humanists and Galenists, they were aware of contemporary realities; their eyes were open to read not only Greek and Latin books in the library, but the book of nature. It is significant that they influenced Paracelsus; this shows that they were not conventional academicians, but there was in them something higher and more vital.

The next champion of Galen was Rabelais. We may assume that our audience needs no introduction to the immortal creator of *Pantagruel* and *Gargantua,* but it may not know so well the physician and the humanist. François Rabelais was born *c.* 1494 at Chinon,[84] his father

27

being a lawyer; François was educated at Chinon and Angers in Benedictine and Franciscan schools; he received the minor and major orders.
In 1521 (*aet.* 26), we find him in Puy-Saint-Martin, a Cordelier[85] monastery in Fontenay-le-Comte (Bas-Poitou); among his brethren in that
house was a Hellenist, Pierre Amy, who brought him into touch with
Guillaume Budé,[86] and he was befriended by a citizen of Fontenay, André
Tiraqueau,[87] legist and humanist.

It is pleasant to think of these young Cordeliers, Amy and Rabelais,
combining their monacal duties with the study of Greek, but their peace
was interrupted in 1523. Erasmus' paraphrase of St. Luke had caused
the anger of many theologians, and the Faculty of Theology of Paris
decided to forbid the study of Greek in France.[88] The abbot of Puy-
Martin confiscated the Greek books which were used in his house.
Happily, Rabelais was permitted to move from the Franciscan monastery
to a Benedictine one of the neighborhood, St. Pierre in Maillezais
(Vendée), the abbot of which, Geoffroy d'Estissac, was a humanist; his
permission to pass from one monacal order to another was confirmed
by Clement VII (pope, 1523-34). Rabelais' distinction was such that he
was selected by Geoffroy as his secretary, and traveled with him from
time to time to the priory of Ligugé (near Poitiers) and to Poitiers itself,
a university city. His restlessness continued, however, and he left in 1527;
we don't know what he did in the following years—perhaps he was
accomplishing his "tour de France" in a scholarly way, passing from one
university or college to another. We may be certain that he was studying
all the while, for he gradually accumulated a mass of learning, which
was not very deep but extensive. For example, he must have obtained a
certain amount of medical knowledge, because he was immatriculated on
17 September 1530 by the Faculty of Medicine of Montpellier, and obtained his B.M. six weeks later. According to tradition during the "petit
ordinaire" of 1531 (from Quasimodo Monday to St. John) he gave lectures based upon the *Aphorisms* of Hippocrates and the *Ars parva* of
Galen, and referred frequently to the Greek text. That was a significant
gesture illustrating the medical renaissance in Montpellier, the Greek,
anti-Arabic revival. It drew attention to the new bachelor who was
appointed physician in the hospital of Lyon; the appointment, dated
1 November 1532, was not very remunerative, but it was flattering to be
called "médecin du Grand Hostel Dieu de Notre Dame de Pitié du Pont
du Rhône." Rabelais' activities were very complex, for he was first a
priest, then a physician, third a scholar, a Hellenist, yet the first part of
Pantagruel appeared in the same year. It is a little difficult to explain
the combination, except with the word "extraordinary genius" which
simply labels the miracle. As to his scholarly books of that *annus mirabilis*,
we shall come back to them presently. By this time Rabelais was in touch

with many humanists, such as his publisher Sébastien Gryphe,[89] Etienne Dolet, Guillaume Budé, even with Erasmus.

His horizon was much extended soon afterwards by his first visit to Rome, as secretary and physician to the bishop (later cardinal), Jean du Bellay. The visit lasted three or four months (January-April 1534); after spending the rest of that year in Lyon, he returned to Rome with the same patron (February-November 1535). Jean du Bellay was a grand seigneur, with many livings, among them the Benedictine abbey of Saint Maur les Fossés (near Paris), which he managed to transform into a collegiate church, selecting his friend Rabelais as one of the canons. The new canon was still restless and returned to Montpellier where he got his M.D. on 22 May 1537. Soon after that he is back in Lyon where he gives a public exhibition of anatomy, dissecting the body of a hanged man (such exhibitions were still uncommon). The fact is mentioned to illustrate the growing complexity of his labor—canon in St. Maur, physician in Montpellier, anatomist in Lyon, always a satirical observer of everybody and everything around him, his mind obsessed by Gargantuan fantasies. In 1538, he was in the train of Francis the First at Aigues-Mortes, where the king met Charles Quint. In the following year he was taken into the service of Guillaume du Bellay,[90] governor of Piemonte, who took him to Torino; his service was as complex as his own personality, for he was acting as secretary, physician, botanist, humanist. His novels got him into trouble, and no wonder. The *Tiers Livre* particularly (1546), in spite of its being dedicated to the Queen of Navarra,[91] was condemned by the Sorbonne, and he had to make himself scarce. He drifted to Metz, where he was appointed "orator" to the city. Once more the cardinal rescued him, and they spent two years together in Rome.

This was his third stay in the Eternal City and one can easily imagine how deeply his imagination would be stirred by all the memories alive in it, and his scholarship enriched. His last years are mysterious, but we know that he died in Paris in April 1553.

Now his work. The fantastic novels form the immortal background; let us give them their dates rapidly to provide a kind of frame (that frame is fundamental, for Rabelais would hardly be remembered today but for his romances): *Pantagruel* (Lyon, 1532), *Gargantua* (Lyon, 1534),[92] *Tiers Livre* (Paris, 1546), *Quart Livre* (Paris, 1552), the fifth book *L'isle sonnante,* posthumous (?, 1562). First edition of the whole (Lyon, 1565). The printers of these first editions were different for each one, and there were a good many other contemporary editions.

His most important scientific publication was printed by his friend, Sébastien Gryphe, in Lyon, 1532. It was the fruit of his first lectures in Montpellier after he had obtained his B.M., as small and thick as a prayer book.[93] It included the Latin translations of five medical treatises, plus the Greek text of the *Aphorisms* partly based upon a MS in his own possession (happy time when a poor scholar could ramble around the bookshops and find precious MSS which were not above his means). The five treatises were (1) the *Aphorisms* of Hippocrates and four Galenic ones, (2) *Praesagia*, (3) *De natura humana,* (4) *De ratione victus in morbis acutis,* and (5) the *Ars parva.* The selection was neither arbitrary nor original[94] and Rabelais was simply revising older translations, those of (1) and (5) by Leoniceno, of (2) and (4) by William Cop of Basel, and of (3) by Andreas Brentius. It was an *editio variorum* but not a critical edition (in our sense), and he was an amateur philologist; it may be disregarded today but it is an interesting monument illustrating the devotion of one of the greatest writers of the French Renaissance[95] to the most illustrious doctors of the Greek past. Rabelais used it to express his gratitude to his old friends, for it began with a preface to Geoffroy d'Estissac (dated 15 July 1532) and was dedicated to Tiraqueau.

This was not his first medical work. In the spring of the same year, he had prepared a new edition of the medical letters of Giovanni Manardi (589 pp.; Lyon: Sébastien Gryphe, 1532),[96] and in his dedication to Tiraqueau he explained that the first condition of medical progress was the recovery of Greek and Latin classics in new editions, cleaned from medieval accretions and properly elucidated. His commentary, however, was purely philological, not experimental.

During his first Roman stay he had tried to rediscover the traces of the ancient city and this induced him to edit the *Topographia antiquae Romae* of the Milanese Marliani[97] (Lyon: Séb. Gryphe, 1534); this book was very properly dedicated to Jean du Bellay.

Bibliographic note. The most elaborate study of Rabelais is the one by Jean Plattard (60 ill.; Paris: Van Oest, 1928; reprinted without the illustrations, Paris: Boivin, 1932). Jean Porcher: *Catalogue de l'exposition organisée à l'occasion du quatrième centenaire du Pantagruel* (Paris: Imprimerie nationale, 1932).

Critical edition of the novels by Abel Lefranc (1863-1952) and others (Paris: Champion, 1912—). Another edition was prepared by Plattard for the Association Guillaume Budé (5 vols.; Paris: Belles Lettres, 1929). Edition in one volume by Jacques Boulenger (Paris: Pléiade, 1933).

Anatole Félix Le Double: *Rabelais anatomiste et physiologiste* (454 pp., 32 facs., 174 ill.; Paris: Leroux, 1899), elaborate survey of Rabelais' knowledge in systematic order. Jean Plattard: "Les publications savantes de Rabelais," *Revue des études rabelaisiennes 2,* 67-77 (1904). René Sturel: "Rabelais et Hippocrate," *ibid. 6,* 49-55 (1908).

The Galenic work which had been so brilliantly begun by one Englishman, Thomas Linacre, was continued in the following generations by another, John Caius.[98] He was born in Norwich in 1510, was educated in that city and then at Gonville Hall,[99] Cambridge. The new Greek learning was stimulated in that city by the activities of Erasmus and of Cheke.[100] In 1539, he went to Padova where he lectured on the Greek Aristotle, studied medicine under Montanus[101] and anatomy under Vesalius who was then preparing his *Fabrica;* he resided eight months in the latter's house, the Casa degli valli near the Ponte della paglia. He must have learned to know Vesalius very well and one cannot help regret that he did not publish his reminiscences of him; he obtained his M.D. in Padova in 1541. During the two or three following years he traveled considerably in Italy, France, and Germany, meeting humanists and hunting for MSS of Galen and Hippocrates. Soon after his return home in 1544, he was charged by Henry VIII to deliver anatomical lectures in London and continued to do so for twenty years. He practised medicine and distinguished himself during an epidemy of the sweating sickness which he was one of the first to describe, first in English, then more elaborately in Latin.[102] He was physician to Edward VI, Mary, and Elizabeth, but the last named dismissed him in 1568 when he was known to be a Catholic. He had been converted probably in Padova, and his Catholicism caused increasing hostility against him under Elizabeth, especially after the Massacre of St. Bartholomew (24 August 1572); he died a year later in London (29 July 1573).

Before speaking of his Galenic contributions we must complete his portrait by a brief account of his educational and medical activities. He became a Fellow of the College of Physicians in 1547 and was elected nine times its president. He defended the physicians very successfully against the surgeons and obtained for them the permission to dissect the bodies of criminals who had been executed. In 1557, he reorganized his alma mater which was known from then on as Gonville and Caius, and he became its Master in 1559.

Caius was a good Hellenist, a man of great learning, presumably a good doctor and certainly a faithful defender of his profession and of his college, but he was stern, ungenial, and excessively conservative. He had enough medical experience to make good observations (e.g., of the sweating sickness) and to recognize good observations in ancient writings. His editions of many Galenic treatises and his English translations of a few were carefully made and obtained a well-deserved popularity not only in England, but also on the continent.

His first translation was of *De medendi methodo* (Basel, 1544; reprinted in Louvain, 1556, and Basel, 1558). This was dedicated to Sir William Butts (d.1545), physician to Henry VIII. His second publication (1544), dedicated to the king himself, contained six Galenic treatises[103] and one Hippocratic, all in Greek, and the first, *De placitis Hippocratis et Platonis,* with a Latin translation (this text had not been included in previous editions of Galen). Among the other Galenic texts we must mention one of immense importance, *De anatomicis administrationibus libri IX;* this was not a novelty but Caius' text was improved and annotated.

A few years later, he edited the Greek text of Galen's hygiene, *De tuenda valetudine* (Basel, 1549), dedicated to Edward VI. His *Opera aliquot et versiones* (Louvain: Bergagne, 1556) included reprints of *De medendi methodo* and *De ephemera britannica* (sweating sickness) and new Latin versions of Galen's two autobibliographic tracts, etc. Finally, the Greek text of a few more Galenic books was edited by him (Basel, 1557).

At the end of his life he wrote two Latin tracts on English dogs and the varieties of races (*De canibus britannicis libellus, de variorum animalium et stirpium historia libellus*), together with his own autobibliography (72 titles). The first of these tracts had been written for Conrad Gesner, who died in 1565. These three tracts were published together by William Seres[104] in London, 1569-70. The first two were translated into English by Abraham Fleming, *Of Englishe dogges, the diuersities and the properties,* and published by R. Johnes (London, 1576).

To complete our survey of Galenism during the Renaissance we must still say a few words about Brasàvola, who did for Galen what Foes did a generation later for Hippocrates.

Antonio Brasàvola[105] was born in Ferrara in 1500 and studied medicine in his native city under the direction of Niccolò Leoniceno. He distinguished himself so much and became so learned that he was patronized by the dukes of Ferrara, and was appointed physician to Francis I, Charles Quint, and Henry VIII, and to popes Clement VII, Paul III, and Julius III. Francis I gave him the name Musa, which was a way of flattering himself as well as his doctor.[106] One realizes that those appointments were honorific rather than practical and one wonders what Brasàvola had done to deserve them all; it is likely that each honor enabled him to obtain others; the favor of the lords of Ferrara would recommend him to kings and popes; it was a kind of chain reaction. After Leoniceno's death (in 1524) and even more so after Manardi's (in 1536), he was the main scientific ornament in the court and the University of Ferrara. He died in 1570.

His practical fame among physicians rested probably on a whole series of partial pharmacopoeias, which he began to publish in 1536, the title of each of them beginning with the words *Examen omnium* . . . :

Examen omnium simplicium medicamentorum quorum in officinis usus est (Rome: A. Bladus, 1536).

Examen omnium syruporum . . . (Venice: A. Bernardino, 1538).

Examen omnium catapotiorum vel pilularum . . . (Lyon: J Pullonus, 1545).

Examen omnium trochiscorum, unguentorum . . . (Venice: Juntae, 1551).

Examen omnium loch, id est linctuum, suffuf,[107] *id est pulverum, aquarum, decoctiorum, oleorum, quorum apud Ferrarienses pharmacopolas usus est ubi de morbo gallico diligentissime copioseque tractatur* . . . (Venice: Juntae, 1553).

De medicamentis tam simplicibus quam compositis catharticis . . . (Lyon: S. B. Honoratus, 1555).

There are various editions of these books; I have quoted the edition of each which I took to be the first. The main point is that Brasàvola was devoting much of his time to the publication of treatises dealing with separate classes of drugs according to their shape or to pharmacodynamic properties.

He wrote commentaries on Hippocrates and Galen, a treatise *De hominum aequalitate et quare alter alterum excellat* (Venice: S. Bernardino, 1537),[108] etc., all of which is mentioned simply to complete our picture of him.

His main help to the Galenic tradition was the preparation of an index which was elaborate, intelligent, and extremely useful. He provided a key to Galen which was the best available until the publication of the one by Fr. Guil. Assmann in 1833.[109] The index was made on the basis of the Juntine editions of Galen and was incorporated with these editions, but also sold separately: *Index refertissimus in omnes Galeni libros*. It was first added to the second Juntine edition (Venice, 1550), then to the subsequent ones until, at least, the ninth one (Venice, 1625).

If we wanted a set of reference books for the study of medical erudition during the Renaissance, we could not find better ones than the Galenic index by Brasàvola (1550), the Avicennian index by Palamedes (1562), the Hippocratic index by Foes (1588), the *Dictionarium medicum* by Henri Estienne (1564), and the *Definitiones medicae* by Gorraeus (1564). These five works were used by hundreds of learned physicians and exerted upon them a normative influence; they helped to stabilize the terminology and the opinions.

5. The Early Byzantine Physicians

THE GREEK TEXT OF SORANOS DISAPPEARED IN WESTERN EUROPE, BUT it was not lost and parts of it can be traced in the early Byzantine writings. One can even claim that irrespective of Caelius Aurelianus, Soranos was never completely lost in the West, because the works of the Byzantine physicians who referred to him were edited in Greek or at least in Latin by Renaissance scholars. Similar remarks apply to Rufus (in Oribasios there are many more references to Rufus than to Soranos).[110] The main

33

basis of the Byzantine writings, however, was Hippocratic and Galenic, and we must assume that Oribasios and his followers had easy access to a fairly good corpus of Greek medicine, a corpus in which Hippocrates and Galen held the lion's share.

It is essential, therefore, to consider Byzantine medicine in any survey, however brief, of the medical transition from Antiquity to the Renaissance. That tradition occurred along three main streams: (1) Latin (like Celsus, Caelius Aurelianus, Cassius Felix, Marcellus Empiricus), (2) Byzantine, then Latin, (3) Arabic-Latin-Hebrew. The first stream was the least important, and the second the most important, not only in itself, but also because the third was really a continuation of it. The only Byzantine physicians who deserve to be considered now are those who were pre-Islamic and made possible the main tradition, which may be summarized by the words *Byzantine-Arabic-Latin*.

These outstanding physicians of the pre-Islamic period were four: (1) Oribasios of Pergamon (IV-2), physician to Julian the Apostate; (2) Aëtios of Amida (VI-1), who flourished under Justinian; (3) Alexandros of Tralleis (VI-2), brother of Anthemios, one of the architects to whom the reconstruction of Hagia Sophia was intrusted in 532 (after long travels, Alexander finally settled down in Rome); (4) Paulos of Aigina (VII-1), who flourished in Alexandria and remained there after the Muslim invasion (640).[111]

The last two, but chiefly Paulos, exerted a great influence upon Arabic medicine, and their books continued to be read in the Byzantine world: witness a compilation like that of Nicetas (IX-2) and the Greek writings of later physicians. We are concerned at present mainly with the attention which Renaissance scholars paid to them.

Oribasios wrote an encyclopedia of medicine in seventy books (*Iatricai synagōgai*) including all the ancient Greek medicine that had come to him; it was the more precious because many ancient fragments (otherwise lost) were quoted verbatim. The work was so bulky, however, that it failed to be preserved completely; only one-third of it has come down to us.[112] He also wrote two smaller works, the *Synopsis* and the *Euporista*. The *Synopsis* in nine books was dedicated to his son Eustathios; the *Euporista*,[113] still shorter and more popular, in four books dedicated to Eunapios. The two shorter works were completely transmitted, and they were translated into Latin not later than the seventh century and possibly much earlier, in any case before the Iron Curtain separating the

Greek from the Latin world had been firmly established. The Arabic translators were more ambitious than the early Latin ones. A translation of the seventy books of Oribasios (that is, of his great encyclopedia) is ascribed to Iṣṭifān ibn Bāsīl (IX-2), that is, Stephanos son of Basilios, and to 'Isā ibn Yaḥyā (IX-2), both of whom were immediate disciples of the great Ḥunain ibn Isḥāq (IX-2) and his collaborators. This suggests that our knowledge of Oribasios' text may be eventually completed by the discovery of Arabic MSS.

The Western tradition of Oribasios was presumably built at first upon the early Latin translations. We may assume that such doctors as Simon of Genoa (XIII-2) and Francesco di Piedimonte (XIV-1) derived their knowledge of him from them, though they may have had access to Greek MSS; Simon at least knew Greek and Francesco flourished at the court of Naples where Hellenists were available.

During these medieval centuries, Galen's fame was growing fast. Oribasios' references to him were so numerous and full of praise that he helped to increase at the same time the Galenic supremacy and his own popularity. Only a small part of his work was printed in Greek in the sixteenth century, but much of it appeared in Latin. The first Latin translation was that of the *Euporista* by Johannes Sichardt (Basel: H. Petri, 1529); then followed a translation of Oribasios' commentary on the *Aphorisms* by Johann Günther (Paris: Sim. Colinaeus, 1533).

The main Latin translator, however, was Giovanni Battista Rosario, who published the *Collecta medicinalia*. These were printed by Turrisanus in Paris, 1555, by Isingrinius in Basel, 1557, and a third time by Etienne in Paris, 1567; there is also an undated Aldine edition. Rosario also published the *Synopsis ad Eustathium* (Venice: P. Manutius, 1554) and the *Euporista ad Eunapium* (Venice: ex officina erasmiana Vincentii Valgrisii, 1558). The preface of the last-named book was dated January 1557 and thus we understand that the *Opera omnia*, as Latinized by Rosario, could appear in the same year (Basel: Michael Isingrinius, 1557).

Giovanni Battista Rosario, who did so much to introduce Oribasios to the Renaissance physicians, deserves to be introduced himself to our readers. He was born in 1517 in Valduggia near Novara, Piemonte, and died in Pavia in 1578. He studied in Milano and Pavia and taught rhetoric and Greek in Venice for twenty-two years (c.1552-74). At the request of Philip II of Spain he accepted the chair of rhetoric in Pavia, but died four years later, 1578. He was a member of the Accademia degli Affidati in Padova. He published many translations from Greek into Latin, but none was medical except his Oribasios. There is no evidence that he was otherwise interested in medicine.[114]

The Greek text of Oribasios was hardly available before the nineteenth century. We owe to the Frenchman, Charles Daremberg (1817-72), and the Dutchman,

Ulco Cats Bussemaker (1810-65), an excellent Greek-French edition of the whole works in six large volumes (Paris: Imprimerie Nationale, 1851-76). They were able to see vols. 1-4 (1851-62) through the press; these volumes contain whatever remains of the *Synagogai*. Vols. 5-6 (1873-76) were edited posthumously by Auguste Molinier. These six volumes contain not only all the works of Oribasios in Greek and French but also the early Latin translations of the *Synopsis* and the *Euporista* and an excellent index. They constitute one of the finest monuments of French learning, next to Littré's Hippocrates, and were in fact dedicated to him.

The edition of Oribasios in the *Corpus Medicorum Graecorum* was undertaken by Joannes Raeder; the *Synopsis* and the *Euporista* appeared in 1926; the *Collecta medicinalia* were published in four parts, 1928-33. Unfortunately, many parts of Raeder's edition were war casualties and are no longer available. Indices are being prepared by M. Häsler.

We must deal a little more rapidly with the three other Byzantine authors.

Aëtios of Amida (VI-1) wrote a shorter medical encyclopedia than Oribasios. It extends to four times four books and the Greek text of Books I to VIII was published by Aldus Manutius and Andreas Asulanus in Venice as early as September 1534 (the rest remained unpublished).[115] A Latin translation of the whole work was prepared by Joh. Bapt. Montanus and Janus Cornarius (Basel: Froben, 1533-35); a better translation by Cornarius alone appeared a few years later (Basel: Froben and Episcopius, 1542). This second translation was reprinted at least twice in the sixteenth century by Farrea in Venice, 1543-44, and by the brothers Beringen[116] in Lyon, 1549.

The most original and valuable of Aëtios' sixteen books was the seventh, treating eye diseases. This was known in medieval times and used by Arabic ophthalmologists such as Ṣalāḥ al-dīn ibn Yūsuf (XIII-2).

A critical edition of Aëtios is in course of publication in CMG. Books I to VIII were edited by the late Alexander Olivieri (1935-50—*Isis 42*, 150-52). The edition of the remaining books was almost completed by him in MS at the time of his death.

We do not know the exact limits of Aëtios' life, but he flourished under Justinian (emp., 527-65). Our information concerning Alexander of Tralleis (VI-2) is a little better; he was born in Tralleis, Lydia, *c.*525, and after many peregrinations settled in Rome; he died in 605. He was thus a younger contemporary of Aëtios; while the latter was established in the new capital, Constantinople, Alexander moved to the old one. This is very interesting in many respects. Was Greek still understood in Rome at the end of the sixth century and did Greek learning receive any appreciation? It is true Alexander's learning was medical, practical, of immediate use. His encyclopedia was reduced to twelve books, and like that of Aëtios included new facts as well as old ones (e.g., the earliest references to intestinal worms or to the drug rhubarb).

It was translated (or parts of it were translated) into Latin, Syriac, Arabic, and known not only to Byzantine physicians but also to Latin ones such as Roger of Salerno (XII-2), Roland of Parma (XIII-1), Lanfranchi (XIII-2), Matthaeus Sylvaticus (XIV-1), Joannes Jacobi (XIV-2). He was almost the only one of the early Byzantine doctors to be represented in the incunabula, that is, if the *Practica Alexandri yatros greci* was really printed before 1501.[117] His *Biblia iatrica* (as the encyclopedia was called) was completely edited in the original Greek by Jacques Goupyl before the middle of the sixteenth century (Paris: Rob. Etienne, 1548), but the princeps had been preceded by Latin versions, the partial ones already referred to (1500?, 1504). An incomplete Latin translation by Albanus Torinus was printed in 1533 (Basel: Heinrich Petrus), improved and completed *ibidem*, 1541. Latin translation of the twelve books by Günther (Strassburg, 1549) was reprinted in Lyon, 1560 and 1576. Günther's translation was also reprinted with the Greek text by Heinrich Petrus[118] of Basel in August 1556.

We must stop to salute the editor of the princeps, Jacques Goupyl, born c.1525 at Luçon in Poitou. He studied in Poitiers and Paris, obtaining his medical degree in 1548, and was so much appreciated that Henry II appointed him as successor of Jacques Dubois (Sylvius, 1478-1555) in the chair of medicine of the Collège Royal. He was a Hellenist as well as a physician; he had accumulated a large collection of MSS and printed books the destruction of which in 1563 during a tumult hastened his death, which occurred in the following year. He edited many Greek medical classics.

Albanus Torinus, whose original name was Alban Thorer, was of Swiss origin. He was born in Winterthur in 1489, studied philology in Basel, became rector of the Peterschule and professor of rhetoric in the Academy. It was only then that he began the study of medicine; he obtained his M.D. in France (?) and became physician to the Markgraf Ernst von Baden and professor of theoretical medicine in Basel (1537). He died in that city in 1550. He translated many medical classics into Latin and devoted many studies to Greek medicine.

A critical edition of the Greek text was prepared by Theodore Puschmann and published with a German translation (2 vols.; Wien, 1878-79); French translation by F. Brunet (4 vols.; Paris, 1933-37—*Isis 30*, 141). A fifth volume advertised to include the Greek text has not yet reached me.

The last of the great Byzantine physicians, Paulos, hailed from the island of Aigina in the Saronic Gulf; he flourished in Alexandria and was there at the time of the Arabic invasion (640) or soon after. He wrote a new medical encyclopedia in seven books (the encyclopedias of Oribasios, Aëtios, and Alexander extended respectively to seventy, sixteen, and twelve books), of which the most important were probably those dealing with surgery and obstetrics. His influence upon Muslim medicine was enormous; this is not surprising considering that he lived in Egypt in contact with Arabic doctors and that his encyclopedia was the last word in Greek medicine. It was translated into Arabic by Ḥunain ibn Isḥāq (IX-2), either in Jundīshāpūr or in Baghdād, and from then on became part and parcel of the treasure of knowledge available to Arabic readers. The surgery of Abulcasis or Abū-l-Qāsim al-Zahrāwī (X-2), a treatise almost unique of its kind in Arabic literature, was largely derived from Paulos' surgery (Book VI of his encyclopedia). Paulos' work was naturally preserved in the Byzantine libraries, was used by Nicetas (IX-2), Nonnos (X-1), referred to by Suidas (X-2), etc. On the other hand, his influence upon Catholic Europe was very small because an Iron Curtain was now separating it almost completely from the Orthodox world. Book III, however, dealing with topical diseases from head to foot was Latinized in South Italy as early as the IX/Xth century.[119] A few medieval physicians, such as Simon of Genoa (XIII-2), Francesco di Piedimonte (XIV-1), Guy de Chauliac (XIV-2) were somewhat acquainted with his work.

The Greek text was printed for the first time by the Aldine press in Venice, 1528; a second Greek edition with additions by Hieronymus Gemusäus was issued by their rival, Andreas Cratandrus, in Basel, 1538.

Latin translations had begun to appear early in the sixteenth century, the earliest being one by William Cop, of the first book only (Paris: Henri Etienne sr., 1510); the first complete Latin translation was prepared by Günther of Andernach and printed by Simon Colinaeus[120] (Paris, 1532); it was reprinted by Wendelinus Richelius (Strassburg, 1542), by Turrisanus (Venice, 1553 or 1554), by G. Rovillius [121] (Lyon, 1553). An almost complete translation by Albanus Torinus was printed by A. Cratandrus and J. Bebelius (Basel, 1532); it lacked the surgical book (VI), of which the same printers published a translation by J. Bern. Feliciano in the following year. The incompleteness of Torinus' translation was thus deliberate. The whole text (Torinus plus Book VI) was printed by Balthasar Lasius (Basel, 1538) and by J. Oporinus (Basel, 1546). A third translation by Janus Cornarius was printed by J. Hervagius(Basel, 1556).

To these early Latin editions should be added the French translation of Book VI (surgery) by Pierre Tolet, printed by Etienne Dolet (Lyon, 1540).

Pierre Tolet (born in Lyon *c.*1502; died in the eighties) studied medicine in Montpellier with Rabelais, who befriended him and mentioned him in *Pantagruel*. He was physician of the Hotel Dieu of Lyon, distinguished himself in the epidemics of 1564 and 1577, and was attached to the service of Charles IX, Henri III, and Catherine de Médicis. Some five books are ascribed to him of which *La chirurgie de Paulus Aegineta* (Lyon, 1540) seems to be the most important[122].

His printer, Etienne Dolet (1509-46), born in Orléans but established in Lyon, was not only a publisher but a distinguished Latinist, one of the leading French humanists of his day, whom one must name together with Guillaume Budé (1467-1540) and Robert Estienne (1503-59). He was a defender of free thought, and various pamphlets issuing from his shop caused him to be denounced by the Sorbonne and burnt alive in the Place Maubert in Paris, 1546. On that account, he has become the most famous of all the sixteenth-century printers, the martyr printer, and many biographies help to immortalize him.[123]

Our own contemporaries have a complete English translation by Francis Adams (3 vols.; London: Sydenham Society, 1844-47), a Greek-French edition of Book VI by René Briau: *La chirurgie de Paul d'Egine* (Paris, 1855), and a critical edition of the Greek text prepared by J. L. Heiberg for the CMG (2 vols.; 1921-24).

6. AVICENNA (XI-1)

THE TRADITION OF ORIBASIOS, AETIOS, ALEXANDROS, AND PAULOS HAS prepared us to consider Arabic medicine. We have seen that Byzantine medicine was preserved very imperfectly by Latin translations and much better in the original Greek, but the Greek text was not known on this side of the Iron Curtain before the sixteenth century. What happened to it in the meanwhile? While the physicians of the Greek world, especially those living in cultural centers like Constantinople, Alexandria, Antioch, Pergamon, Trebizond, Thessalonica had been able to consult the MSS if they had sufficient curiosity to do so, a warmer reception was given to those very MSS in Eastern cities, such as Jundīshāpūr at first, later Baghdād where they were translated into Syriac and into Arabic. The main translators were Ḥunain ibn Isḥāq (IX-2) and the members of his school. Thanks to their almost incredible zeal, the best of Greek and Byzantine medicine was available to Arabic readers by the end of the ninth century.

Then followed a century of cogitation and experience, and there emerged something new—Arabic medicine—built upon a Greek basis but with many original additions. Let me just repeat a few names to awaken your memory (I quote first the Latin form with which you are more familiar than with the Arabic which is more correct; and we must go back to the first half of the ninth century, because Arabic medicine developed before the Greek corpus had been completely Arabicized) : Mesuë major or Yūḥannā ibn Māsawaih (IX-1) and 'Alī ibn Sahl ibn Rabbān al-Ṭabarī (IX-1), the latter already bringing to light novelties borrowed from Hindu sources as well as from Greek ones or from their own experience; Rhazes or Muḥammad ibn Zakariyā al-Rāzī (IX-2), who lived until 925;[124] Serapion senior or Yaḥyā ibn Sarāfyūn (IX-2); Isaac Judaeus or Isḥāq al-Isrā'īlī (X-1); Haly Abbas or 'Alī ibn 'Abbās (X-2); Abulcasis or Abū-l-Qāsim al-Zahrāwī (X-2); Ibn al-Jazzār (X-2) —and we may add Abū Manṣūr Muwaffaq (X-2), who wrote in Persian; Mesuë junior or Māsawaih al-Māridīnī (XI-1), who died in 1015 in very old age; Canamusali or 'Ammār ibn 'Alī (XI-1); Jesu Haly or 'Alī ibn 'Isā (XI-1).

Two of these writers had already found it necessary to compile medical encyclopedias: the *Kitāb al-ḥāwī* (*Continens*) of al-Rāzī (IX-2) and the *Kitāb al-malikī* (*Liber regius, Regalis dispositio*) of 'Alī ibn 'Abbās (X-2). The popularity of these two works is attested by the existence of many incunabula; *Elhavi sive Continens* was printed by J. Britannicus in Brescia, 1486; the *Liber Almansoris* (an abbreviation of the *Continens*) was printed thrice before 1501; an Italian translation of its *Liber tertius* was printed twelve times and the *Liber nonus* was often printed with other medical books; the *Regalis dispositio* was published by Rizus for Nigro in Venice, 1492.[125]

Avicenna or Ibn Sīnā (980-1037) was the climax not only of the Greek efforts, which had covered more than eleven centuries, but also of the Arabic ones, which had extended the Greek experience by at least two centuries. Let us consider a moment his gigantic personality and his *Canon*. There are but few greater personalities in the history of science than Avicenna; he was great not only as a physician but also as a philosopher, and his influence in both fields was so persuasive and durable that it is still reaching us today. He was born in Afshana near Bukhārā, in Transoxiana, in 370 (= 980/81) and died in 428 (= 1036/37)[126] in Hamadhān where his grave is visited by pilgrims to this day. Should we call him an Arab (he wrote in Arabic), a Persian, or a Turk?[127] We need not worry about that, for he is one of the greatest world citizens, and transcends all the boundaries. His personality illustrated the complexities of language, race, and religion which obtained in his part of the world, but we are concerned only with his work. He was a man of encyclopedic genius and on the basis of the immense treasure of Greco-Byzantine-Arabic knowledge which he had inherited he composed a philosophical encyclopedia, *Kitāb al-shifā'*, and a medical one, the *Qānūn fī-l-ṭibb*, which superseded the earliest medical encyclopedias and remained a kind of medical bible for at least six centuries. It was the medical bible not only of the Middle Ages, but also of the Renaissance, and it survived the latter by at least a century and a half.

By the way, the Greek-Arabic culture out of which Avicenna emerged is symbolized by the title of his book, as it was by the title of Ptolemy's. *Almagest* is a bastard Greek-Arabic word; *Canon* or *Qānūn* (as it is written in Arabic) is entirely Greek. The Greek word *canōn* designates a straight rod, a carpenter's rule, a standard (Lat. *norma*); its plural *canones* referred to classics (standard books); *canon* or *canones* was used also to designate laws, decrees, official standards, or collections (such as the Biblical ones). Avicenna's work was a kind of codification of Greek (and Arabic) knowledge, like Galen's but more elaborate, and it had the advantage of being a single monument. For the physician, the words *Canon* and Avicenna were almost interchangeable, whereas the Galenic authority was dispersed in a number of separate works, each with a tradition of its own.

It was easy to outline the tradition of Oribasios or Paulos, but it would be very difficult or rather long and tedious to retrace the Avicennian tradition because hundreds of names would have to be mentioned and the reader would be completely bewildered.[128] The *Canon* was so large a work that copyists might be frightened by its mass, yet there are a number of MSS in Arabic, Latin, and Hebrew; and smaller MSS containing parts of it are innumerable.[129]

There is one moment of the medieval tradition which must be evoked. The *Canon* was translated into Latin by Gerard of Cremona (XII-2) and that translation remained the basis of almost every Latin edition. Gerard had come from Lombardy to Castile in order to study Arabic and found ideal conditions in Toledo, which was then a Christian city with a large Arabic-speaking population.[130] Under the patronage of the archbishop of Toledo and the direction of a great man, Gerard of Cremona, an incredibly large number of Arabic books were translated into Latin, the two most important being the *Almagest* (1175) and the *Canon*.

In spite of its immense size the *Qānūn* was printed in Latin at least a dozen times before 1501. Some fourteen Latin incunabula are listed by Klebs (131); but one at least, the first (Milano or Padova, end of 1472), was restricted to Books I-III. To these Latin incunabula must be added a Hebrew one. The Hebrew translation of the whole *Qānūn* was made by Nathan ha-Me'ati in Rome, 1279, and revised by Joseph Ibn Vives ha-Lorqi before 1402 (*Introd. 2,* 854); it was edited by Asher ben Perez Minz and Abraham ben Jacob Landau and printed by 'Azri'el ben Joseph in Naples, 1491. It was published in three parts, totaling 476 leaves, folio, printed in two columns (Klebs 132; *Osiris 5,* 109; facsimiles on pp. 148-49).

We must still mention the first Arabic edition, a splendid folio printed by the Typographia Medicea in Rome, 1593. It is one of the Arabic "incunabula,"[131] and the largest one, being almost equaled by the Arabic Euclid which issued from the same press in the following year.[132]

What astonishes one with regard to the Latin incunabula is not only their number but also the number of printers who were in competition. At the present time a work of such size could hardly be printed at all; it certainly could not be printed on a commercial basis. In the fifteenth century, however, there were presumably so many potential buyers of that medical bible that many printers were trying to satisfy them. These incunabula were printed in Strassburg, Lyon, and no less than five Italian cities: Milano, Padova, Bologna, Pavia, and Venice. In Venice no less than five different printers were competing with one another. This speaks volumes for the importance of the Venetian book trade; we know that it was international and the local market would have been unable to support it.

The basic text of all the early Latin sixteenth-century editions was the translation of Gerard of Cremona (XII-2), but some editions contained additional material. Out of the fourteen incunabula, two of them included another text of Avicenna, the *Cantica de medicina,* and nine of them his *De viribus cordis.* The richest incunabulum was the last, printed by Bevilaqua (Venice, 1500); it included those two texts plus the *Quaestio de febre* and other treatises by Gentile da Foligno (XIV-1). As the fourteen incunabula of the *Canon* (with addenda or without) were issued by fourteen different printers, I shall not attempt to discuss them individually.

A few remarks must suffice. The edition printed by Joannes Herbort in Padova, 1476, was revised by two physicians, the Paduan Prosdocimus Mutius (Muzio?) and the Venetian Petro Rochabonelle. It is a folio of 482 leaves with *seven* colophons. The notes of these two doctors were reproduced in the Venetian edition of 1490 and possibly in others. The edition printed by Baptista de Tortis in Venice, 1494, has a preface by Antonius Gratarolus. These editors are otherwise unknown to me.

Choulant lists thirteen sixteenth-century editions; his list is probably incomplete, but sufficient for our survey. These thirteen editions were printed by an entirely new set of printers, one in Pavia (1510-11), another in Lyon (1522), another in Basel (1556), and four in Venice. The Venetian printers were Paganinus (1507), Filippo Pinzi (1523), Vinc. Valgrisius, and the Juntae; the last named, the Juntine firm, issued seven editions between 1527 and 1597.

The sixteenth-century editions varied in contents as much as the incunabula, if not more, as each publisher must try to offer some kind of novelty, but the basis remained medieval. The main innovation occurred in the Juntine editions wherein the old translation by Gerard of Cremona was revised by Andreas Alpagus and explained by Benedict Rinius (Venice, 1527, 1544, 1555, 1582, 1595).

This introduces a very curious episode in the history of Arabic learning in the West. Andrea Alpago[133] of Belluno (Veneto) was born *c.* 1440; he spent some thirty years in the Near East, residing for a long time (*c.*1487 ff.) in Damascus where he was physician to the Venetian colony. He obtained a fluent knowledge of Arabic and translated various Arabic books into Latin. His main translation was that of Avicenna's *Canon*. He left Damascus *c.*1517-20, resided a few years at Nicosia, Cyprus, then returned to Italy; he taught medicine at Padova, but died soon afterwards in 1521. He added to his translation of the *Canon* an elaborate Arabic-Latin glossary; this was edited by his nephew, Paolo Alpago, who had been with him in the Near East. A deeper study of the Juntine editions would reveal to what extent Alpago modified the medieval translation of the *Canon*. Was Gerard's translation erroneous in any important respect? It will not be possible to answer such questions until we have a critical edition of the Arabic text, and the translations of the twelfth and sixteenth centuries have been collated, a tremendous undertaking which would require a scholar's lifetime.

Each publisher tried to enlist the coöperation of a distinguished scholar who would revise the text, add notes, or write a preface. For example, the edition published by Jacques Myt (Lyon, 1522) included notes by Symphorien Champier. The Juntine edition of 1544 contained the Latin translation of an Arabic biography[134] of Avicenna by Niccolò Massa. This is puzzling: Massa was an outstanding anatomist, professor in Padova, discoverer of the prostate (d. 1569). Did he know Arabic? Did he know it well enough to translate an Arabic text from MS? Of course, the translation might have been made for him or he might have been helped by an Arabic-speaking man of whom there may have been quite a few in the Venetian district. Massa's translation was reprinted in many other editions (1556, 1582, 1595, 1608).

The Juntine edition of 1562 is sometimes called the Palamedes edition because it contains an *Index in Avicennam* compiled by Julius Palamedes.[135] The index was reprinted separately: *Index in Avicennae libros nuper Venetiis editos Julio Palamede Adriensi medico auctore* (76 leaves, folio; Venice: Juntae, 1584). The edition printed by Vinc. Valgrisius (Venice, 1564) was prepared by J. Paulus Mongius and J. Costaeus, who revised the Alpagus text. Giovanni Costeo was born in Lodi, practised medicine in Torino, taught it in Bologna, and died in 1603. He wrote various medical books, also commentaries on Mesuë and Avicenna.

The Juntine edition of 1582 which I used and described (*Introd. 1,* 711) combines many features of the previous ones.

The seventeenth-century editions do not concern us because they are definitely post-Renaissance, but we may remark that some continued to be published until the end of the century. The latest complete edition of the *Canon* known to me was the Juntine of 1608 (2 vols., folio), but many partial editions appeared later.

The most important of the incomplete editions was the one prepared by an illustrious professor of medicine, Plempius,[136] and printed in Louvain, 1658. Tomus I (the only one published; in 2 parts, folio) included Books I and II of the *Canon,* and *fann* 1 of Book IV dealing with fevers. Apparently, Plempius had planned to publish the whole *Canon.*

Let me mention a few other partial editions. The most interesting is the one by the German, Peter Kirsten,[137] restricted to Book II of the *Canon* in Arabic and Latin (132 pp., folio; Breslau, 1609-10).

There are many commentaries on this or that part of the *Canon,* and following an old tradition these commentaries generally included the original text (in Latin). The medical generalities (*fann* 1 of Book I) attracted the attention of medical professors. For example, the commentary *ad hoc* by the scientific physician, Santorio,[138] was printed in Venice, 1625; again, 1646, 1660. A singular case is that of Pierre Vattier[139] (1623-67), physician to Gaston, duke of Orléans; it is said that Vattier studied Arabic for the sake of reading Avicenna in the original and became so proficient that he was appointed professor of Arabic at the Collège de France. We owe him many translations from the Arabic into French or Latin, particularly his Latin translation of the Avicennian psychology (fifteen chapters of Book III, and one of Book IV) published in Paris, 1659. A commentary on Book III by Diversus[140] of Faenza was published in Padova, 1673 (folio). The book on fever (Canon IV, 1) was often reprinted with commentaries, e.g., by J. B. Pasquati (Padova, 1659). An earlier commentary by Giovanni Arcolani[141] of Verona (d. 1460 or 1484) was printed in Ferrara, 1488; Venice, 1496 (Klebs 80); Venice, 1512; Lyon, 1518; Venice, 1560; Padova, 1685 (1685!).

These post-Harveian editions were not published to satisfy the curiosity of dilettanti or scholars, but for medical use (*Isis 43,* 54). The fame of Avicenna was so great that medical progress did not shake it and there was still a professional market for the *Canon* during the whole of the seventeenth century. Could a better example of spiritual inertia be found?

The survival of his fame is the more inexplicable when we remember that the efforts of the humanists since Petrarca had been primarily directed against Arabic medicine. Their main purpose was to resurrect Greek knowledge and to clean it of medieval (Arabic) additions; indeed, their love of Greece and Rome was nourished by their hatred of Islām.

It may be true to say that the medical humanists of the Renaissance were Greek-minded, antimedieval and anti-Oriental, and yet they could not bury Avicenna, who was almost as alive in the sixteenth century as were Hippocrates and Galen. They succeeded so little in overcoming him that a new Arabic Renaissance was initiated in the seventeenth century. While the learned physicians of the sixteenth century studied Greek in order to improve their medical knowledge, we come across two physicians of the seventeenth century, the German Kirsten and the Frenchman Vattier, who learned Arabic for the purpose of reading Avicenna in the original.

7. MEDICAL COLLECTIONS

IN ORDER TO APPRECIATE THE RENAISSANCE OF ANCIENT MEDICINE, WE must still say a few words of various collections. Some of them have already been referred to as we went along, but it is useful to consider them together.

The two oldest and most popular were the *Articella* and the *Fusciculus medicinae*.

The *Articella* (Klebs 116) was a collection of seven medical treatises printed in Padova in an unknown shop before 1476. A second edition including four more treatises was printed by Liechtenstein (Venice, 1483). The following editions contained the eleven texts, six of them Hippocratic, two Galenic, the books on pulse and urine by Theophilos Protospatharios (VII-1), and the *Isagoge Johannitii ad Tegni Galeni* of Hunain ibn Ishāq (IX-2). There were altogether six incunabula editions, all Venetian, except the first incomplete one. There were at least eight more editions in the sixteenth century, the last in Lyon, 1525 (Choulant, 402). The editor of the *Articella* collection is not known, but the other collection, the *Fasciculus medicinae*, was put together by Joannes de Ketham, a German physician perhaps identical with Johann von Kirchheim, professor at Vienna, c.1460. It is certain that he was a German and very probable that he flourished not long before the publication of the *Fasciculus medicinae* (say, after 1450).

The *Fasciculus medicinae* (Klebs 573-75) was published later than the *Articella* (first ed. of *F.m.*, Venice: Gregoriis, 1491), but it was equally popular and it is far more important. It contained more novelties and was beautifully illustrated with woodcuts. There are eight incunabula editions, four in Latin, one in Italian, and three in Spanish. The Latin and Italian editions were all by the same printer, Gregoriis in Venice; the three Spanish editions appeared within fourteen months, the first in Saragossa (1494), the two others (1493) in Burgos and Pamplona. In addition, there were at least five sixteenth-century editions, two in Latin (1513, 1522) and three in Italian (1508, 1509, 1522). These thirteen editions are very different in content (for a simple analysis, see Klebs), but the main ingredients are medieval. Indeed, elements of the *Fasciculus* had been circulating in MS a century before its appearance in print and the six full-page woodcuts of the first edition (1491) symbolized medieval medicine: a circle of urinals, the vein man, the zodiacal man, the pregnant woman, the wound man, the disease man; they constituted the first series of didactic medical illustrations to appear in print.

The *Articella* was a collection of ancient and early medieval treatises; the *Fasciculus medicinae* was not by any means modern at the time of its appearance, but it contained, in addition to texts by Rhazes (IX-2) and Michael Scot (XIII-2), the anatomy of Mondino (XIV-1) and the plague treatise of Pietro da Tossignano (XIV-2); the Spanish incunabula even included another plague treatise by Valesco de Taranta, who wrote at the beginning of the fifteenth century (*Introd. 3,* 1199).

The popularity of the *Fasciculus medicinae,* continuing at least until 1522, shows that the Renaissance doctors preferred to drink from ancient and medieval sources.

The text and illustrations of that famous medical work are well known, thanks to the splendid facsimile editions of the first edition (Latin; Venice, 1491) by Karl Sudhoff and Charles Singer (Milan, 1924—*Isis 6,* 547-49) and of the second (first Italian; Venice, 1493) by Singer (Florence, 1925—*Isis 8,* 350). Both editions include elaborate introductions, notes, and abundant illustrations.

Still a third medical collection was started before the end of the fifteenth century, the so-called *Collectio chirurgica veneta,*[142] a collection of surgical writings clustered around the *Chirurgia* of Guy de Chauliac (XIV-2); it includes writings of Canamusali (XI-1), Jesu Haly (XI-1), Roger of Salerno (XII-2), Roland of Parma (XIII-1), Theodoric of Cervia (XIII-1), Lanfranc of Milan (XIII-2), Bruno da Longoburgo (XIII-2), Leonardo Bertapaglia (XV-1), and Tura da Castello (XV-2). This was published in Venice, 1498 and 1499 (Klebs 494), a smaller collection again in Venice, 1500 (Klebs 497). Later editions, 1513, 1519, 1546 (Choulant, 417). The six editions mentioned were all published in Venice, at least four printing shops being involved.

The many collections which originated in the sixteenth century must be listed briefly; none enjoyed the popularity of the fifteenth-century ones. At any rate, they were not reprinted as frequently, but we must bear in mind that the editions were probably larger.

Albanus Torinus (Alban Thorer of Winterthur, 1489-1550) published a collection[143] of ancient medical treatises with *index locupletissimus* (Basel: Cratandrus, 1528).

The *Collectio diaetetica,* first published by Henry Sybold in Strassburg, 1530, was reprinted in Paris, 1533, and Frankfurt, 1564, 1571. It included texts by Polybos of Cos (IV-1 B.C.), Aristotle, the *Hortulus* of Walafrid Strabo (IX-1), and many pieces by a contemporary, Helius Eobanus Hessus (Elias Göbbchen, d. 1540); the collection is literary, poetical, rather than scientific; Eobanus the Hessian was professor of poetry in Marburg.

A collection of veterinary writings was edited by Jean Ruel of Soissons (1479-1537) and printed by Simon Colinaeus (Paris, 1530). It includes all the ancient writers especially Apsyrtos (IV-1) and Hierocles (IV-2). A similar collection was edited in the Greek original by Simon Grynaeus (1493-1541) and printed by J. Valderus (Basel, 1537). Other collections were published in Italian (Venice: Mich. Tramezino, 1543), in French by Jean Massé, Champenois (Paris: Charles Périer, 1563) and in German by Gregor Zechendorfer (Eger: Hans Burger, 1571). These vernacular editions were needed, because the average "vet" was not a Latinist.

Joannes Caesarius[144] edited together (Strassburg: Jac. Cammer-lander, 1534) the *Isagoge in artem parvam Galeni* by Ḥunain ibn Isḥāq (IX-2), the *Ars medendi* of Copho of Salerno (XII-1) and the *Diaeta* of Niccolò Bertruccio (XIV-1).

A similar collection was edited in the same year by Christopher Heyll, physician in Wiesbaden (Mainz: Johann Schoeffer, 1534). It includes Heyll's translation or paraphrase of Galen's *De constitutione artis medicae,* the commentary of John of Saint Armand (XIII-2) on the antidotary of Nicholas of Salerno (XII-1), a treatise by Niccolò Bertruccio (XIV-1), and a common index to the antidotaries of Mesuë Junior (XI-1) and Nicholas.

The *Experimentarius medicinae* (Strassburg: J. Schott, 1544) offered to its readers texts by Hippocrates, Oribasios (IV-2), Theodorus Priscianus (IV-2), Trotula (XII-1), Hildegard (XII-2), with a few woodcuts illustrating Eva's creation, her expulsion from Paradise, and the saints Cosmas and Damian, the first with a urinal, the second with a spatula.[145]

Note the strong medieval character of these medical collections of 1534 and 1544 printed at about the same time as Vesalius' *Fabrica* (1543).

The surgical collections which I shall mention now are necessarily more scientific. The earliest, the Venetian one (1498 to 1546), has been discussed above. The second or Parisian collection, edited by Guido Guidi (d. Pisa, 1569) and published by P. Galterius (Paris, 1544), was less modern, being restricted to Hippocrates, Galen, and Oribasios. This is significant, because Guidi must have handled one or the other edition of the *Collectio veneta,* yet decided that it was better to publish only the more ancient treatises.

The *Collectio tigurina,* edited by the illustrious Conrad Gesner (1516-65) and printed by the brothers Gesner (Zürich, 1555), was a welcome reaction, which its title reveals: *Chirurgia, de chirurgia scriptores optimi quique veteres et recentiores, plerique in Germania antehac non editi, nunc primum in unum conjuncti volumen.* It includes the writings of many modern surgeons, even contemporaries, and is illustrated with woodcuts.

We have abandoned the chronological order a moment for the sake of comparing the three early surgical collections: Venice, 1498 to 1546; Paris, 1544; Zürich, 1555. Though available at about the same time, they were strikingly different. The earliest was the most popular.

The sons of Aldus, who controlled the great Aldine typography of Venice, published in 1547 a medical collection of ancient authors and a few medieval ones like Walafrid Strabo (IX-1), *Macer floridus* (XI-2), Trotula (XII-1). Nothing newer except a letter by Janus Cornarius, *De hippocraticae medicinae dignitate,* which is more in the nature of editorial commentary.

One might perhaps insert here the *Commentarii* of Joachim Camerarius the elder (1500-74), published by J. Hervagius (Basel, 1551), a folio of xliv pp., 498 col., plus index. The *Commentarii utriusque linguae in quibus est . . . diligens exquisitio nominum, quibus partes corporis humani appellari solent . . .* is an elaborate anatomical dictionary with Latin and Greek indices. Two other medical dictionaries were published in Paris thirteen years later (see below).

Ancient and medieval physicians were much interested in balneology (the use of springs, of baths, and all that goes with them) and a collection of writings *ad hoc* was issued by the Juntine press (Venice, 1553), *De balneis omnia quae extant apud Graecos, Latinos et Arabas, tam medicos quam quoscunque ceterarum artium probatos scriptores . . . ,* a thick folio with a few illustrations. The contents are rich and the unnamed editor must have been very learned.

The two dictionaries referred to a moment ago were both published in Paris in the same year, 1564. The first was the *Dictionarium medicum* compiled and published by Henri Estienne II (1528-98), better known under his Latin name Stephanus. The second, the *Definitiones medicae,* was compiled by Gorraeus.[146] Both were large dictionaries needed for the understanding of the Greek medical writings. The second was many times reprinted (1578, 1601, 1622). There was great need of such tools, because every learned physician was anxious to understand the ancient classics as well as possible.

Three gynecological collections were published in the second half of the sixteenth century. The first was edited by Caspar Wolf (Basel: Th. Guarinus, 1566); the second, by the Swiss botanist and anatomist, Gaspard Bauhin, 1560-1624 (Basel: Conrad Waldkirck, 1586), the third, by Israel Spach, with woodcuts (Strassburg: Laz. Zetzner, 1597).

The Aldine collection of 1547, *Medici antiqui omnes . . . ,* was superseded by a much richer one edited by Henri Estienne: *Medicae artis principes post Hippocratem et Galenum, Graeci latinitate donati* (2 vols., folio; Paris, 1567). Another collection of the same kind but much smaller was prepared by Junius Paulus Crassus (d. 1574) and edited posthumously by his son (Basel: Pt. Perna, 1581). A series of Greek, Latin, and Arabic treatises on fever (all in Latin) was printed by Gratiosus Perchacinus, at the expense of Gaspard Bindoni: *De febribus opus sane aureum* (Venice, 1576). It was reprinted by Rob. Meiettus (Venice, 1594).

This was the last of the Renaissance collections of ancient and medieval medicine; similar collections were published in the following centuries, but excellent examples had been given in the sixteenth century and they had involved the efforts of physicians of many nations. The list given is probably incomplete, yet it is very impressive. Never was the elite of the medical profession so deeply concerned with the past.

In spite of the fact that I tried to keep my enumeration as brief as possible, I have generally named the editor and printers. During the Renaissance four categories of learned men were gradually differentiated: authors, editors (of a definite text or of collections; this includes translators and commentators), publishers, printers. Some printers were very learned, every one of them was interested in knowledge, the best of them might be called patrons of learning.

8. A Few Words of Conclusion

THE PRECEDING CHAPTERS ILLUSTRATE DIFFERENT KINDS OF MEDICAL tradition which did not vary very much. The main purpose of the learned physicians was to establish the text of their authorities as exactly as possible. In the case of Latin writers like Celsus, all that was needed was to collate and edit the MSS; in the more general case of Greek authors, it was necessary to edit the Greek text, to translate it, or to revise earlier translations. In every case, the Latin editions had to be completed with explanations and commentaries; it is significant that the commentaries were philological rather than medical.

The fact that the learned doctors attached more importance to ancient and to medieval medicine than to the more modern ones reveals a strange feeling of insecurity. How could they trust so much the ancients and so little the physicians who were their own contemporaries? They suffered from what we would call an inferiority complex. What caused it? Our first guess is that their feeling of inferiority was the result of insufficient experimentation, and yet many physicians, most physicians, were practising medicine, and is not medical practice an endless series of experiments?

We shall perhaps understand the situation better and be more tolerant when we remember that American medicine of, say, the last century was often too subservient to European medicine. Many American doctors had more confidence in treatises originally published in Paris,

London, Edinburgh, Leipzig, or Vienna than in those which were of American origin. It took quite a while before American medicine obtained enough confidence in itself. The comparison is not fair, however, because methods of medical research were known in America in the nineteenth century, while they were practically unknown during the whole of the Renaissance.

This gives a clue to the real answer. Medical research did not exist in the sixteenth century, or whatever there was of it was rudimentary and inchoate. During two thousand years many observations had been made, but these observations had not been collected under new headings: there was no system in gathering them or in explaining them. The theories explained by Hippocrates and Galen had not been invalidated.

The new anatomical knowledge put together by Vesalius in his *Fabrica* in 1543 started further anatomical research, but there was nothing equivalent to that in physiology or medicine. Hence, that fantastic situation, of which many examples have been given above: the subordination of clinical medicine to philology.

The best road to medical progress was supposed to be the study of Greek, or at least of classical Latin. That was also the best road to medical preferment. A new edition of a Greek text or a new Latin translation of it was the best title a physician could have in order to secure a medical chair in a university or to be appointed royal archiater or town physician.

The medical Renaissance was essentially philological (not clinical or physiological); it was humanistic with a vengeance. Its humanism discouraged the discovery of new methods, and it was largely restricted to Greek and Latin literature. Therefore, it was anti-Oriental, anti-Arabic. Every effort was made by the medical pedants to clean ancient medicine from Arabic interpolations and deviations. Nevertheless, the prestige of Arabic medicine and especially of Rhazes and Avicenna was so great and pervasive that it was almost impossible to get rid of them. We should remember that Arabic medicine was known only in its Latin dress and hence was less outlandish and offensive than it would have been otherwise.

The defeat of Avicenna and his exclusion from the medical schools was hardly possible without a revolution. Such a one was attempted by Paracelsus when he was teaching at the medical school of Basel. During the traditional revelry of St. John's Day (Midsummer Night) he threw a copy of the *Canon* in the bonfire.[147] Paracelsus' gesture was symbolic, but futile. It could not drive Avicenna out of the schools; MSS and printed copies of the *Canon* (and other books of Arabic origin) continued to circulate.

For example, consider the popularity of the *Practica* written by Ferrari da Gradi.[148] This was a commentary[149] upon the ninth book of Almansor with fragments of its text. In spite of its very large size, nine editions of it appeared before 1560. It was derived not only from al-Rāzī but also from Ibn Sīnā. The latter was quoted 3100 times; al-Rāzī, 1280; Galen, 1160; Hippocrates, only 140. The readers of Ferrari's *Practica* were drinking far more deeply from Arabic than from Greek sources.

Another example is the one given by Niccolò Leoniceno, though it is perhaps too exceptional to be significant. Leoniceno was a good Hellenist, but he remained independent and nonconformist: witness his anti-astrological attitude. He often criticized Ibn Sīnā, but he criticized also Pliny and Dioscorides. Instead of blaming the Arabic doctors systematically he recognized their merit, whenever they appeared to him to have any. He was fully aware of the medical greatness of al-Rāzī. He was one of the few medical humanists who tried to appeal from the written words to the eternal realities. In this respect, he was comparable to Petrus Severinus, who flourished not like himself at the beginning of the Renaissance but toward the end of it, and not in Ferrara but in Copenhagen.

The average medical humanist, however, was anti-Arabic and became more and more so as time went by. He was convinced that medical truth had been explained in the best manner by the Greek physicians. His main concern was not to drive the Arabs out, but rather to vindicate the Greeks more completely, by publishing better editions, translations, and commentaries of their classics. By the end of the sixteenth century, the market was flooded with them.

Learned humanists continued to dominate medical teaching in the seventeenth century, but their golden age was the Renaissance. After that period, their importance diminished gradually, and they were obliged to give way, step by step, to anatomists, physiologists, and clinicians. Their task had not been useless, but it was done and overdone.

LECTURE II
NATURAL HISTORY

1. THE FOUR MASTERS

THE IDEAS OF THE ANCIENTS ON NATURAL HISTORY, AND MORE specifically on living creatures, plants and animals, were best represented by the works of four masters, three Greek ones—Aristotle, Theophrastos, and Dioscorides—and one Latin, Pliny the Elder. These writings had never been lost for a long time and the medieval students of nature had borrowed from them either directly or indirectly. During the Renaissance, all were available in Greek or Latin in printed editions as well as in MSS, and we may safely assume that every learned naturalist of the sixteenth century was familiar with them.

After all, that was not very difficult, and when we bear in mind the enormous libraries with which we ourselves are burdened we cannot help feeling a little jealous of our ancestors of four centuries ago. Any one of them who had perused the works of those four men and who had in his bookpress copies of them—whether in print or in handwriting—for ready consultation, such a man might be deemed well informed. We shall see in a moment that some of them were much better informed, for they had read also in the book of nature.

In the following sections discussing the tradition of each of those great four, the reader must always remember that an editor of, say, Dioscorides was almost equally familiar with the other three, as his footnotes or commentaries would reveal. For the sake of convenience, we shall deal with some of the sixteenth-century naturalists apropos of Aristotle, with others apropos of Theophrastos, and so forth, but we must bear in mind that the real differences obtaining between them were of a deeper nature.

One general classification may be indicated at once. Zoölogists would be more interested in Aristotle and secondarily in Pliny, while botanists would study Pliny, but above all Theophrastos and Dioscorides.

Another general remark. The naturalists were more original than the physicians of equal genius, because plants and animals are more tangible, more brilliant, and more arresting than nosological entities could ever be.

2. ARISTOTLE OF STAGEIROS (IV-2 B.C.)

WE ARE CONCERNED HERE ONLY WITH THE ARISTOTELIAN WRITINGS on animals, the *Historia, De partibus, De motu, De incessu, De generatione animalium,* to which one might add *De anima* for the psychological aspect of biology.

No ancient writer was more completely available to the Renaissance scholars than Aristotle. Not only could one obtain the text in Greek or Latin, but added to it the commentaries of Averroes (XII-2) and of many others. We shall not attempt to give a complete list of all the editions but we must mention enough of them to illustrate the abundance of opportunities.

To begin with the *Opera omnia*—the first Latin edition was printed by Canozius de Lendeneria in Padova, 1472-74; this included Averroës' commentary, and so did three early Venetian editions (1483, 1489, 1495/6). The first edition of the *Opera* without Averroës was printed in Augsburg, 1479 (very incomplete); more complete editions in Venice, 1482, 1496, and Cologne, 1497. In short, there were no less than eight incunabula Latin editions. Not only that, but before the end of the century Manutius published a magnificent edition of the Greek works, all of them plus the botanical treatises of Theophrastos (5 vols., folio; Venice, 1495-98).[1]

Another Greek edition prepared by Erasmus, corrected by Simon Grynaeus,[2] was printed by Johann Bebel (2 vols., folio; Basel, 1531), reprinted by the same firm in 1539 and 1550. A third one was prepared by J. B. Camotius (6 vols.; Venice: Aldus, 1551-53) and a fourth one by Friedrich Sylburg[3] (11 vols.; Frankfurt: Wecheli heredes, 1584-87). A fifth Greek edition including Latin translations by various persons and commentaries was printed by J. Bubonius (2 vols., folio; Lyon, 1590). Thus, before the end of the sixteenth century five editions of Aristotle's works were already available in the original Greek.[4]

To return to the Latin translations of the *Opera*, a whole series of them were printed by Oporinus in Basel, 1538, 1542, 1548, 1563; by Frellonius in Lyon, 1549, 1561; by the Juntae in Venice, 1550-52, 1562, 1573-75; by Cominus de Tridino in Venice, 1560; and perhaps by others.

We may assume that almost every one of these "complete" editions included the biological works, but there were also separate editions of these in Greek and Latin. Of course, a separate edition like that of the

Greek biological works by F. Sylburg (Frankfurt, 1585) might be simply one of the volumes of his edition of all the works. The Latin translation by Theodoros Gaza was first printed by John of Cologne (Venice, 1476).[5] It was reprinted by three other Venetian printers in 1492, 1495, 1498 (Klebs 85.1-4)[6] and many times more in the following century: Lyon, c.1505; Venice, 1513, 1546; Paris, 1524, 1533; Basel, 1534, etc. The Greek was also reprinted by the Juntae in Florence, 1527, etc.

That is not all. To the editions and translations of *De animalibus* might still be added those of separate zoölogical books and those included in commentaries, but that would carry us too far. Let us give a few examples.

A translation of the spurious Book X of the *Historia animalium* was made by the elder Scaliger[7] (Lyon, 1584). The Latin text of the *De partibus animalium* was printed with the scholia of Michael of Ephesos[8] (Basel, 1559) and the Latin text of *De generatione animalium,* with the commentary of John Philoponos (VI-1).

The most interesting examples concern the *De anima,* the appeal of which was not restricted to naturalists but extended to metaphysicians. The Greek text of *De anima* with Philoponos' commentary was edited by Trincavella[9] (Venice: Bart. Zanetti, 1535). Another Greek edition with the commentary of Jacques Lefèvre[10] appeared a few years later (Basel: T. Platterus, 1538). There were also Greek-Latin editions (Paris, 1554; Frankfurt, 1596), and, of course, a good many Latin editions, beginning with seven separate incunabula (Padova, 1472, etc.; Klebs 84.1-7) in addition to many other incunabula wherein *De anima* was but one of the ingredients. The *De anima* was used in schools with suitable commentaries, not only ancient ones by Simplicios and Philoponos but chiefly with scholastic explanations, e.g., by Thomas Aquinas (XIII-2) (Venice, 1507, 1560), by M. de Palacio (Salamanca, 1557), by Agostino Nifo (Venice, 1559). A familiar explanation of the *De anima* prepared for the gymnasium of Kraków was published in that city as early as 1513.

The scholars who were editing the Greek text of the zoölogical books, or Latin translations and commentaries, were most of them philologists who were interested in the Master's words and had no curiosity to see the animals themselves, but we must pause a moment to consider four glorious exceptions[11]—the first English, two others French, one Italian.

The Englishman was William Turner[12] (c. 1510-68), who published a book on birds derived from Aristotle and Pliny, yet containing new observations of his own. The Rev. Turner, a native of Northumberland, educated at Pembroke Hall, Cambridge, was primarily a theologian, and in the second place a botanist. We shall speak of his botanical writings later, and of his theological writings we can only say that they were very controversial and often violent. He was twice Dean of Wells, but made himself obnoxious by the strength of his anti-episcopalianism and was finally suspended for nonconformity. He spent two long periods of his life on the continent, the first (1540-47) for study, chiefly with Luca Ghini in Bologna and with Conrad Gesner in Zürich, the second during Mary's rule (1553-58) when his strong Protestant feelings would have put him into dire trouble. He returned to England at the time of Elizabeth's accession and died in London in 1568.

In addition to the books on birds, he also wrote an account of English fishes which was included in Gesner's *Historia animalium 3*, 1294 f. (1557). The *Avium praecipuarum, quarum apud Plinium et Aristotelem mentio est, brevis et succincta historia* was dedicated to Henry VIII and printed in Cologne by Joannes Gymnicus, 1544.[12] Out of the abundant publications (some twenty-three) of this extraordinary Englishman we must still quote two in order to give an idea of his versatility —a treatise on balneology, *A book of the natures and properties of the bathes in England* (Cullen = Cologne: Arnold Birckman, 1562), and *A new boke of the nature of all wines* (London: W. Seres, 1568).[14] In spite of its being largely derived from Aristotle and Pliny (as the title declared) the *Avium historia* may be called the first modern book on birds; it contains many new observations, and its point of view is not medical, as that of older treatises, but scientific. As his translator, A. H. Evans, put it (1903, p. ix): "It is not too much to say that almost every page [of his book] bears witness to a personal knowledge of the subject which would be distinctly creditable even to a modern ornithologist." This does not mean that it is free from errors and superstitions; for example, it retells the old story of the breeding of the Bernicle Goose, but does so with a modicum of skepticism.

Turner was a good man who would probably have been a better naturalist if his mind had not been obsessed by theological controversies. The two Frenchmen were less handicapped by circumstances and their scientific genius spoke louder in them.

Guillaume Rondelet (1507-66) and Pierre Belon (1517-64) were almost complete contemporaries and their main works appeared in the same decade, but Rondelet was a Southerner, while Belon came from a little town in Maine (a province in NW France whose capital was

Le Mans). The climatic and psychologic distance between Le Mans and Montpellier was considerable.

Rondelet was the son of a druggist of Montpellier; presumably a man of modest means, he was able to make long studies, first of medicine in Paris and Montpellier, then in Paris again for additional Greek training. He finally obtained his M.D. in Montpellier in 1537 (at the age of thirty) and eight years later became a professor of anatomy in that university. In 1556, an anatomical amphitheatre was built for him by Henri II, and he organized public dissections. He was one of the physicians attached to Cardinal François de Tournon,[15] another being Symphorien Champier. The cardinal took Rondelet with him on various errands to Antwerp, to Saintonges, and on an Italian journey (Rome, Venice, etc.) in 1549-51. Apparently, Rondelet was left sufficient freedom for his own avocation, the study of fishes. He seems to have had Protestant velleities but realized their danger, and in 1552 burned the forbidden books which he had collected; he may be identical with Rondibilis, one of Rabelais' creatures. His most illustrious disciple was the Fleming, Matthias de Lobel,[16] to whom he bequeathed his botanical MSS. He died in 1566 in Réalmont (Tarn, Albigeois).

Rondelet was an anatomist and a naturalist; his writings are devoted to medical subjects and to ichthyology, and it is the latter which have made him immortal. His main work on sea fishes, *Libri de piscibus marinis in quibus verae piscium effigies expressae sunt,* was printed by Matthieu Bonhomme[17] (folio; Lyon, 1554); it was followed by the *Universae aquatilium historiae pars altera cum veris ipsorum imaginibus* (folio; Lyon, 1555). Both volumes were dedicated to the Cardinal de Tournon, and according to the "good usage" of that time their prefaces were followed by congratulatory poems. One of the poems in volume 1 was contributed by Carolus Clusius. The two volumes were soon translated into French and published with the same illustrations and portrait by Bonhomme (2 vols., folio; Lyon, 1558). These Rondelet volumes were beautifully printed; the copies I have seen in the Harvard Library look like de luxe editions. Was this due to the munificence of the Cardinal de Tournon?

Rondelet dealt with nearly 250 fishes or aquatic animals, such as whales, and his descriptions are generally sufficient for identification with definite genera.

The life of Rondelet was the simple life of a professor in a famous university; the life of his friend and rival, Belon, was far more adventurous and picturesque.

Pierre Belon[18] was born *c.* 1517[19] in the hamlet of Soultière,[20] and was educated in Brittany among "French heretics." He must have been a born naturalist, interested in plants and animals from an early age, and he must have inclined to Protestantism, because he chose to continue his studies in Wittenberg (the very place where the Reformation had begun in his own birth year); he interviewed Luther and worked under the guidance of Valerius Cordus; then Valerius and he and some ten students traveled across Saxony, Thuringia, Pomerania, crossing the forests of Germany and Bohemia, visiting mines and herborizing (this kind of expedition was something new and full of promise). In 1542, he returned to Paris and entered the service of Cardinal de Tournon. What did he do for the Cardinal? Perhaps he was used as an apothecary or perhaps as a newsgatherer. At any rate, he was sent on a kind of mission to Switzerland and Germany in that same year; he was held in Geneva by the Calvinists and spent six months in prison. After his liberation, he went to Lyon and Luxemburg and rejoined his old friend, who was exploring Provence and Italy with some students. Their new expedition cannot have lasted very long, because Cordus died in Rome in September 1544. Think of these two men of genius of about the same age, exploring nature together in Germany, Provence, and Italy; what a strange conjunction. Belon returned probably in the service of Cardinal de Tournon, and he was able to visit the curiosities which were gathered by François I at the court of Saint-Germain-en-Laye.

A stranger conjunction was this one. François I needed information concerning the Near East, and Belon, who was planning to translate Dioscorides and Theophrastos into French, was inhibited at every step by the difficulty of identifying the plants and animals which were dealt with in the ancient books. He realized more and more deeply the need of going to the East and seeing with his own eyes the original creatures which the Greek naturalists had described. Thanks to the largesse of the Cardinal de Tournon, it was possible to attach Belon to an embassy sent to the Near East by the king under the direction of Gabriel d'Aramon.[21] There were two scientific attachés to the embassy: Pierre Gilles of Albi, whose business it was to find Greek MSS and antiquities; and Belon, whose business we already know. The embassy left in December 1546, sailed from Venice in February. We are very well informed concerning its motions because of Chesneau's account, and Belon's own travels have been narrated by himself in *Les observations de plusieurs singularitez et choses mémorables trouvées en Grèce, Asie, Judée, Egypte, Arabie et autres pays estranges, rédigées in trois livres* (Paris: G. Cavellat, 1553), a book which was immediately popular and reprinted in the same place in 1554, 1555, 1588, and also by Plantin in Antwerp in 1555. The same Plantin published in 1579 and reprinted in 1605 a Latin translation made by no less a person than Clusius. The extensiveness of Belon's travels may be judged from the names of a few of the places where he stopped or sojourned: Ragusa, Corfu, Zante, Cythera, Crete, Constantinople, Lemnos, Mt. Athos, Salonica, Egypt, Sinai, Judaea, Damascus, Lebanon, Cilicia, Armenia, back to Constantinople overland, and then by sea to Venice. He had been absent more than two years. After his return, his main pied-à-terre, thanks to the Cardinal de Tournon, was the abbey of St. Germain des Prés in Paris, but he was frequently absent: he was with the cardinal in Rome for the conclave[22] in 1549-50; visited England twice; in 1553, he was physician to the Comte de Vieilleville, appointed governor of Metz after that city had been taken from the Spaniards. Belon took advantage of this to explore Lorraine, but the country was unsafe, and he was seized by a gang of Burgundians in Spanish service; he was imprisoned in Thionville (1555) but ransomed by one of Ronsard's friends.[23]

Belon had gradually realized that many of the plants which he had seen in other countries could be acclimatized in France and become sources of agreement and profit. He had admired botanical gardens in Italy and wanted to establish similar ones in France. He explained his views to Henri II who gave him a pension. His ideas were not realized but some plants were actually introduced by him. In the meanwhile, he began medical studies in Paris and obtained his license in 1560 (there is no evidence that he ever obtained his M.D.; it may be that his Greek and Latin were a bit rusty). His life was embittered (as were the lives of all good men) by the increasing nastiness and violence of the struggle between Catholics and Protestants. Belon's torment was perhaps greater because of his ambivalence; he had had Protestant leanings in his youth, but a long life in the service of cardinal and king had changed his state of mind; after the colloque of Poissy[24] (1561), if not before, he was bitterly anti-Huguenot. The new king, Charles IX (1560-74), continued the protection extended to him by Henri II and granted him lodgings in the Château de Madrid, which he had just built in the Bois de Boulogne. On an evening in April 1564, as Belon was returning to Madrid from Paris, he was murdered in that forest. The murderer and the reasons for his deed are unknown; it is useless to guess. Pierre Belon was then only forty-seven years of age and much more could be expected from him.

We have already spoken of one of his books, which was not the first but by far the most popular. His first book was *L'histoire naturelle des estranges poissons marins avec la vraie peincture et description du Dauphin* (Paris: Regnaud Chaudière, 1551). Two other books of his dealt with fishes and other aquatic animals:

Petri Bellonii Cenomani (i.e., of Le Mans) *De aquatilibus, Libri duo, cum eiconibus ad vivam ipsorum effigiem, quoad eius fieri potuit, expressis* (Paris: Charles Estienne, 1553). This is a small album of 16 leaves plus 448 pp., 160 x 95 mm., with a great many full-page illustrations.

La nature et diversité des Poissons avec leurs pourtraicts representez au plus près du naturel (Paris: Charles Estienne, 1555). Same size as the preceding volume, 19 leaves plus 448 pp., illustrated. It is the French translation of the preceding work, the text and illustrations being presumably the same, though Belon might have introduced corrections and additions in the French book appearing two years later than the Latin. I had no time to collate both works page by page, and line by line as should be done, and to compare all the illustrations. Many of Belon's ichthyological observations were integrated by Conrad Gesner in his *Historiae animalium Liber IIII qui est de Piscium et Aquatilium Animantium natura* (folio, 1297 pp., ill.; Zürich: Christ. Froschover, 1558; reprinted in Frankfurt by A. Cambierus, 1604 and 1620).

Belon was interested primarily in fishes, but not exclusively; witness the two following books, the first dealing with birds, the second with birds and other animals, except fishes:

L'histoire de la nature des Oyseaux avec leurs descriptions et naïfs portraicts, retirez du naturel escrite en sept livres (folio, ill., 14 leaves plus 381 pp.; Paris: G. Cavellat, 1555). The same book was published in the same year by another Parisian printer, G. Corrozet.

Portraits d'Oyseaux, animaux, serpens, herbes, arbres, hommes et femmes d'Arabie et Egypte . . . (10 + 122 leaves; Paris: Guillaume Cavellat, 1557).

Two more books of his must still be mentioned. First, *De arboribus Coniferis, resiniferis aliis quoque nonnullis sempiterna fronde virentibus, cum earundem iconibus ad vivum expressis* (8 + 32 leaves; Paris: B. Prévost, 1553). This is not only the first treatise on cone-bearing trees, but the first monograph of a plant group in Western literature.[25]

In our brief account of Belon's life, we told that after his return from the Near East, his mind being full of images of all the plants and animals he had seen there, he bethought himself that some of them might be acclimatized in his own country for the pleasure and benefit of the French people. The king showed some interest in his plans but nothing came of them; Belon may have managed to introduce a few plants in a small way, but systematic acclimatization was not begun in France until much later.[26] Belon realized not only the usefulness of introducing foreign plants but also the need of taking better care of the domestic ones, and his last publication was devoted to both purposes: *Les Remonstrances sur le default du labour et culture des plantes et de la cognoissance d'icelles, contenant la manière d'affranchir et apprivoiser les arbres sauvages* (20 + 80 leaves, small octavo; Paris: Corrozet, 1558). Clusius translated this into Latin (87 pp., Antwerp: Chr. Plantin, 1589), reprinted by the same firm together with their Latin translation of Belon's *Observationes* (Antwerp, 1605).

The number and variety of Belon's books is astonishing when one considers the brevity of his life, but what is more important is their scientific quality. As distinguished from the majority of his learned contemporaries, Belon was primarily a naturalist, not a humanist.[27] The distinction was as clear then as it is now, but real naturalists caring for the objects of nature rather than for literal descriptions of them were very rare. It is passing strange that it took so long for intelligent men writing about nature to discover their opportunities, for in the sixteenth century he who was willing to observe nature with his own eyes and to travel in foreign climates, as Belon did, was bound to discover innumerable novelties.

Moreover, the best zoölogical work of the ancients, that of Aristotle, could not be appreciated except by men who took the trouble of renewing his observations. For example, one of the glories of Aristotelian zoölogy is the account of the reproduction of a certain kind of shark; not only does that fish (dogfish) bring out its young fully shaped and alive, but there is a connection between the embryo and the maternal uterus, somewhat like the placenta of mammals. Pierre Belon in 1553 and Guillaume Rondelet in 1554 were the first to rediscover that extraordinary fact, and their merit will appear in its fulness if we add that their observations remained largely unnoticed, except by Niels Stensen (1673), until their rediscovery and complete explanation by the German physiologist, Johannes Müller (1839-42).[28] That is great: Belon and Rondelet did not simply comment upon Aristotle's words, they recreated some of his best observations with their own genius, and they were the only men of the Renaissance capable of doing so.

Before leaving Belon, we must come back for a moment to an older contemporary of his, Pierre Gilles[29] (1490-1555), who was his companion in M. d'Aramon's embassy and whom he has been accused of pilfering. That is silly, because Belon was a genuine naturalist and a great one, while Gilles was a humanist and archaeologist. Pierre Gilles was born in Albi (Tarn; Languedoc). He became interested in zoölogy because of his study of Aristotle, Ailianos, and Pliny. He was perhaps more interested in fishes than in other creatures and observed many of them in the Adriatic and the Mediterranean seas. After his return to his province, he found a congenial protector in Georges d'Armagnac[30] and wrote his treatise *De vi et natura animalium* the essential parts of which are translated from Ailianos (III-1), but he added information taken from many other Greek authors. The work was divided into sixteen books devoted to particular groups of animals, Book I to elephants, Book II to lions, Book III to dogs, Book IV to horses, etc. In his dedication to François I,

Gilles explained the need of exploring the countries of the Near East which had been constituent parts of the ancient world and the curiosities of which, natural or archaeological, had been described or referred to in classical literature. François I permitted himself to be persuaded of that necessity and commissioned him to explore Turkish territories.

From this point on, the vicissitudes of his life are not clear to me, because he was a member (at least a temporary member) of the embassy of M. d'Aramon, yet, we are told that after a while he found himself abandoned in Turkey without resources. The only explanation is that he had been dropped by the ambassador and lost his job. In order to survive, he was obliged to enlist in the army of Sulaimān I the Great (sulṭān, 1520-66; François' ally) and lost all his collections during the Turco-Persian war. Later, he managed to return to Constantinople and was repatriated by the French ambassador in 1550. Soon after his homecoming, he rejoined his old patron, Georges d'Armagnac, who was then cardinal in Rome. He spent the last five years of his life in that city, presumably engaged in research and writing.

Gilles' first publication, already mentioned, was entitled *Ex Aeliani historia per Petrum Gyllum latini facti itemque ex Porphyrio, Heliodoro, Oppiano, tum eodem Gyllio luculentis accessionibus aucti libri XVII De vi et natura animalium* . . . (14 leaves, 598 pp., no ill.; Lyon; Sébastien Gryphe, 1533).[31] To this was added a list of fish names in Latin and French, and an index of all the animals (terrestrial, aquatic, flying; special index of fishes).

In the course of his travels (presumably while he was still on M. d'Aramon's staff), he wrote letters to his protector, the Cardinal d'Armagnac, describing a journey from Constantinople to Tabriz, then back to Aleppo; the most interesting event described by him was the dissection of an elephant. That particular letter, *Elephanti descriptio missa ad R. cardinalem Armaignacum ex urbe Berrhoea Syriaca,* was first printed in the third edition of his Ailianos (Lyon: Guillaume Rouillé I, 1565).[32] Gilles' interest in elephants had already been illustrated by the fact that in his book he gave pride of place to those animals and not, as was usually done in the Middle Ages, to the lions. This elephant item was not available to me, and I have no means of appreciating its scientific value. In any case, it appeared after Belon's death. Gilles' other publications were historical and archaeological rather than zoölogical. Belon may have used one of the earlier editions of Ailianos (1533 or 1535); it was his duty to use it, as did Conrad Gesner, very fully in his Greek-Latin edition of the same author (Zürich, 1556).

The Italian, Ippolito Salviani (1514-72), was born at Città di Castello,[33] Umbria, was trained as a physician, practised medicine in Rome, and was archiater to Julius III (pope, 1550-55), Marcel II (1555), and Paul IV (1555-59). He developed early a passion for natural history, especially ichthyology, and it is said that his office at the papal court made it easier for him to obtain many specimens of fish. The outcome of his studies was a magnificent folio entitled *Aquatilium animalium historiae liber primus cum eorumdum formis aere excusis* (16 + 256 leaves, 88 pl.; published by the author himself, 1554-58). The eighty-eight copperplates reproduce ninety-two Italian fishes. The title page, including the author's portrait, bears the date 1554, but the book was not completed until 1558, and the "liber primus" was not followed by any other. The splendid illustrations were often reprinted in later works, such as those of Gesner and Aldrovandi.

It is clear that Salviani had taken considerable pains to do his work as well as possible, and he was fully conscious of his merit. He wanted the text and images to be published beautifully, and the work to be launched in the best manner. One can see that he was familiar with courts and knew how to puff his book up in royal style. He began as early as 1551, if not before, to obtain patronage for it and he succeeded remarkably well judging from the introductions printed at the very beginning, written by Julius III (s.a.), Charles Quint (1551), Henri II (1554), Còsimo de' Medici, duke of Florence (1552). These royal testimonia were followed by no less than twenty-six laudatory poems composed by sixteen poets or poetasters. Then came synoptic tables (56 leaves) giving the names of the aquatic animals in Latin, Greek, vernaculars; and in seven columns, references to Aristotle, Oppianos, Pliny, Athenaios, Ailianos, etc. The book itself is divided into ninety-two chapters each of which contains the description of an animal together with a magnificent copper plate. Then full indices. On folio 256, occurs the colophon stating that publication of the work was completed by the author himself in Rome, January 1558.

This was the main work of Salviani's and almost the only one, and it is certainly sufficient to immortalize his name. In spite of its size and expensiveness, it was reprinted in Rome, 1593 (?), and in Venice, 1600, 1602. He composed a medical treatise *De crisibus ad Galeni censuram, liber omnium crisium cognitionem brevi et miro ordine continens* (127 pp.; Rome: ex officine salviana, 1556; reprinted, 1558). This imprint means that Salviani continued to be his own publisher and perhaps his own printer.

LECTURE II: NATURAL HISTORY

One might object to my inclusion in this lecture of men like Rondelet, Belon, Gilles, and Salviani, none of whom was primarily an interpreter of Aristotle or of other ancient authors, but were naturalists, and we might even say ichthyologists. Yet, they had all of them studied the ancient texts and derived from these very texts their first inspiration. They were very different. Rondelet was a professor of medicine in Montpellier; Belon and Gilles obtained their fame as explorers in the Near East, but Belon became a real zoölogist, one of the greatest ornithologists as well as ichthyologists of his time, and one of the pioneers in the study of comparative anatomy, while Gilles remained closer to philology and archaeology; Salviani, papal physician and courtier, published one of the outstanding books on fishes of the Renaissance.

The four men were humanists and philologists, but in various degrees, and their efforts illustrate the task which Renaissance naturalists had to accomplish. They were brought up on the Greek classics and they had to be gradually weaned from them. We shall explain presently how their weaning was finally completed.

3. THEOPHRASTOS OF ERESOS (IV-2 B. C.)

LET US PASS TO THE BOTANISTS AND THIS MEANS IN THE FIRST PLACE the interpreters of Theophrastos and secondarily of Dioscorides and Pliny, but takes us away from Aristotle.

This is correct, but only with the following qualification which we hasten to add. The two books on plants which are generally ascribed to Nicholas of Damascus (I-2 B. C.) were long credited to Aristotle himself and included in his *Opera,* as well as in collections like the *Aristotelis varia opuscula,* edited by Friedrich Sylburg (1536-96) and printed by Wechel's heirs in Frankfurt a.M., 1587. Moreover, Julius Caesar Scaliger (1484-1558) devoted a commentary to these books: *In libros duos qui inscribuntur de plantis, Aristotele autore, libri duo* (Paris: Michael Vascosanus, 1556), reprinted in 1566 and 1598.

Scaliger was primarily a philologist, and his book was not illustrated; yet, his botanical knowledge was not purely verbal; it was based upon frequent autopsies of the living plants. In his preface to Gabriel Minutius, governor of Rouergue, Scaliger remarks that the identification of the plants dealt with by the ancients is made difficult because the plants vary from country to country and from one season to another. Moreover, the ancient descriptions were often careless and insufficient, and the plants were badly grouped together. Yet, the vested interests of the herbalists are such that his criticisms are likely to be ill received. The local herbalists, he remarks, should be called verbalists.[34] That is very remarkable, quite in the spirit of the German "fathers of botany" of whom we shall speak later. Incidentally, Scaliger's title "In libros qui inscribuntur de plantis, Aristotele autore" was misleading, but he corrected it in the heading of his preface "In libros de plantis falso Aristoteli attributos."[35]

We must assume, however, that the majority of Renaissance botanists were so used to accepting Aristotle's authority in every field, that they accepted it also in botany on the basis of that spurious work as well as of the other botanical references in the Aristotelian corpus.

The Greek text of *De plantis* is lost; the original was preserved in an Arabic translation by Isḥāq ibn Ḥunain (IX-2), but that translation is also lost, and our only witness is a translation from Arabic into Latin by Alfred of Sareshel (XIII-1).

The Latin medieval translation was edited by the historian of botany, E. M. F. Meyer: *Nicolai Damasceni de plantis libri duo Aristoteli vulgo adscripti* (158 pp.; Leipzig, 1841). The Greek text *Peri phytōn* in the Bekker edition (f. 815-30) is a retranslation from the Latin into Greek,[36] thrice removed from the original! It is better to use Meyer's Latin text or the English translation by Edward Seymour Forster in the English Aristotle (Oxford: Clarendon Press, 1913), vol. 6, which includes references to other Aristotelian writings.[37]

At any rate, whatever Aristotelian there was in Greek botany was soon integrated with the writings of Aristotle's disciple and successor, Theophrastos of Eresos (IV-2 B.C.). The medieval tradition of his botanical writings was singularly inert. Almost the only Christian scholar who read Theophrastos in a creative way and looked at the plants themselves was Albert the Great (XIII-2).[38] It will thus suffice for our purpose to consider the Renaissance tradition.

The integration of Theophrastos' botany with the Aristotelian corpus was completed by the early printers. The Greek princeps of Aristotle, the splendid five volumes published by Aldus Manutius in Venice, 1495-98 (Klebs 83.1), included in vol. 4 (1497) the two great works of Theophrastos, *Historia plantarum* and *De causis plantarum*. A Latin translation of them by Theodoros Gaza (*c.* 1400-75) had been printed previously by Confalonerius (Treviso, 1483; Klebs 958).[39] Thus, Theophrastos was widely available to botanists in Greek or Latin before the end of the fifteenth century.

All the works of Theophrastos were edited in Greek with a preface by Hieronymus Gemusaeus (Basel: J. Oporinus, 1541). There are copies of that edition with a different title page and a longer preface by Joachim Camerarius.

The Latin translation by Theodoros Gaza was reprinted by the Aldine counterfeiters together with Aristotle's *De natura animalium* (Lyon, 1506?). It was reprinted by C. Wechel (Paris, 1529) and again in Lyon, 1552. There are probably other sixteenth-century editions in Greek or Latin (no Greco-Latin ones before the seventeenth century); the combination of Theophrastos' writings with those of Aristotle makes a full bibliography more difficult. The main point is that sixteenth-century naturalists could easily obtain the botanical works of Theophrastos in Greek or Latin, having the choice of many editions.

LECTURE II: NATURAL HISTORY

One could be very familiar with Theophrastan botany, however, without having read his botanical treatises, because his views were quoted verbatim or integrated by many commentators and constantly referred to by every Renaissance botanist. Among the commentators let us select four: the Frenchman, Jean Ruel (1536); the Swiss, Conrad Gesner (1541); and in the last quarter of the century, the Italian, Andrea Cesalpino (1583) and the Bohemian, Adam Zalužansky (1592).

Before speaking of them let us mention briefly the modern editions of Theophrastos: Greco-Latin edition by Friedrich Wimmer, with full indices (Paris, 1866); Greek-English edition of *Enquiry into plants* by Sir Arthur Hort (2 vols.; Loeb Library, 1916—*Isis 3, 92*).

Jean Ruel's profession was medicine. Born in Soissons in 1479, he was educated in Paris and became dean of the medical faculty of that city in 1508-9; he was also one of the physicians to François I, but his medical activities were largely of the literary kind. He published translations of Dioscorides and of other medical and veterinary texts. After his wife's death, he obtained a canonry at Notre Dame. His main work was an enormous botanical treatise derived from all the Greek and Latin authors, principally Theophrastos: *De natura stirpium libri tres* (folio 395 mm., 6 + 884 + 124 pp.; Paris: Simon Colinaeus, 1536).

This might be considered an encyclopedia of ancient botany, exceedingly rich, and the first edition (the only one which I have seen) is a monument of early typography. In spite of its large size, the book was reprinted at least thrice within seven years, by Froben in Basel, 1537 and 1543, and by Pederzanus in Venice, 1538.

Ruel's memory is immortalized by that monument and by a genus of herbs and shrubs of tropical America, the Ruellia, so-named by the French botanical explorer, Charles Plumier (1646-1706).

The *De natura stirpium* was dedicated to François I. It contains no illustrations whatsoever, but an "index copiosissimus" of 124 pp., mainly of plant names. It was printed in large type on folio pages with generous margins. The work is divided into three books and 454 chapters, and but for twenty-two introductory chapters, each is devoted to one or two plants or to a small group.

Ruel died soon after the publication of his magnum opus, in his native city, on 24 September 1537.

Conrad Gesner (1516-65) will be dealt with in a separate section below, and it is enough to mention the book which concerns us at present: *Historia plantarum et vires ex Dioscoride, Paulo Aegineta, Theophrasto, Plinio et recentioribus Graecis juxta elementorum ordinem . . . Adjecta ad marginem nomenclatura qua singulas herbas officinae, herbarii et vulgus gallicum efferre solent* (index plus 262 pp.; Paris: Joh. Lodoicus Tiletanus, 1541).

This book written in his youth was of the same type as Ruel's, that is, verbal, the work of a philologist rather than of a naturalist, but later he accumulated a large amount of materials for a *Historia plantarum*, to be a companion work to his *Historia animalium*. Some fifteen hundred drawings had been prepared to illustrate it, but his untimely death at forty-nine thwarted his purpose, and his fame as a botanist has suffered accordingly. A few of his drawings were shown by Josias Simler in his *Vita Conradi Gesneri* (Zürich: Froschauer, 1566), but his botanical work was not published until two centuries later, and then incompletely (see below).

The title of his book of 1541 is typical of his lack of historical sense, for the Greek authors are quoted pell mell, the oldest and main one being named third after Paulos of Aigina (VII-1) who came almost a thousand years later, and his enumeration ends with "the more recent Greeks" who could not be (on that scale) much more recent than Paulos.

To return to the book which he published at the age of twenty-five. It is a small book (14 cm.), the size of a prayer book. It is a pocket dictionary of botany wherein the plants are arranged in Latin alphabetical order from Abrotonum and Absinthium to Zea and Zizipha (jujube); Greek and vernacular names are neatly printed in the margins.

Andrea Cesalpino[40] (1519-1603) was born in Arezzo, Toscana, and studied medicine in Pisa and Bologna. During the Renaissance, anatomy and botany constituted the scientific core of medical studies. The teaching of botany had been considerably improved in Northern Italy by the creation, in the first place, of special chairs and, in the second place, of botanic gardens. The earliest chairs devoted exclusively to botany[41] were those of Padova, founded in 1533, and of Bologna, founded in the following year. The first incumbent of the latter was Luca Ghini[42]. The oldest botanic gardens were those of Padova (1545) and Pisa (1545); this second garden was established by Luca Ghini soon after his hegira from Bologna to Pisa in 1544. A third botanical garden was started in Bologna and was first directed by Ulisse Aldrovandi (1522-1605). Now, Cesalpino studied botany in Pisa under Ghini and succeeded Aldrovandi as director of the garden of Bologna.[43] He was thus one of those fortunate beings who appear at the beginning of a new development, when the main battles have already been fought by others, and time is ripe for victory. Victory, it should be remembered, is never won by the pioneers, but by the people who turn up hopefully a generation or two later.

Another instrument of botanical progress (next to specialized teaching and the organization of botanical gardens) was the collecting of dried plants (what is now called herbarium). Strange as this may seem, no one is known to have thought of making a herbarium for himself before the sixteenth century. The earliest person whom one can mention in this connection is Luca Ghini (the greatest pioneer in Italy, pioneering in the three directions). It is significant that the earliest herbaria referred to in botanical literature were made by three of his pupils, William Turner, Aldrovandi, and Cesalpino. Other herbaria were made at about the same time, though I think a little later, by the Swiss Conrad Gesner, the Frenchman Jehan Girault (who completed his collection in 1558), and the German Conrad Ratzenberger (who began his in 1556). More than twenty herbaria formed or at least begun in the sixteenth century are preserved in European collections.[44]

Cesalpino was thus walking in the footsteps of Ghini and Aldrovandi and, what is better still, observing the living plants in the university garden and preserving specimens of them in his study. He was one of the first to attempt a better classification of plants and though he was wrong in building it upon too narrow a basis (the seed), he influenced his followers—even as late a one as Linnacus. For all his modernity, he was a faithful student of Theophrastos and his great book, *De plantis*[45] continued and amplified the tendencies which were discernible in the books of Ruel and Gesner, discussed above. He was, however, more scientific than they, a little closer to nature; yet, his reverence for the ancients was unshaken.

The fourth example in this chapter is a Bohemian, Adam Zalužansky[46] (1558-1613), whose great book *Methodi herbariae libri tres* appeared in Prague before the end of the century, being printed by Georgius Daczicenus (George of Dačic) in 1592. It was reprinted in Frankfurt a.M., 1604, with a list of plant names.

He was a member of the lesser nobility, his father, Matthew, a kind of government official.[47] Educated at home, then at Prague, he obtained his B.A. in 1581. In 1583, he wrote a Latin poem, *De peste bohemica*. Having received his M.A. in the following year, he became head of a school at Svatý Jindřich and in 1585-86 taught at the famous school of Králův Hradec. Interests in science sent him abroad and he was in Germany at various universities and came back with a doctorate in medicine in 1587. He joined the faculty of the Charles University and taught classics. In 1589 he was Provost of the Collegium Carolinum and Professor of Greek Literature; in 1591, Dean of the Philosophical Faculty; and in 1593, Rector of the University.

His reputation for wide erudition brought him favor with the Emperor, Rudolf II, who, in 1593, gave him a reaffirmation of his title of nobility. The nobility also were favorably disposed to him and William of Rožmberk set up a botanical garden on Adam's specifications.

In 1594, he married the daughter (or niece) of a professor of Hebrew, but as marriage was forbidden the professors, he had to give up his rectorship and professorate. He then began medical practice in the Old Town of Prague, and was active during the plague of 1599. His educational and scientific experience convinced him that the University needed a reorganization, and he got together with other medical doctors—also well-educated men—and wrote memoranda suggesting how the whole curriculum could be improved. This activity had some result. When the University was expressly put under the Utraquist Estates by the Letter of Majesty of 1609, he was named head of a Commission to reorganize scientific studies at the University. The Estates approved their report, but political disturbances prevented any real effectuation of the reforms. He died in 1613 of the plague.

His main work is the *Methodus herbariae* of 1592, which is a textbook of botany. It has been claimed that it contains an account of the sexuality of plants, but that claim cannot be substantiated. His other writings were medical, theological, or academic. One of these is given a Latin title, *Apothecariorum regulae et taxae medicinarum* (Prague, 1592), but is also given a Czech one, *Rád apatekařský*. It was written by him after his appointment as inspector of the apothecaries in Prague. Was it in Latin or in Czech, or perhaps in both languages? He also wrote a Czech calendar, *Minucí česká s pranostykou*. The other titles explain themselves:

Animadversionum medicarum in Galenum et Avicennam libri VII, dedicated to Rudolf II (2 parts; Frankfurt: E Collegio Paltheniano, 1604).

Oratio pro anatomia et restauratione totius studii medici in inclyto regno Bohemiae (Prague, 1600).

De consensu ordinum Regni Bohemiae integra coena sacra utentium et quid inter se differunt (Prague, 1609).

De pace et concordia ac de restauranda academia (Prague 1609).

According to a statement of his quoted by Mrs. Arber[48] he was one of the early defenders of botanical science, for botany's, not simply medicine's, sake. The establishment of botanical science is indeed one of the achievements of his time. He pointed out more clearly than his predecessors the rich diversity of vegetal forms and the deep differences obtaining between the lower and the higher kinds of plants.

These four men—Ruel, Gesner, Cesalpino, Zalužansky—illustrate the gradual development of the old Theophrastean tradition and the gradual emancipation of botany from medicine and philology. A similar emancipation was carried through at the same time by another band of botanists, the authors of illustrated herbals of whom we shall speak presently.

4. DIOSCORIDES OF ANAZARBOS (I-2)

THE DIOSCORIDEAN TRADITION WAS FAR MORE CONTINUOUS THAN THE Theophrastean one, and that is not surprising, because the botanical writings of the latter were more scientific and less attractive to medieval minds than those of Dioscorides. Latin translations were made as early as the sixth century (*Introd. 1*, 431, 434). It was not simply the text which was transmitted in Greek and later Latin MSS but also the illustrations, some of which date back to Cratevas (I-1 B. C.). The iconographic tradition is gloriously represented by the *Codex Aniciae Iulianae,* an enormous and magnificent MS of Dioscorides with abundant illustrations of plants, which was written and limned for an imperial princess in 512, was re-discovered in Constantinople by the Flemish diplomat Busbecq[49] (*c.* 1560) who caused the emperor to obtain it, and is to this day the most precious MS of the library of Vienna.[50]

Not only was Dioscorides soon translated into Arabic, but there were two Arabic traditions, Eastern and Western. The first translation was made by Stephanos, son of Basilios (IX-2), and corrected by Ḥunain ibn Isḥāq (IX-2). The Western tradition began in the following century when Constantinos VII Porphyrogennētos presented a Greek MS of Dioscorides to the caliph of Cordova 'Abd al-Raḥmān III. It was translated into Arabic by the latter's Jewish minister, Ḥasdai ibn Shapruṭ (X-2), helped by the Greek monk, Nicholas. The translation was corrected and the text commented upon in 982 by another Cordovan scholar, Ibn Juljul (X-2).

The Latin tradition was also double. The first was begun as early as the sixth century and was probably incomplete and imperfect; at any rate, it was superseded by the second ascribed to Constantine the African (XI-2). This second translation, arranged in alphabetic order, was very

popular, especially after having been revised by Pietro d'Abano (XIV-1).
While in Constantinople, Pietro had seen a Greek MS of it. Was this
the *Codex Aniciae Iulianae* of 512?

We need not speak any longer of the medieval tradition. Suffice
it to say that the text of Dioscorides was available to any doctor reading Greek, Arabic, or Latin. The plant illustrations which existed only
in a few MSS were less well known and hence the iconographic tradition remained incomplete and exceptional.

Let us pass now to the incunabula.[51] The first printed Dioscorides
was the Latin version by Petrus Paduanensis (i.e., Pietro d'Abano) and
J. Allemannus de Medemblick (Walbeck) in Colle, 1478 (Klebs 343).
The Greek princeps was printed by Aldus Manutius in Venice, 1499
(Klebs 342). There were only those two incunabula, but each of them
was many times reprinted with or without changes and additions.

Consider the Greek text. The text of 1499 was revised by Hieronymus
Roscius, a Padovan physician who made use of new MSS, especially
those discovered by Niccolò Leoniceno (Venice: Aldine press, 1518).
This was almost unavoidably followed by a Basel edition, prepared by
Janus Cornarius and printed by Joannes Bebel (1529). To these Greek
editions may be added the Greek-Latin ones, by Marcellus Vergilius
(Cologne: Soteris, 1529-30), by Jacques Goupyl (Paris: widow of Arn-
old Birkmann, 1549),[52] by Janus Ant. Saracenus (Frankfurt a.M.:
Wechel's heirs, 1598).

The two first Latin editions contained the text of Pietro d'Abano
(XIV-1), Colle, 1478; and Gilbert de Villiers, Lyon, 1512. Later Latin
editions offered new translations, by Hermolaus Barbarus (d. 1493)
(2 vols.; Venice, 1516) and by Jean Ruel (Paris: H. Estienne, 1516).
Ruel's translation was often reprinted, e. g., in the Greco-Latin edition
of 1549; by Marcellus Vergilius (Florence: Juntine, 1518. Reprinted
1523, 1528; again Cologne, 1529*);[53] by Pietro Andrea Mattioli (Venice: Vinc. Valgrisius, 1554); by Janus Cornarius (Basel: Frobenius,
1557); by Saracenus (Frankfurt, 1598*).

The popularity of Dioscorides extended outside the learned circles
as is proved by sixteenth-century editions in no less than four vernaculars.

It was translated into Italian thrice: by Fausto di Longiano (Venice,
1542); by P. A. Mattioli (Venice: Bascarini, 1544)—this was the first
publication of Mattioli's famous commentary, the Latin versions of which
appeared only ten years later—it was often reprinted; and by Marco
Antonio Montigiano (Venice: Juntae, 1546-47). The German translation by J. Danz von Ast was printed in the year of his death (Frankfurt a.M.: Cyriaco Jacobi, 1546). The Spanish translation by Andrès
de Laguna was printed in Antwerp, 1555, and Salamanca, 1560 (often
reprinted). There were no less than three French translators: Martin
Mathée (Lyon: Payan, 1559), Ant. du Pinet (Lyon, 1561), and J. des
Moulins (Lyon, 1572, 1579).

Few of the early Latin editions were illustrated, while all the German, Spanish, and French ones included woodcuts. This is significant: the vernacular point of view was concrete and matter of fact; as soon as one ceased to be fascinated by Greek or Latin terms, the interest in the natural objects and their graphic representation was increased. There was even published a book by Juan de Jarava—*Historia de las yervas y plantas sacada de Dioscoride y otros insignes autores* (523 pp.; Antwerp: Byrcman's heirs, 1557)[54]—which was simply an album of woodcuts with very brief text.[55]

To this long enumeration should still be added the commentaries which appeared in the sixteenth century with increasing frequency. The line is often difficult to draw between a commentary and a translation, for the two were often combined in various degrees. We shall not worry about that, but simply introduce the main translators and/or commentators. Our selection is so narrow that it is unavoidably artificial, every botanist of the sixteenth century was in a sense either a translator of, or commentator on, Dioscorides—or both.

There is no need to enumerate later editions, except the very latest to which every student of Dioscorides must necessarily refer: Greek-Latin edition by Curt Sprengel in the Kühn's corpus of Greek medicine (1829-30), vol. 25-26; critical edition of the Greek text by Max Wellmann (3 vols.; Berlin, 1907-14); German translation by J. Berendes (572 pp.; Leipzig, 1902); Old English translation of John Goodyer (1655), edited by Robert T. Gunther (Oxford University Press, 1934—*Isis 23*, 261-62).

Ermolao Barbaro (1454-93) had completed before his premature death a collection of notes on Dioscorides which was edited by another Venetian, Giovanni Battista Cipelli (J. B. Egnatius, or Egnazio, 1473-1553): *Hermolai Barbari in Dioscoridem corallariorum libri quinque* (Venice, 1516; Cologne, 1530).

We shall speak longer of him in the next chapter, because he is more famous as a critic of Pliny the Elder.

We have already mentioned the Spanish translations of Dioscorides which Andrès de Laguna dedicated to Philip II, first printed in Antwerp (Juan Latio, 1555), reprinted in Salamanca, 1560, etc. Before that, he had published *Annotationes in Dioscoridem* (340 pp.; Lyon: G. Rouillius, 1554) in which he criticized the Latin version of Jean Ruel (Paris, 1516).

This Andrès de Laguna was a very remarkable man, primarily physician and anatomist, but humanist as well. A doctor of his time would have no social standing if he were not very deep in Latin and if possible in Greek. He was born in Segovia in 1499, and educated in the universities of Salamanca, Alcalá de Henares, and Paris. While in Paris, in 1535, he published his *Anatomica methodus,* which includes the first description of the ileocaecal valve[56]. In the following year, he returned to Alcalá to teach Greek and Latin and obtained his M.D. in Toledo. He was appointed physician to Charles Quint and was present at the fatal lying-in of the empress. It is possible that it was that accident which caused him to leave Spain. At any rate, he spent the following five years in Metz, where he befriended Johann Guenther of Andernach and helped to fight the plague. Then he moved to Cologne, to Nancy, to Bologna, where he taught medicine until the Emperor took him in his retinue on his way to Rome. Laguna became physician to Paul III and Julius III and sojourned about twelve years in Rome and its vicinity. His *Epitome Galieni* [*sic*] (Basel: M. Isingrinus, 1551), often reprinted, was composed by him in Cicero's villa of Tusculum. About 1555, he visited Antwerp, which helps to explain how his best-known work, the Spanish translation of Dioscorides, was printed in that city (1555). He wrote many medical books, some of these very technical and derived from personal experience; in spite of that, his fame is based upon his many studies of Galen and his translation of Dioscorides. In 1557, he returned to his native city where he died three years later (1560); he is buried in the church of San Miguel.[57]

Andrès de Laguna deserves our respect not only because of his learning and medical experience but also because he was one of the first to give a rational account of the phenomena classified under witchcraft. This he did in his Spanish translation of Dioscorides published in 1555, eight years before the *De praestigiis daemonum* of Johann Weyer, i.e. Joannes Wierus (Basel: Joan. Oporinus, 1563).[58]

The sixteenth century was the golden age of the Hispanic peninsula, and we are not surprised to meet another great doctor, Amatus Lusitanus (1511-68),[59] a little younger than Laguna, Portuguese not Spanish, and certainly Jewish.

His original name was Juan Roderigo, and he was born in Castelo Branco[60] in 1511 of a Marrano family. Amatus was his baptismal name, and he is best known under the name Amatus Lusitanus. He studied medicine in Salamanca, obtaining his M.D. *c.* 1530; he practised medicine in Lisbon but was obliged to leave Portugal for Antwerp *c.* 1533 on account of the violent anti-Semitic prejudices which were focused upon the neo-Christians.[61] It was in Antwerp that he published his first work, the *Index Dioscoridis* (Antwerp: widow of Martin Caesar, 1536), and his reputation grew to the extent that the Duke of Este invited him to be professor of medicine in Ferrara (1540). While lecturing on ancient medicine, he took part in the medical activities of the university, studying botany with Brasàvola[62] and John Falconer,[63] anatomy with Canano[64] and others. He resigned his professorship in 1547, with the hope of obtaining the place of town physician in Ragusa, but his hope did not materialize, and he settled down in Ancona (which had recently become papal territory, 1532). It was in Ancona that he completed his first *Centuria* (1549, pr. 1551), and his commentary on Dioscorides (pr. 1563). He practised medicine in Ancona and Rome, and enjoyed papal patronage until the election of Paul IV (1555-59), who began to persecute the Jews and Marranos. Amatus was one of the victims of that persecution; it is sad to think that his own misery was probably caused, or aggravated, by the enmity of his mean rival, Pier Andrea Mattioli. We find him as a kind of refugee in Pesaro, Ragusa, finally in Salonica where he died at the beginning of 1568, at the age of fifty-seven.

In spite of the vicissitudes of his life and the miseries which blackened the last dozen years, his medical activities were enormous. His fame rests upon two kinds of works—the *Centuriae* and the Dioscoridean commentary.

The *Curationum medicinalium centuria prima* (391 pp.) was printed by Laurentius Torrentinus in Florence, 1551. It is a collection of a hundred case histories with an introduction explaining clinical methods and bedside manners. During the rest of his life, he published many more centuries, seven in all, the last in 1566.[65] Judging from the number of editions, these experimental centuries obtained considerable success. Practical physicians were given seven hundred histories fully discussed in the learned manner of Renaissance humanism, yet based upon individual cases. It might be worth while to analyze these cases and to reconsider them in the light of our own knowledge.

The Dioscoridean commentary interests us more immediately at present. It was equally popular and perhaps among the same group of readers. The *Index* of 1536 was not reprinted as such, but the *In Dioscoridis de medica materia libros quinque enarrationes eruditissimae*—first printed by Gualterus Scotus (Venice, 1553)—was frequently reprinted: in Strassburg, 1554; Venice, 1557; Lyon, 1558 (two editions by two printers).

Amatus was at one and the same time one of the leaders of clinical medicine and one of the foremost exponents of Dioscorides.

The next group is the German or German Swiss: Valerius Cordus, Conrad Gesner, and Caspar Wolf. We have already spoken of Gesner, and we shall speak again of him in a later section because he is one of the giants of the scientific Renaissance. It will suffice to recall here his *Historia plantarum et Vires ex Dioscoride, Theophrasto, etc.* (Paris:

Joannes Lodoicus Tiletanus, 1541), and also the work done by him for the sake of his ill-fated teacher, Valerius Cordus.

Valerius Cordus[66] is famous, but no one can imagine how much greater his fame would have been if he had been permitted to live longer; he was the victim of an accident and of travel exhaustion and died in Rome before he was thirty. He belonged to a learned family, his father Euricius Cordus (1486-1535) being a botanist and humanist. He studied in Marburg and began his professional career explaining Dioscorides to the students of Wittenberg. In the way we would put it, he was teaching materia medica; from the Renaissance point of view, he was teaching Dioscorides. Like other naturalists of genius, he realized the need of escaping from verbalism and started the hunt for plants, first in his own country, later in Provence and Italy. He was a pioneer in the teaching of live botany, taking students with him in his botanical excursions. He did not husband his strength and died prematurely in Rome, in the course of his last excursion. Fortunately, devoted disciples took care of the writings he had left behind, edited them, and saved his name from oblivion.

A collection of medical recipes taken from his writings was circulated for some time in manuscript form and finally published by the magistrates of Nuremberg: *Pharmacorum omnium, quae quidem in usu sunt, conficiendorum ratio. Vulgo vocant Dispensatorium pharmacopolarum . . . authore Valerio Corde* (Nuremberg: Joh. Petreius, 1546).

This work generally called *Dispensatorium* may be considered the first pharmacopoeia. It is available in a beautiful facsimile edition published by the Gesellschaft für Geschichte der Pharmazie (Mittenwald, Bayern, 1934—*Isis 24,* 215). The word pharmacopoeia appeared for the first time in the fifth book of that kind (Augsburg, 1573). There is no point in enumerating the editions of Cordus' *Dispensatorium* of which there are many, but is interesting to mention an early French translation: *Le guidon des apotiquaires, c'est à dire la vraye forme et manière de composer les médicamens. Premièrement traittée par Valerius Cordus. Traduite de latin en françois et répurgée d'une infinité de fautes . . .* (Lyon: Loys Cloquemin, 1578).

This French edition included the notes added by a Flemish apothecary, Pierre Coudenberg[67], first published in the *Valerii Cordi Dispensatorium* (Antwerp: Ch. Plantin, 1568). Coudenberg's annotations were reprinted some fifteen times in Latin, Dutch, and French, the last reprint being as late as 1662 (in Dutch, Amsterdam).

We have devoted more space to the *Dispensatorium* than it perhaps deserves from the purely scientific point of view, though the importance of the first pharmacopoeia can hardly be exaggerated.

Cordus' main scientific works, his *Historia stirpium* and his commentary on Dioscorides, were edited after his death by Conrad Gesner: *Valerii Cordi Adnotationes in Dioscoridis materia medica, eiusdem his-*

toriae stirpium libri IIII (Strassburg: Josias Rihelius, 1561).

The *Adnotationes* alone had been published previously, together with the *Botanologicon* of his father Euricius (Paris: G. Morel, 1551).[68]

The kind services which Gesner rendered to Valerius Cordus (and no man could do anything kinder to another than to edit well his unpublished writings) were rendered to himself by one of his own friends. Though Gesner had the inestimable privilege of living twenty years longer than Valerius Cordus (living twice longer we might put it), his botanical work was left unfinished at the time of his death in 1565. He handed over his MSS to his friend, Caspar Wolf,[69] who was not able to publish them but kept them together, and a part of them were finally published by Casimir Christopher Schmiedel: *Conradi Gesneri Opera botanica . . . vitam auctoris et operis historiam, Cordi librum quintum cum adnotationibus Gesneri in totum opus, ut et Wolphii fragmentum historiae plantarum Gesnerianae, adjunctis indicibus iconum . . .* (folio, 186 pp., pl.; Nuremberg: J. M. Seligmann, 1751-54).

This volume includes the biography of Valerius Cordus by Hieronymus Schreiber. The *liber quintus* and biography of Cordus have a separate title page dated 1751; that is why I gave the date 1751-54 for the whole book. Note that this publication of Gesner's *Historia stirpium* was made almost two centuries too late.

The number of sixteenth-century Dioscorideans is exceptionally large, because every student of botany or of materia medica was one, either directly and explicitly, or not. We shall end this chapter with a study of the most influential of them and finally with a briefer account of another Italian, Fabio Colonna.

Pier Andrea Mattioli (1500-77) was born in Siena but spent his early life in Venice, where his father was a physician. He studied medicine in Padova and graduated in 1523; he then practised it in Siena, Perugia, and Rome which he left at the time of the sack of 1527.[70] He then moved to Trento and Gorizia (Trient and Görz). We must assume that throughout these years he continued his studies of Dioscorides and botany, because his great work appeared first in 1544. This first edition was in Italian: *Dioscoride libri cinque della historia et materia medicinale tradotti in lingua volgare italiana* (Venice: Nicolo de Bascarini, 1544).

The Latin text was not published until ten years later and assured the author's renown; Mattioli was perhaps the most famous botanist of the Renaissance. We shall see presently to what extent that fame was justified, but let us first complete the history of his life.

His *Commentaries* attracted the attention of the imperial court: he was called to Vienne and became physician to the Hapsburg emperors, Ferdinand I (1556-64), who ennobled him, and Maximilian II (1564-76). This office being honorific did not oblige him to remain near the imperial court and very soon (*c.* 1562) he withdrew to Innsbruck, Tirol, and finally to Trento where he died of the plague in 1577.

His *Commentaries* on Dioscorides (based on Ruel's translation) had been facilitated at the beginning by his knowledge of the Italian flora which was closer to the Dioscoridean one than that of central Europe. His travels extending from South Italy to Austria enabled him to obtain considerable experience of living plants and of their varieties; he discovered new ones, especially in the Tirol, and as his fame increased more correspondents were willing to communicate to him their discoveries. He became a magnet of botanical information even as Linnaeus was to be two centuries later. For example, what we know of the botanical observations made by the Flemings Busbecq and Quackelbeen in Turkey, we know only through the reports which the latter sent to Mattioli.[71] To decry Mattioli's work on the ground that many botanical observations were not made by him is unfair; he deserves to be praised almost as well as the original observer because of his publication which was often the first and always the most pregnant.

The editions and translations of his *Commentaries* were so numerous that we can give only a very brief account. Not only were the editions numerous, some were exceptionally large.[72]

The original Italian edition of 1544 has already been mentioned. This was reprinted by another Venetian firm, V. Valgrisi, which became Mattioli's exclusive printers, in 1548, 1549, 1550, 1551, 1559, 1568, 1573, 1581, 1585, etc. In the meanwhile, the Latin text had been published by them: *Commentarii in libros sex Dioscoridis de materia medica* (Venice: V. Valgrisi, 1554). And this was reprinted by the same Valgrisi in 1558, 1559, 1560, 1563, 1565, 1569, 1570, 1583, etc. These editions vary in content; some include other works of his, and the *Commentarii* were gradually increased and were illustrated with more abundant, better, and larger figures.

To these Latin editions of the *Commentarii* must be added those included in Mattioli's collected works which appeared in Frankfurt at the end of the century: *Petri Andreae Matthioli Opera quae extant omnia* (2 parts in 1 folio vol.; Frankfurt: N. Bassaeus, 1598). Reprinted in Basel, 1674.

The interest of this edition lies in the fact that it introduced a new commentator, Caspar Bauhin[73] (1560-1624), the most illustrious member of an illustrious family of Basel, anatomist and botanist, collector of a large herbarium still preserved in the University of Basel. His most important works appeared in the seventeenth century, however, and he represents that century rather than the Renaissance.

In spite of the fact that the Latin editions made Mattioli available to every scholar of Europe, it was found necessary to publish translations in vernaculars. In 1572, two Lyonnese printers published separate French translations, one by Jean Des Moulins (G. Rouillé), the other by Antoine du Pinet[74] (widow of G. Cotier). This second one was often reprinted by different printers, all in Lyon (1605, 1620, 1627, 1642, 1655, 1680). This shows the growing currency of the French language from the end of the sixteenth century on.

A German translation was published in Prague, 1563; another one was made by Joachim Camerarius (Frankfurt a.M., s.a.; preface dated 1586); the book was printed (or reprinted) in Frankfurt in 1600, 1611, and in Basel, 1678 (this is called the fourth edition of Camerarius' version).

Two Czech translations were made by T. Hagek (Hajek?) and by Adam Huber and published in Prague (1582, 1596).

Fabio Colonna[75] was born in Naples, 1567, and lived until 1650. He was thus younger than Bauhin, yet a typical Renaissance personality. His father, Gerolamo Colonna (1534-86) of Naples, was a very learned man, who had collected a large library, and provided for him the best education. Fabio obtained the appointment of prefect of Zagarolo (Rome). Unfortunately, he was epileptic and the story goes that, intelligent and learned as he was, he tried to find a remedy and made a deep study of Dioscorides for that purpose (this is typical of the Renaissance faith in Dioscorides' wisdom). Fabio's diligence was rewarded; he found the remedy "to phu" (Dioscorides 1, 10)—that is, valerian—[76]used it, and cured himself. At any rate, he developed a passion for botany and devoted to it his best-known work, written at the age of twenty-four: *Phytobasanos, sive Plantarum historia . . . Accessit etiam piscium aliquot plantarumque novarum historia* (2 parts in 1 vol.; Naples: Carlinus, 1592). The *Phytobasanos* (meaning the plant touchstone) was reprinted much later (186 pp., ill.; Milano: Viviani, 1744).

In 1606, he published another book in the same vein, with another Greek title, *Ecphrasis* (description), and the same combination of plants and fishes: *Minus cognitarum stirpium aliquot ac etiam rariorum nostro coelo orientium Ecphrasis. Item de aquatilibus aliisque animalibus quibusdem paucis libellus* . . . (2 parts in 1 vol.; Rome, 1606). The illustrations include his own portrait reproduced by A. Arber (p. 98). Reprinted in 1616.

Colonna was interested in natural curiosities and he wrote a treatise on glossopetra and another on purpura.[77] His books were well illustrated, and he was trying to improve the description and classification of plants. In his *Annotationes* to the natural history of Mexico by Francisco Hernandez (1514-78), he introduced the new term petalum (petal) in the description of flowers. This takes us again into the seventeenth century. Colonna knew of Hernandez's work only in the Latin version of Nardo Antonio Recchi (Rome, 1628) and his own *Annotationes* were published posthumously in the second edition (Rome, 1651).[78]

The *Phytobasanos* of 1592 is a little book (20 cm.) dedicated to the cardinal Marco Antonio Colonna. In his preface, "Ad lectorem," the author refers to the fit of epilepsy of which he was cured. The book is divided into two parts each with its own pagination, 120 pp. for the plants and 33 for the fishes, this being followed by the index which as usual is not paginated. The botanical part contains long descriptions, discussions of some twenty-seven plants, each being illustrated with a good image taken from nature and engraved on copper with a curious frame.[79] Almost all these plants are taken from Dioscorides and the last one is the phu (or valerian) in the description of which he refers very briefly to his own experience with it.

This charming little book, with its queer illustrations, is a singular monument of botanical learning at the end of the Renaissance. Its learning is still largely bookish, but not exclusively so; it is clear that Fabio was interested in the plants themselves, examined them with his own eyes, and loved them.

It has been claimed that he made the drawings himself and even engraved them. If that is true, and if he drew and etched also his own portrait illustrating his *Ecphrasis* (1606), he was a distinguished artist, but is it true?

5. Pliny the Elder (I-2)

THE NATURAL HISTORY WHICH PLINY DEDICATED TO THE EMPEROR Titus in the year 77 was one of the most influential books ever published. It was the favorite scientific encyclopedia of medieval times. It was written in Latin, but was derived very largely from Greek sources;

Pliny quoted 327 Greek authorities against 146 Roman ones, and half of the Roman ones were Greek in Latin garb. When one wishes to investigate ancient and medieval knowledge on a definite topic, it is always convenient to consult Pliny first, then, maybe at his own suggestion, earlier authorities, and finally later ones. What did Pliny know? How did he know it? How was his knowledge transmitted to us and gradually improved?

Take the case of fossil ivory. Pliny spoke of it, repeating the statement of Theophrastos (IV-2B.C.). Ailianos (III-1) added stories of his own which encouraged prospectors in search of the ivory needed for the arts. The medieval trade in fossil ivory was observed by al-Māzinī (XII-2). References to it might perhaps be found in other books, but the *Natural history* was the main center of information[80] and was available in every library.

It is curious, by the way, that medieval scholars confused the two Plinii, Pliny the Elder (23-79), the naturalist, and his namesake and nephew Pliny the Younger (61-c.114), the author of the *Epistolae,* man of letters and moralist. One of the first to recognize their duality was Giovanni de Matociis (XIV-1), priest of the cathedral of Verona, who discovered a MS of the *Epistolae.* Giovanni believed that the two Plinii were Veronese like himself, but both were born in Como, far away from Verona though in the same region.

During the whole Middle Ages, Pliny meant primarily, if not exclusively, the author of the *Natural history,* and for the average scholar this meant natural history itself. The botanically-minded person studied Pliny next to Theophrastos and Dioscorides, or he studied books derived from Pliny, like the *Medicina Plinii* (IV-2?), or *Apuleius Platonicus* (V-1?), or the *De herbis femininis* (VI-1?). The *Apuleius* or *Herbarium Apulei,* was thrice printed in the fifteenth century, by the same printer, Lignamine, in Rome (1481, 1482, 1483; Klebs 505.1-3). Friedrich Wilhelm Tobias Hunger (1874-   ): *The herbal of Pseudo-Apuleius* (Leiden: Brill, 1935—*Isis* 27, 96-98) was a facsimile of the edition of 1481 and of a ninth-century MS in Monte Cassino. This *Herbarium Apulei* exerted a great influence, evil rather than good, upon the later herbals of which we shall speak presently.

As to the *Natural history* itself, its text was never lost, and it has come to us in its integrity. There is an abundance of MSS reproducing the whole of it, or parts, or anthologies. Pliny's popularity was due not only to the richness of his information but even more so to his informality. He was not a man of science in the Aristotelian or Theophrastian sense, but rather an encyclopedist and collector of information on a level which was lower but more pleasant. His information was bookish,[81] his curiosity concerning the objects themselves was minimal; in that respect, he gave his medieval followers the worst of examples and it took the combined efforts of the best Renaissance naturalists to drive him out, or at least to lessen the evil which he was doing.

The medieval popularity of the *Natural history* is confirmed by the interest of the early printers. There are no less than fifteen incunabula editions of the Latin text, plus three of the Italian version.[82] All these editions were printed in Italy, in five different cities, one each in Treviso and Brescia, two in Rome, three in Parma, and eleven in Venice. We are always astonished by the multiplicity of printers. For example, the eleven Venetian editions were produced by no less than nine printers. Nine printers in the same city were competing for the publication of the selfsame book, a large book, the composition of which must have been expensive. The eighteen incunabula editions (Latin and Italian) were issued by no less than fourteen Italian presses. The place of honor among them must be given to Johannes de Spira who brought out the princeps (Venice, 1469).

The producer of that princeps, Johannes de Spira, was the first printer of Venice in 1469. He came from Speier on the Rhine; he was probably one of the many Mainz printers whom the sack of that city in 1462 scattered all over Europe.[83] The *Natural history* was his third book, a more ambitious attempt than the preceding ones; it is a large folio (356 leaves, 285 x 164 mm.) the printing of which took three months and was completed by the middle of September 1469. Only a hundred copies were issued. Johannes de Spira died the following year and his business was continued with increasing activity by his brother Vindelinus. Their first competitor in 1470 was the more famous Nicolas Jenson (who came from Sommevoire, near Troyes). Before the end of the year three printing presses were active in Venice, and they worked so hard that a trade crisis arose in 1473. By this time, Venetian printing was in full swing and it became the main industry of the city before the end of the century. The Venetian output was so abundant that it flooded Europe with books.

Modern editions. The best edition of *C. Plini Secundi Naturalis historiae libri XXXVII* is the one by Ludwig von Jan (1807-69), revised by Karl Mayhoff (5 vols.; Leipzig: Teubner, 1892-1909). English translation with copious notes by John Bostock and H. T. Riley (6 vols.; London: Bohn's Library, 1855-57). Latin-English edition begun by Harris Rackham, continued by W. H. S. Jones (6 vols.; Loeb Library, 1944-52); this covers Books I to XXVII. Latin-French edition by Alfred Ernout and others, Collection Guillaume Budé (5 vols.; Paris, 1950- — *Isis 43*, 58-60; *44*, 104), covering Books I-II, VIII, XI-XII.

As the *Natural history* was written in Latin, fewer scholars were needed to introduce it to the reading public. It sufficed to print the Latin

MS and then to reprint it indefinitely, making use sometimes of better MSS, adding more notes and explanations, more elaborate indexes, and so forth. Commentaries were added to the editions or published separately; controversies followed. There is no point in listing all the sixteenth-century editions, and enumerating their characteristics; we must restrict ourselves to the protagonists in the general emulation which was caused by the Plinian encyclopedia.

In his *Handbuch für Bücherkunde* (Leipzig, 1841), Ludwig Choulant listed forty-three Latin editions of the sixteenth century: his list is probably incomplete but sufficient for a first approximation. Of these forty-three editions, twelve were printed in Venice, eight in Paris, eight in Basel, seven in Lyon, two in Cologne, two in Frankfurt, and one each in Hagenau, Alcalá de Henares, Leiden, and Geneva. In short, the *Historia naturalis* could be found in every library and could be bought in every bookshop.

Before speaking of the commentators, let us say a few words of the early translators. The Italian translation was very early indeed and is represented by three Venetian incunabula printed by Nicoles Jenson (1476), Filippo di Pietro (1481), and Bartolommeo de Zanis (1489) (Klebs 787.1-3). These three printers published the same translation, made by the Florentine Cristoforo Landino[84] (1424-1507), who was secretary to the Signoria di Firenze and wrote an often quoted commentary on the *Divina commedia* (1481).

. - The translations in other languages were relatively late. The French translation was made by Antoine du Pinet whose acquaintance we have already made. It was published by Claude Senneton (2 parts in 1 vol., folio; Lyon, 1562. Reprinted by the same in 1566, and by other Lyonnese printers in 1581 and 1584). The English translation was even later; it was made by the greatest Tudor translator, Philemon Holland (1552-1637), and was printed by A. Islip (London, 1601). No other vernacular translation of the whole work appeared in the sixteenth century, but there are partial translations in German.

No less than four commentaries were printed before the end of the century: those of the Italians, Barbaro, Leoniceno, Collenuccio, and of the Frenchman, Robert de Valle.

The most curious of these personalities is the first—Ermolao Barbaro, who was born in Venice, 1454, and died in 1493 when he was not yet forty. He studied in Rome and Padova and was professor of philosophy in Padova, where his lectures on Aristotle were very well attended. He was primarily a humanist. He translated Aristotle's *Rhetoric,* Dioscorides, and Themistios (IV-2), and copied a MS of Athenaios of Naucratis (III-1). A younger humanist, Pietro Bembo (1470-1547), said that he had surpassed all the Venetians in Greek and Latin learning. Having returned to his native city, the Republic of Venice decided to use him for diplomatic errands and he was sent to Milano and to Rome. He captured the favor of Innocent VIII (pope, 1484-92) to such an extent that he was appointed patriarch of Aquileia (1491); Aquileia was then a Venetian dependency.[85] Barbaro, having accepted the patriarchate without the leave of his own government, was punished and his estates confiscated. He gave up the patriarchate and died soon afterwards.

Before his untimely death, he had completed his criticism of Pliny —he claimed to have corrected five thousand errors in the text—and his work *ad hoc* was edited by another Venetian scholar, Egnazio. Pliny emended by a young Padovan don who had become patriarch of Aquileia—is not that a strange concurrence of events?

The book is entitled *Hermolai Barbari patricii veneti patriarchae Aquiliensis Castigationes plinianae. . . .* It is a folio of 348 leaves (304 x 208 mm.) printed by Eucharius Silber in Rome in 1492/93 and dedicated to Alexander VI (Innocent VIII's successor, pope 1492-1503). It is in two parts bound together and the second part includes the "castigationes" of Pomponius Mela (I-1).

The publication must have been begun when Barbaro was still alive and had not yet resigned the patriarchate. Judging from the fact that it was reprinted at least thrice, it was successful. It was reprinted in Venice, 1493-94 (s.a.l.), in Cremona by Darleriis in 1495 (Klebs 143.1-3), and in Basel by J. Valderus in 1534.

Niccolò Leoniceno (1428-1524) wrote a book like Barbaro's at about the same time: *Plinii ac plurium aliorum auctorum qui de simplicibus medicaminibus scripserunt errores notati* (18 leaves, 202 x 143; Ferrara: Laurentius de Rubeis de Valentia, 1492).

It appeared at the very end of the year, on 18 December 1492 (Klebs 598.1), and Barbaro's book was printed in Rome between 24 November 1492 and 13 February 1493. Leoniceno has received credit for more realistic criticism than Barbaro's, his criticism based not upon the MSS but rather upon the plants themselves. His book was reprinted in Ferrara by Jo. Maciochium in 1509 and in Basel by H. Petrus in 1529, 1532.

His criticism was promptly answered by Pandolfo Collenuccio: *Pliniana defensio adversus Leoniceni accusationem* (52 leaves, 144 x 107; Ferrara: Andreas Belfortis, 1493?—Klebs 282.1).

Collenuccio referred not only to Leoniceno's book but also to Barbaro's *Castigationes* "ex urbe Roma . . . nuper editae." He was not a professor like Leoniceno, but a man of an entirely different kidney. He had been podestà[86] in many Italian cities, a dangerous profession which caused him who held it to create many enmities against himself. Toward the end of his life he retired to his native place, Pesaro, where he was thrown into prison and finally strangled by order of Giovanni Sforza[87] for the crime of treason.

Like any other podestà he had to be an orator, but in addition he was a historian and man of letters. He wrote (in Italian) a history of Naples which was often reprinted and was translated into Latin, French, and Spanish; and he composed many literary pieces in prose and verse. His most interesting works to us are his treatise on ancient education (in Italian) and his defense of Pliny against Leoniceno. He must have been somewhat of a botanist, for some of his remarks on Pliny's plants were inserted by Otto Brunfels in Book VI of his *Herbarum vivae eicones* (Strassburg, 1530). A podestà who is not simply an orator, but a historian, poet, and botanist, so much virtue and such a variety of it in a single man, that is typical of the Italian Renaissance.

Collenuccio was rebuked by Lodovico Pòntico Virunio (1467-1520) or Lodovico da Ponte of Belluno, who was primarily a humanist and an abbreviator of Geoffrey of Monmouth (XII-1), and from the botanical point of view by Brunfels: *Invectiva contra Pand. Coll. in defensionem Nic. Leoniceni.* This item is quoted by Choulant (p. 203), but I cannot find it anywhere else.

Robert du Val was a Norman. His Latin name, Robertus de Valle Rothomagensis, suggests that he came from Rouen, but he was born at Rugles (Eure) *c.* 1450 and was canon of Chartres. He wrote: *Compendium memorandorum vires naturales et commoda comprehendens a Plinio data* (122 leaves; Paris: Felix Baligault for Durand Gerlier, 1500) and *Explicatio terminorum historiae naturalis Plinii* (90 leaves; for Gerlier, no date). Both works are recorded by Marie Pellechet (nos. 4537, 4539) and by Klebs (356.1, 357.1).

Let us pass to Spain. The main Plinian scholar of the early Renaissance was Francisco López de Villalobos[88] (1473-1549). Of Jewish origin, he was born not in Toledo but in Zamora (on the Duero R. in León),

Spanish man of letters and physician, best known because of his poem *El sumario de la medicina con un tratado sobre las pestiferas buvas* (28 leaves, double col.; Salamanca, for Antonio de Barreda, 1498—Klebs 615.1), an abbreviation of Ibn Sīnā's *Canon,* first didactic poem in Castilian, including one of the earliest descriptions of syphilis.

We introduce him here because of his *Glosa de los dos primeros libros de Plinio* (Alcalá de Henares, 1524). He was a practising physician and even an illustrious one, being archiater to el Rey Católico (Ferdinand V of Castile) and later to Carlos V (1519). His best-known work was the *Libro intitulado los Problemas de Villalobos que tracta de los cuerpos naturales y morales, y dos dialogos de medicina, y el tractado de las tres grandes, y una Canción y la comedia de Amphytrion* (88 1.; Zamora: J. Picardo, 1543), reprinted in Medina, 1543; Sevilla, 1550, 1574. This title has been quoted in extenso to illustrate the heterogeneity of Villalobos' composition—a Renaissance trait.

Among the editors of the *Historia naturalis,* special mention should be made of Alessandro Benedetti, who was born in Legnano about the middle of the fifteenth century and died in 1525. He was an anatomist and became chief surgeon to the Venetian army fighting Charles VIII (king of France, 1483-98); he was spoken ill of because of his astrological tendencies and of his flight from Venice when the plague flared up. His edition of Pliny printed by Jo. Rubeus and Bernardinus fratresque Vercellences (Venice, January 1507) was far more elaborate than the preceding ones, based upon MSS and well indexed.

Johann Froben of Basel published in 1525 a new edition of the Latin text under the misleading title *Historia mundi.* The editor was no less a person than Erasmus, who added a prefatory letter to the bishop of Olmütz in Moravia. Froben and his associates reprinted the book many times, trying each time to introduce novelties. For example, their edition of 1530 included[89] the elaborate index compiled by Joannes Camers, i.e., the Franciscan Giovanni Ricucci (1468-1546) of Camerino, who flourished in Padova and Vienna. Their edition of 1535 was revised by Sigismundus Gelenius (1497-1554) of Prague, who was one of the leading philologists of his day (Hellenist as well as Latinist) and was established in Basel. That edition included some fifty pages of *Observationes Gelenii* printed without pagination.[90] Gelenius' edition, reprinted in Basel, 1554, was a material contribution to our knowledge of the original text.

The history of translations and commentaries is made complex because the latter may include the former or not, and both kinds of books may concern the whole work or a few books only. Books appearing under a very different title may be in fact largely derived from Pliny.

For example, the *Melchioris Guilandini Papyrus* is a commentary on three chapters of Pliny dealing with papyrus (printed, with two other items, by M. A. Vimus, Venice, 1572). The same author published another partial commentary (152 pp., Lausanne: F. Le Preux, 1576); and long before that, a study of his on plant names had been printed together with a similar study by Conrad Gesner (Basel: Episcopius junior, 1557). Melchior Guilandinus (d. 1589) of Königsberg in Prussia was a naturalist and traveler who was made prisoner in Algiers and ransomed by Gabriele Fallopio (1523-63); he became professor of botany in Padova and director of the botanic garden. His description of that garden, *Hortus patavinus,* was published after his death (Frankfurt, 1608; frontispiece with date 1600).

The French translation of the *Natural history* by Antoine du Pinet was mentioned above, but before its first publication in 1562, a summary of Books I-XVI was published in French by Pierre de Changy: *Sommaire des singularitez de Pline, extraict des seize premiers livres . . . et mis en vulgaire françois* (Paris, 1542).

This Pierre de Changy is perhaps better known by a French translation of the treatise of Juan Luis Vives (1492-1540) on the education of women, *Livre très bon, plaisant et salutaire de l'institution de la femme chrestienne* (Paris, 1543), reprinted in Lyon (s.d.) and Le Havre (1891).

Next to Ruel, the main diffusionist of botanical literature in France was Jacques Dalechamps (or d'Aléchamps, 1513-88) whose *Historia generalis plantarum in libros XVIII per certas classes artificiose digesta* was first published by Guillaume Rouillé (2 vols., folio, 1922 pp.; Lyon, 1586-87).

This includes some 2686 figures, of which 400 are repeated. Reprinted by other printers in Lyon. It was translated into French by Jean des Moulins and printed by Rouillé's heirs (2 vols., folio; Lyon, 1615). This translation enjoyed considerable popularity.

Jacques Dalechamps was born in Caen in 1513; he studied medicine in Montpellier (M.D., 1546) and practised it in Lyon where he died on 1 May 1588. The very long title page of his *Historia* does not mention his name, and therefore it is often quoted impersonally as the *Historia plantarum lugdunensis.* There is no doubt as to his authorship, but he was helped by Jean des Moulins and Guillaume Rondelet (see publisher's dedicatory letter to Charles Emmanuel, duke of Savoy).

He was a philologist interested in plants and plant lore, rather than a learned botanist. He translated into Latin the *Banquet of the learned*

85

of Athenaios of Naucratis (III-1)[91] and into French the *De anatomicis administrationibus* of Galen (Lyon, 1572), annotated Günther's Latin edition of Paulos Aigineta (Lyon, 1567), and edited Pliny's *Natural history*. This edition, printed by Barthélemy Honorat (Lyon, 1587), was based on new MSS; it was reprinted by Jo. Feyerabend (Frankfurt, 1599). Dalechamps was accused by Scaliger of having been too free in his emendations. On the other hand, he was also accused of lacking originality. His *Historia plantarum* was said to be exclusively derived from Theophrastos, Dioscorides, and Pliny; this is not true, for he used also the works of sixteenth-century botanists like Matthias de L'Obel. His work was compiled too hastily; for example, some four hundred illustrations are repeated, some under different names. He could not complete himself the immense compilation and was helped by des Moulins; must the editorial negligence be credited to him or to the latter?

To complete our account of Dalechamps, we must still mention his *Chirurgie françoise,* printed by Guillaume Rouillé I (21 l., 933 pp., ill.; Lyon, 1570. Reprinted in Lyon, 1573; Paris: O. de Varennes, 1610).

His collaborator, Jean des Moulins (or Desmoulins, Molinaeus), was born in Ambert (Puy-de-Dôme) in 1530, studied in Montpellier, was acquainted with Rondelet, practised medicine in Lyon, but was primarily interested in botany. He died *c.* 1620. He was one of the French translators of Mattioli's *Commentarii* (1572). We do not know how much he helped Dalechamps in the documentation and redaction of the *Historia plantarum,* but it was he who translated it into French: *Histoire générale des plantes contenant XVIII livres . . . sortie latine de la bibliothèque de Me Jacques Dalechamps, puis faite française par Me Jean Des Moulins . . . Ensemble les tables des noms en plusieurs langues* (2 vols., folio; Lyon: Rouillé's heirs, 1615). This was reprinted in Lyon, 1653.

Dalechamps' *Historia plantarum* marked the climax of the learned botany of the French Renaissance; it was a monument of learning and typography; it was inferior to the botanical works accomplished on a smaller scale, but on a sounder basis, by the original herbalists of the sixteenth century.

6. THE DEVELOPMENT OF NATURALISM
IN ART AND SCIENCE

IT IS NECESSARY AT THIS POINT TO OPEN A LARGE PARENTHESIS AND explain an intellectual growth which was very different from the recovery of ancient texts, yet converged with it during the Renaissance.

The ancients had not been satisfied to describe and discuss nature by means of words; they had also tried to represent some aspects of it graphically. Ancient artists reproduced animals and plants.[92] Their purpose was purely artistic, yet what they did was the counterpart of scientific description; it took a very long time, however, for men of learning to understand the polarity of artistic and scientific representations.

That polarity was repeatedly obscured and even forgotten, because the artists were not always naturalistic. On the contrary, their tendency was often the opposite; they were influenced by nature but had no desire to imitate natural forms too closely. The objects which they had the opportunity of observing inspired forms or patterns, but these patterns might be so remote from concrete reality that the latter could hardly be recognized. For example, consider the acanthus of Corinthian and Byzantine capitals; the original inspiration was given by a real plant, Acanthus spinosus, but it would not do to illustrate Dioscorides' verbal description with the sculptor's conception of acanthus leaves. Throughout the centuries, artists and men of science followed their several paths; sometimes they drew very close together, sometimes they were very far apart.

To simplify the subject, let us restrict ourselves to botany.[93] The traditions of botanical iconography can be traced back at least to the time of Cratevas (I-1 B.C.) ; that is, he is the first person known to have written a herbal and illustrated it. Of course, plants had been reproduced long before his time by Egyptian artists and by artists of other nations, but Cratevas was the first to use plant illustrations for a scientific purpose. His illustrations are lost, but the tradition was not. A century and a half later, Pliny the Elder (I-2) was complaining that the pictures in the illustrated herbals had become degraded in copying.[94] Illustrated herbals continued to be produced and the earliest specimen which has come to us is the magnificent manuscript of Dioscorides made in 512 for the princess Anicia Iuliana (see above). A few of the illustrations have been traced back to Cratevas. There is a whole series of MS herbals which stretch out to the beginnings of printing. It will suffice to mention four outstanding examples: first, the "Lombard" MS written in Monte Cassino in the ninth century and now preserved in Munich (Cod. lat. 337) ; second, the Oxford MS of Apuleius Barbarus written at Bury St. Edmunds, Suffolk, *c.* 1120; third, the Codex Hamilton 407 in the National Library, Berlin, written for Philippe de Valois before his accession to the throne of France in 1328; fourth, the herbal completed by Benedetto Rinio in Venice, 1410. The tendencies of the MS herbals were continued, and sometimes their very illustrations were copied in the printed ones, but before dealing with them, let us consider for a moment the purely artistic tradition.

The best medieval examples in sculpture are to be found in the floral decoration carved in limestone in the minsters of York and Southwell. For painting, the best examples are found in illuminated MSS, either in separate miniatures or in the margins of missals and other books. Consider the delicate illustrations made by Cybo of Hyères (XIV-2) in a Ligurian MS of the British Museum. Cybo was deeply interested not only in plants but also in insects, snails, etc. His illustrations are very realistic, but his aim was not in the least scientific; it was artistic and perhaps religious, for the beauty and loveliness of his creatures, even the humblest, help us to love God.[95]

Many painters of the fourteenth century and later added flowers, birds, even insects to their compositions and we must assume that many of them had a religious intention (even as the Buddhist painters had in their own world). Their representations were sometimes realistic enough to enable modern naturalists to identify the plants delineated. Just think of some paintings or drawings of Giotto (*c.* 1270-1336), Spinello Aretino (1330?-1410), Botticelli (1444?-1510), Leonardo da Vinci (1452-1519) or, to pass to other countries, Jan Van Eyck (*c.* 1370-*c.* 1440), Holbein (1465-1524), Albrecht Dürer (1471-1528); or evoke the ceramical creations of Bernard Palissy (1510-89). That list could be lengthened indefinitely, and it would be possible to write a "natural history of the Renaissance artists," that is, to draw up the flora and fauna as represented by them and derived exclusively from their works of art. One may see, for instance, in Holbein's "St. Sebastian" (1516, Munich) the variety monophylla of Fragaria vesca, which is now seldom met with.[96] As to Botticelli's "Spring" (1478, Florence) no less than thirty species of plants can be recognized in it. It must be admitted that if Botticelli's spirit was religious, it was certainly not Christian, but pagan, for his "Spring" is an apotheosis of Venus.

These Renaissance paintings, whether Christian or pagan, prove that the artists were increasingly aware of the beauty of nature, and of its individual forms. One should not conclude that naturalism had won forever, not at all. The struggle between concrete representations, on the one hand, and abstractions, on the other, or between realism and symbolism has existed in almost every place and time. It is one of the essential rhythms in art evolution. Art, we should remember, does not progress in one direction as science does; it goes up and down, up and down, without cease. At times, the realists are winning; at other times, symbolism is the fashion.

The representations of natural objects by Renaissance artists were generally realistic, sometimes to an astonishing degree. When the first herbals were printed, the influence of these artists had not yet been felt strongly enough to overcome the inertia of the old medieval tradition. The herbalists had copied the drawings of their predecessors in the same spirit as they had copied the text. Few of them took the trouble of examining the flowers growing in their own meadows and forests, and it had hardly occurred to them that the conventional illustrations which had been transmitted from scribe to scribe might be inadequate and wrong.

The first printed herbals continued the MS tradition; the MS figures were stereotyped in the form of woodcuts. The incunabula herbals, some forty-one of them, are largely medieval. This is true of the three editions of the *Herbarium Apulei* (Rome, 1481 f.), of the eleven editions of the Latin *Herbarius* (Mainz, 1484 f.), of the thirteen editions of the

Herbarius zu Deutsch, Gart der Gesundheit[97] (Mainz, 1485 f.), of the three editions of the *Grant herbier* (Besançon, 1486 f.), of the six illustrated editions of *Macer floridus* (Genève, 1500).[98] The herbals of the early sixteenth century, such as the English ones (London, 1525 f.), were of the same antiquated type. A new era began in 1530 when the *Herbarum vivae eicones* (note the title) of Otto Brunfels was published by Joannes Schott in Strassburg. We shall come back to it in another chapter.

7. PRINTED IMAGES

THE LEARNING AND THE ARTISTRY OF THE RENAISSANCE ARE BOTH well known, but one has not paid sufficient attention to something intermediate, the use of the graphical arts for scientific purposes. The invention of typography changed the face of the world. The more I think of it, the more convinced I am that the age of incunabula was the infancy of the Renaissance itself. The incunabula were the best symbols thereof and wherever printers journeyed to establish a new press, they evoked a new spirit. This was not immediately obvious; yet, it is clear enough in retrospect. The pregnancy of that invention is explained in every historical textbook, but the explanation is seldom complete.

There are at least two fundamental aspects of it which we may call briefly diffusion and standardization. Printing made possible the simultaneous production of hundreds or thousands of copies of the same text. Once a sheet had been composed by the typesetters, it was easy to reproduce it indefinitely. That is clear enough.

The other aspect of the matter, standardization, is equally important. Whereas it was impossible for the best copyists to reproduce the same text without alterations, the sheets printed from the same form were exactly alike. Not only did all those sheets contain the same text, but that text was arranged in exactly the same way. For example, line 5 of page 6 was always the same line, and it was possible to refer to it without ambiguity.[99]

We do not forget that teaching needs caused the wholesale production of MSS before the invention of printing. But those editions of MSS were relatively small, as compared with the editions of printed books, and in spite of every effort to guarantee faithful copying, the copies could never be as close to identity as the printed books issuing at the same time from the same presses. As to reference from one copy to another, it was never as easy and dependable; the owner of a MS did not generally know whether it was a unique copy or one of many similar ones. On the contrary, the owner of a book, say the *De Plinii et aliorum in medicina erroribus* by Niccolò Leoniceno, printed in Ferrara by L. Rubeis and A. Grassis on 18 December 1492, knew for certain that his copy was equivalent to a great many others which in the course of time were distributed all over the world. If he referred to one of Leoniceno's statements (giving its exact location, l. *x*, p. *y*), the reference could be verified eventually by every owner of another copy. This commodity applied not simply to his contemporaries but to the readers of every place or time. A reference to a MS now preserved in the Bibliothèque Nationale of Paris can hardly be checked except by autopsy of that particular MS or of a photograph of it; it is necessary to identify that MS by quoting its number in a given catalogue. On the other hand, Leoniceno's book, or rather that particular edition of it, can be located in a good many libraries. It is Klebs 598.1; it is described in BMC VI, 612, etc. The book can be easily identified, and every statement in it can be referred to in the simplest manner.

We have already pointed out that by the end of the fifteenth century the average scholar had in his library a number of MSS as well as printed books. It must have happened many a time that he had a MS and a printed copy of the same book, and thus it was possible for him to compare them. Sometimes, the differences were, or looked, small. The earliest printers were imitators; they produced "counterfeit MSS"; at least, that is how refined collectors would have put it; the early printers replaced the original MSS by cheap imitations. The use of those early editions was as difficult as that of the MSS themselves, for in both cases, clearness was sacrificed to economy of space. The words were abbreviated and the sentences crowded together without blanks. This did not disturb contemporary readers who did not expect the printed books to be easier to read than the MSS. The printers did not exploit the invention as fully as it could be exploited until later. They learned gradually that there was no point in copying the MSS so slavishly and that the economy of the new method might be transmitted more fully to the readers. Abbreviations were no longer necessary; it was simple enough to introduce blank spaces between the paragraphs, larger ones between the chapters, and so on. Not only was it possible for any reader of a definite book to find a definite sentence in it; it could be found with increasing ease and promptness.[100]

The Renaissance was introduced not by a single invention, typography, but by two collateral inventions which were completed at about the same time and whose early growth occurred in the same period. These two contemporary and complementary inventions are typography and engraving.[101] The first is fully discussed in all the historical books while the second has generally been abandoned to the historians of art, though it was of almost equal importance for many readers and of supreme importance for men of science. Books are dealt with by historians, however, and if they be learned books, by philologists, and the genuine philologists are more interested in words than in pictures. Indeed, they are quite capable of combining a verbal accuracy carried to the limits of pedantry with incredible laxity and nonchalance for iconography;[102] they are like blind guides, which strain at a gnat and swallow a camel. They will quarrel about a single word, a letter, or an accent and accept blindly any illustration, say a false portrait. According to a Chinese[103] proverb "one picture is worth a thousand words"—pedantic philologists are itching to fight about a single word in the text; yet, they accept without demur the equivalent of thousands of them in the figures.

The invention of engraving made it possible to print illustrations, or to illustrate printed texts. This was of great importance for the diffusion of knowledge. One might even say that engraving was more needed than typography itself. Indeed, every educated man could copy a text, while only a few were capable of copying an image; this was not due so much to a fundamental inability but to a lack of training. Artists learned to draw and paint; but the majority of people were not artists and remained graphically illiterate.

It was not necessary to copy a full text. An intelligent scholar who had received permission to read a MS would take notes for his own use; if he were expert in note taking, his summary of it and his anthology of extracts would be more convenient for further use, and therefore more valuable, than the MS itself. If the MS were illustrated, he might try to copy the illustrations but that was far more difficult and was definitely uncongenial. The MS illustrations of an ancient text were often degenerate. The name of a plant, say *Artemisia* or *Valeriana,* might be transmitted correctly (or recognizably) by a chain of a hundred copyists, but the image of it would have suffered a whole series of alterations; these alterations were never corrective; they were cumulative and the illustrations went almost unavoidably from bad to worse.

The invention of engraving made it possible for the first time to publish durable illustrations, illustrations that would not run down and degenerate but would remain standards of graphical accuracy.

"Graphical accuracy," what does that mean? Most of us understand these words, but we may be sure that very few people understood them before 1450, or before 1500. For the majority of educated people, there was no meaning in them, and no problem. This is the more remarkable when we remember that the sophisticated people of the *quattrocento* could be wary judges of the likeness of a painted portrait. Of such there were many excellent ones, and others which were not so good. The friends of Piero della Francesca would discuss whether his self-portraits were good likenesses or not.[104] Was Tiziano's portrait of Gianello della Torre of Cremona, clockmaker to Charles Quint and Philip II, "the Archimedes of his time," a good portrait?[105] Of the many portraits of Erasmus by illustrious painters—Quentin Metsys, Holbein, Dürer—

which came closest to reality?[106] Not only did they criticize the portraits which were given as such, but they could do and did the same with regard to sacred pictures. One could not discuss whether St. George looked like St. George, or St. Sebastian like St. Sebastian, but the painter's friends knew well enough the models whom he had used, and they would debate (sometimes eagerly and warmly) whether his St. George was like the young Luca or not, or whether his Madonna did justice to the loveliness of Monna Ermellina whom they all admired and loved. It is probable that such criticism was soon applied to the engraved portraits of contemporaries; yet, the imaginary portraits of the ancients were stupidly taken for granted. Consider a famous publication like the *Icones medicorum* of the Hungarian, John Sambucus, published by Christopher Plantin (folio; Antwerp, 1574).[107] The etchings were made by the Flemish artist, Pieter van der Borcht, who illustrated many other books for Plantin. Sambucus explains in his preface that they were made from ancient paintings, statues, medals, or MSS. Was not that sufficient identification? We should not judge Sambucus too severely, because there are still scholars in our own day whose iconographic criticism is on the same level.

As to the representations of objects, say plants, the early printers were generally satisfied to reproduce the MS illustrations or to concoct similar ones without bothering too much about reality. That extraordinary incuriosity or inertia was caused by a lack of imagination, or perhaps the ancient portraits had sidetracked them. A publisher might embellish his books with the portraits of Theophrastos, Dioscorides, or Pliny; he might add pictures of plants. It was impossible to check on the portraits. Why bother about the plants? One iconographic tradition could be accepted just as readily as the other.

These aberrations lasted a long time, but they could not last forever. This does not mean that they were eventually stopped everywhere; they are still flourishing today. There are learned books written by accurate scholars, yet offering to their readers images of Plato and Aristotle. Such aberrations are like other superstitions and can never be completely eradicated. Therefore, the protagonists of the graphical accuracy of the Renaissance deserve the warmest admiration.

Let us consider the simple case of plants. In the sixteenth century, the teaching of botany was well organized in all the universities having a medical department. Not only was botany recognized as a basic science for every medical purpose, but a growing number of men were aware of its value even for nonmedical purposes. Botany deserved to be studied for its own sake. The medical needs introduced a modicum of rigor in the determination of certain plants. Any physician should be able, if not to find the necessary herbs, at least to identify them in the drugshop. The establishment of botanic gardens close to each medical school familiarized the students with definite plants. Some pioneers like Valerius

Cordus did even better and took students with them into the fields and the woods to find plants in their natural abode. We have seen that Valerius did not restrict himself to local herborization, but took his flock across Germany, and even to such distant countries as Provence or Italy.

Any botanist who had become familiar with living plants either in a garden or in their habitat could not help being disgusted with the stereotyped images which illustrated the earliest herbals. The next step was to prepare new images drawn from nature. The great innovation was first brought to a sufficient degree of perfection by Otto Brunfels (1530). Once the fundamental idea had been grasped, it could be applied gradually to more and more objects, and the drawings could include more details, illustrate them better from the scientific point of view, and more pleasantly from the artistic one.

The illustrations were not simply valuable in themselves; their existence close to the text must eventually lead to the correction of the latter. It became more and more objectionable to reproduce stereotyped words in the vicinity of correct images.

The draughtsman was trained to observe the plant as a whole and every detail of it. In a sense, one might claim that no one can observe anything completely without the necessity of making a drawing of it. Without such a necessity, we are generally satisfied with an intuitive perception which enables us to recognize it, but hardly to describe it. We may assume that expert rhizotomists and some herb gatherers of every clime and age managed to obtain an astonishing degree of alertness and competence in the discovery of the herbs and roots they were hunting for. Each plant is distinguished by its *habitus,* which may be more significant than any detail and can be perceived immediately from a distance.

A faithful drawing must suggest the *habitus* and general appearance, but it must also indicate every detail as clearly as possible. The botanists undertaking such a task, or commissioning an artist to do it under their supervision, were being gradually trained in botanical analysis. The graphical analysis of the draughtsmen and the commentaries which they evoked prepared the way for the technical descriptions. These were still impracticable during the Renaissance, if only because the terminology was inadequate. The development of botanical anatomy and of classification, the establishment of binomial nomenclature even in their cruder stages, required two or three additional centuries of labor. The great herbalists of the Renaissance provided the graphical introduction.

There is no point in comparing the different herbals produced in Germany and later in other countries. Each might contain novelties— new plants or better drawings of familiar ones; most contained also a number of stereotyped illustrations. This is especially true of the large treatises offering thousands of figures (e.g., the *Historia generalis plantarum* of Jacques Dalechamps, Lyon, 1586-87).

It was tempting for the author or for the publisher to increase the richness of his collections by including old images. We must bear in mind that each illustration required many more pains than those used in modern books, for it was necessary to obtain for each of them the collaboration of a good draughtsman and a good engraver. The two tasks required not a little time. In many cases, blocks used by one printer were borrowed or bought by another and were used again for the illustration of other books. Or a great printing firm like Plantin's in Antwerp was forming a large stock of blocks of which it tried to make the largest use possible. This was natural enough. The printer's stock included various "fonts" (i.e., assortments of type of different sizes and styles); it also included fancy initials, borders, tailpieces, and other ornaments; finally, there accumulated in his drawers all kinds of "blocks"—wood blocks or engraved copperplates—which had been prepared for the illustration of one book but which it would be economical to use again and again for the embellishment of other books. A large firm like Plantin's would have draughtsmen and engravers in its service. Illustrations for the Dodoens' *Frumentorum . . . historia* (1566) were drawn by Pieter van der Borcht; other books of Dodoens were illustrated by the same artist[108], by Arnaud Nicolai, by Jan Van Loo, etc. The blocks were preserved by Plantin and used again in the botanical books of Mathias Lobelius and Carolus Clusius which he published.

Some of the very blocks used by Plantin have been preserved to this day and can be seen in the Plantin-Moretus Museum in Antwerp (*Horus,* 262). Many other blocks of Renaissance printers have come down to us and are preserved in European museums and libraries. A remarkable example is that of the blocks used to illustrate Vesalius' *Fabrica* printed in Basel by Joannes Oporinus in 1543 and again 1555. They had been drawn and engraved by Stephen van Calcar under Vesalius' supervision and were preserved in the Library of the University of Munich.[109] The original blocks (227 in number) were used again in the magnificent *Vesalii Icones anatomicae* published by the New York Academy of Medicine in 1934.[110]

To return to the early naturalists, every time they realized the necessity of adding to their texts illustrations reproducing the natural objects and were able to attain their purpose, the literary tradition was replaced or supplemented by a new tradition derived directly from nature. The endless struggle between *verba* and *realia,* between erudition and experimental science, was won by the latter. In some cases, the figures of a book were much in advance of the text and even of its commentaries, but gradually a better text or a better commentary was substituted until the time came when the ancient texts disappeared completely from the scientific textbooks, and treatises on natural history were finally written which contained hardly any reference to the ancient elucubrations.

This is another aspect of the Renaissance, the gradual triumph of autoscopy and its graphical results over textual literalism. The cycle was now completed. The early naturalists had felt the imperative duty of rescuing the ancient writings; the early criticism had been purely philological. This excited a new kind of criticism based upon the objects, and finally the study of nature replaced the study of Greek and Latin sources.

The printed image was the savior. As soon as scholars realized the need of illustrating the ancient texts by means of illustrations drawn from nature itself, the artists did their work and drove the philologists away. The main evil of Renaissance science was its love of words; that evil was finally compensated and redeemed by the love of clear and good images. Humanists had turned their back to nature, the artists did the opposite. Science was the winner.

8. THE NEW HERBALS

THE TITLE OF THIS CHAPTER, "THE NEW HERBALS," IS USED TO DESIG-
nate a new kind of herbal essentially different from those which continued the Dioscoridian-Plinian tradition in that they were based upon the autoscopy and the delineation of living plants. The title is vague and this is unavoidable because the line between the "old" and the "new" herbals is not easy to draw. The change from the former to the latter was not abrupt and complete, but gradual and full of compromises. The first new herbalists were Germans and these have sometimes been called the German Fathers of Botany. Their great achievements have been described by Edward Lee Greene (1843-1915) in his *Landmarks of botanical history* (Washington, 1909) and by Agnes Arber in *Herbals* (Cambridge University Press, 1938—*Isis 30,* 131-32), which is admirably illustrated.

A summary suffices for our general purpose. The story of the early herbals can be restricted to four capital events dated 1530, 1542, 1546, and 1561. The last date is artificially late; the early new herbals were composed within less than twenty years. The protagonists were Germans and Lutherans. They took part in two simultaneous revolutions: the Reformation of the Church and the revelation of the vegetal world.

(1) The first new herbal was prepared by Otto Brunfels (so called because of his native place, Braunfels, near Mainz). He was a Carthusian monk but abandoned his monastery at the time of his Lutheran conversion in 1521. He lived for some nine years in Strassburg, teaching school and herborizing. The fruit of his studies was the *Herbarum vivae eicones ad naturae imitationem summa cum diligentia et artificio effigiatae, una cum effectibus earundem in gratiam veteris illius et jamjam renascentis herbariae medicinae per Othonem Brunfelsum recens editae 1530. Quibus adjecta ad calcem appendix isagogica de usu et administratione simplicium* (3 vols. in 1, folio; Strassburg: Johann Schott, 1530-36). German edition, *Contrafaÿt Kreüterbüch nach rechter vollkommener Art*

und Beschreibungen der alten besst-berümpten Artzt (2 parts, folio; same printer, 1532-37; also 1539-40).

I have not seen the German editions, but inasmuch as they were issued by the same printer we may assume that they contained the same illustrations. These had been made by Hans Weiditz, who deserves as much praise as Brunfels himself. Indeed, the illustrations were better than the text, which was very conservative. His descriptions were dominated by the ancient ones, which were sometimes incongruent, as the varieties which he could observe in the Rhine district were generally different from those of the Near East. As to the plants which had no Latin name he called them *herbae nudae*.

(2) The second herbal illustrated from nature was the work of Leonhart Fuchs of whom we have already spoken. Fuchs was far better educated than Brunfels and his personality more complex. He was a Bavarian, born in 1501 at Wemding; he studied in Erfurt and Ingolstadt, became a Lutheran, practised medicine in Munich, then taught medicine in Ingolstadt and Tübingen. At the time of the plague of 1529, he distinguished himself so much that he received calls from the University of Pisa and the king of Denmark; he preferred to remain in his native country. During his medical practice he studied the plants available to him and published his great herbal—the greatest of the early ones: *De historia stirpium commentarii insignes maximis impensis et vigiliis elaborati, adjectis earundem vivis plusquam quingentis imaginibus numquam antea ad naturae imitationem artificiosius effectis et expressis, Leonharto Fuchsio . . . authore* (897 pp., fol. ill.; Basel: Isingrinus, 1542. Reprinted Paris: J. Bogard, 1543; Paris: J. Gazellus, 1543; Paris: G. Guillard, 1546, 1547; Lyon: G. Gazellus, 1547; Lyon: B. Arnolletus, 1549, 1551, etc.)

German translation (Basel: Isingrinus, 1543; reprinted in 1550?). French translation (Paris: widow of A. Byrkman, 1549; Lyon: B. Arnoullet, 1550; Lyon: G. Rouillé, 1558; Lyon: Pesnot, 1575; Rouen: R. Mallard, 1593). Abbreviated Spanish translation by Juan de Jarava (Antwerp: heirs of A. Byrkman, 1557).

In the preparation of his work, Fuchs could and did avail himself of the *Vivae eicones* of Brunfels, as well as of the botanical *texts,* published by Tragus in 1539 and by Gesner in 1541, but his descriptions (far superior to any preceding ones) were largely derived from his own observations. As to the excellent woodcuts, the drawings were made under Fuchs' supervision by Heinrich Füllmaurer and Albrecht Meyer and the engraving by Veit Rodolf Speckle. Fuchs explained how the work was done by himself and by his collaborators. They are immortalized by his praise and by their portraits, which are engraved in the book (the book also contains his own portrait).

The illustrations of Fuchs' herbal were frequently copied in later times until the end of the eighteenth century. In fact, they are copied to this day, for no history of botany is complete without some of them.

The scope of his herbal was considerable; he dealt with some four hundred native plants plus a hundred foreign ones; we must again bear in mind that as far as the text was concerned and the selection of plants, Fuchs could use Bock as well as Brunfels.

(3) Jerome Bock (Hieronymus Tragus) was a Bavarian like Fuchs. He was born in 1498, was a schoolteacher at Zweibrücken in the Palatinate, then a Lutheran pastor and physicus in Hornbach. After various vicissitudes, he returned to Hornbach where he died in 1554. He must have devoted much time to the study of plants, because his herbal appeared for the first time in 1539, that is, before the one by Fuchs: *New Kreütter Buch von Underscheydt, Würckung und Namen* (Strassburg: Wendel Rihel, 1539).

This first edition was not illustrated, however, and therefore hardly counts in our brief history.[111] The second and following editions were fully illustrated.

Second edition, illustrated: *Kreuter Buch darin Underscheid, Würckung und Namen der Kreuter so in Deutschen Landen wachsen, auch der selbigen . . . Gebrauch im der Artznei fleissig dargeben* (2 parts, folio; Strassburg: Wendel Rihel, 1546. Reprinted Strassburg, 1551, 1560, 1572, 1577, 1595, etc.).

De stirpium maxime earum quae in Germania nostria nascuntur, usitatis nomenclaturis propriisque differentiis neque non . . . facultatibus commentarionum libri tres, germanica primum lingua conscripti, nunc in latinam conversi, interprete Davide Kybero . . . His accesserunt . . . praefationes duae: ultera D. Conradi Gesneri . . . rei herbariae scriptorum . . . catalogum complectens; altera ipsius authoris herbariae cognitionis laudes . . . continens. Practerea . . . adjectus est Benedicti Textoris . . . de stirpium differentiis libellus (1264 pp., plus index, ill. quarto; Strassburg: Wendel Rihel, 1552).

The Latin translator was David Kyber. The text by Benedictus Textor had been printed before in Venice by St. Bernard in 1537. The name Textor is well known to humanists, because it was the maiden family name of Goethe's mother, Katherina Elizabeth.

Verae atque ad vivum expressae imagines omnium herbarum, fructicum et arborum, quarum nomenclaturam et descriptiones H. Bockius in suo herbario comprehendit (Strassburg, 1553). A copy of this book in the BM, I have not seen. I assume that this is a collection of the figures, without the text, except legends in Latin and German, the original blocks being used.

Bock's artist was David Kankel, who worked from natural plants yet used to some extent the work of his predecessors, the assistants of Brunfels and Fuchs. This is unavoidable in any scientific undertaking; a man has no right to overlook the attempts of his predecessors. His descriptions were vastly superior to Brunfels' in their originality, and they were anterior to those of Fuchs. Brunfels did not live long enough(he died in 1534) to see the herbals of Bock and Fuchs but he was aware of their work and encouraged the former whose garden he visited. Kankel's illustrations matched the originality of Bock's descriptions; there was already then artistic emulation between the designers of plants. These artists of the first half of the sixteenth century realized already the complex duty of a scientific illustrator: his drawings must be accurate, yet attractive, even beautiful. Many of the flowers drawn by them please our souls as much as they satisfy our intelligence.

(4) The fourth or latest of the early monuments is strictly contemporary with the preceding one, because its author, Valerius Cordus,[112] died very early in 1544, at the age of twenty-nine. He died ten years before Bock and twenty-two years before Fuchs.

Valerius Cordus was a botanist of genius, the author of the first pharmacopoeia, and he gave the first account of the chemical substance, ether. That would be very much for any man; it is astounding for one who did not live to be thirty. As to the botanist, he realized more deeply than others the need of extensive herborizations and the need of carrying them into foreign countries in order to be able to compare specimens of different floras. He organized botanical excursions and expeditions with colleagues and students and went as far as Rome, where he died of fever and exhaustion in September 1544. He left unpublished notes but had the good fortune in his misfortune to excite the curiosity, zeal, and charity of an illustrious naturalist, Conrad Gesner, who edited them: *Valerii Cordi Adnotationes in Dioscoridis de medica materia libros V, eiusdem historiae stirpium libri III . . . posthumi nunc primum in lucem editi . . . Omnia studio Conradi Gesneri collecta et praefationibus illustrata* (folio, 300 leaves; Strassburg: Josias Rihel, 1561).

The descriptions are excellent, but the book is not illustrated; we cannot blame Cordus for that, and we do not know how he would have published his book if he had been given the opportunity of doing so.

These four men—Brunfels, Fuchs, Bock, and Valerius Cordus—deserve to be called the German Fathers of Botany. Among the multitude of Renaissance scholars, they form a little group—German and Lutheran —of remarkable homogeneity and distinction.

The herbals of these four men were in a sense the best of their kind in the German Renaissance. More ambitious books were published at the end of the century, wherein good observations were diluted in a greater mass of erudition. It will suffice to mention two of them.

Joachim Camerarius junior (1534-98) published the *Hortus medicus et philosophicus in quo plurimarum stirpium breves descriptiones continentur* (3 parts in 1 vol., quarto, fig.; Frankfurt a.M.: S. Feyerabend usw., 1588), a well-illustrated book partly based upon the earlier works but also upon many observations of his own made in his Nuremberg garden and in other gardens and wilds of Germany, Hungary, and Italy. He obtained his M.D. at Bologna, befriended Andrea Cesalpino in Pisa, and translated Mattioli. He was a very learned man and was ready to make botanical observations and to collect information *ad hoc* wherever he went.

In the same year, the work of another German, Jacob Dietrich (1520?-90), began to be printed: *Neuw Kreuterbuch* (Frankfurt a. M.: Nicolaus Bassaeus, 1588-91). This book was published in three parts, of which the last two were edited and completed by N. Braun. The second edition was corrected by Caspar Bauhin (1560-1624) of Basel (Frankfurt a.M., 1613).

In the meanwhile, the illustrations had been published separately: *Eicones plantarum seu stirpium, arborum nempe, fructicum, herbarum, fructuum . . . quae partim Germania sponte producit, partim ab exteris regionibus allata in Germania plantantur . . . Curante N. Bassaeo* (3 parts with Latin and German legends; Frankfurt a.M., 1590).

The author was called in Latin Theodorus Tabernaemontanus (after his birthplace, Bergzabern, in the Palatinate); he had been in touch with the very founders, Brunfels and Bock. He dreamed of redoing their work on a larger scale, and actually described some three thousand plants with abundant illustrations. The fact that those illustrations were reprinted separately is significant; there was a growing body of botanists and gardeners who cared for little else. The bulk of his illustrations were borrowed from other books. Many of his wood blocks were eventually bought by an English printer, John Norton, and used by him to illustrate the *Herball or Generall Historie of plantes* of John Gerarde (London, 1597).

All these books were too scientific, too rational, to satisfy a large part of the German public whose minds were corrupted by astrological fancies and needed some kind of "astrological botany." The best examples of that debased kind of botanical book are the following by Winckler, Carrichter, and Thurneisser:

Nicolaus Winckler: *Chronica herbarum, florum, seminum, fructuum, radicum, succorum, animalium, atque eorundem partium quo nimirum tempore singula eorum colligenda atque in usum adferenda sint medicum* (Augsburg: Michael Manger, 1571). This was a kind of astrological calendar reviving the superstitions of the herb gatherers. Winckler was an Augsburg physician who wrote tracts on the plague and on the comet of 1577.[113]

Bartholomaeus Carrichter: *Horn des Heyls menschlicher Blödigkeit, oder Kreütterbuch, darin die Kreütter des Teutschenlands auss dem Liecht der Natur nach rechter Art der himmlischen Einfliessungen beschriben durch Philomusum Anonymum . . . jetzunder erzt durch Doctorem Toxiten allen Medicis, Pharmacopoeis und Chyrurgis auch andern zü gefallen in Truck geben* (188 pp., index, folio; Strassburg: C. Müller, 1576). The title of this book reveals its occult tendencies. Carrichter was born in Reckingen (on the Rhine, at the south end of the Black Forest) and was physician at the imperial court. He was accused of having caused the death of Ferdinand I in 1564 by malpractice. The dates of his own birth and death are unknown.

Leonhardt Thurneisser zum Thurn: *Historia sive descriptio plantarum omnium . . . earundem virtutes necnon icones proponens atque partium omnium corporis humani . . . picturas et instrumentorum extractioni chymicae . . . delineationem usumque complectens* (folio; Berlin: Michael Hentzske, 1578). German translation (same printer and year). The Latin text was reprinted by Johannes Gymnicus (Cologne, 1587). Thurneisser was a more important personality than Carrichter, richer in good and evil. He was a Paracelsian doctor, alchemist, adventurer, quack, and crook.[114] He was born at Basel in 1530, traveled considerably, died in a monastery of Cologne on 9 July 1596, and was buried at his request near the tomb of Albert the Great (XIII-2).

It was well to mention him to recall the shadiest side of the Renaissance; that side is, unfortunately, represented by thousands of books the influence of which was the more evil because relatively few people, even among the learned, were able to draw the line between science and superstition.

The pioneers were Germans, but their most illustrious followers were three Flemings, best known by their Latin names: Dodonaeus, Clusius, and Lobelius. They all belong to the end of the Renaissance; the first died in 1585 at the age of sixty-eight, the second in 1609 at eighty-three, the third in 1616 at seventy-eight.

They were standing on the shoulders of the German fathers and did better what the latter had done before them. Their knowledge of botanical anatomy was deeper and they had a keener sense of the relationships (or classification) of plants. They were familiar with a multitude of plants (exotic and tropical as well as domestic) of which the early herbalists had no inkling. In short, their botanical experience was immeasurably richer.

Rembert Dodoens was born in Malines in 1517, was physician to Maximilian II, and then professor at the University of Leiden where he died in 1585. Charles de l'Ecluse was born in Arras[115] in 1526, studied in Montpellier under Rondelet, was director of the botanical garden of Vienna for fourteen years, and finally professor of botany in Leiden until his death in 1609.[116] Mathieu de L'Obel, born in Lille in 1538, studied also in Montpellier, flourished for a time in Delft as physician to William of Orange, then was called by James the First to London; he died in Highgate on 2 March 1616.

It is hardly possible to choose between these three men whose fame was attained in similar ways. They are immortalized by the generic names *Dodonaea, Clusia,* and *Lobelia.*[117] Many of their books were published by the Plantinian presses in Antwerp and Leiden. Christopher Plantin (1520?-89) had accumulated many blocks which served to illustrate their works; that is, in addition to the woodcuts prepared for each volume there was a common fund of blocks which might be used in any one of them.

To these three Flemings must be added a fourth, who was a diplomat but with a genuine interest in plants, Ogier Ghiselin de Busbecq (1522-92). Busbecq's observations were elaborated and written out by his physician, Quackelbeen, and published by Mattioli. It is to them that we owe the introduction from the Near East to Western Europe of the horse chestnut, the lilac, and the tulip![118]

This is not a history of botany and zoölogy in the sixteenth century, but inasmuch as we have mentioned the main naturalists of Germany and of the Netherlands, we might evoke rapidly their outstanding contemporaries in other countries. We might begin with Switzerland—that is, the German part of it.

The two outstanding Swiss naturalists were Conrad Gesner (1516-65) of Zurich, of whom we shall speak at greater length presently, and at the end of the century, Caspar Bauhin (1560-1624) of Basel.

In Italy, which was the cradle of the Renaissance and remained its best nursery, we must expect to find many virtuosi who loved nature and the classics almost equally: Antonio Brasàvola (1500-55) of Ferrara, the modern "Musa," physician to many kings and popes; Bartolommeo Maranta of Venosa, Luca Ghini's pupil in Pisa and student in the garden of Naples; Luigi Anguillaria, who died in Ferrara in 1570; Pier Andrea Mattioli (1501-77) of Siena (it is a pity we do not know the name of his skillful engraver "G.S.") ; Francesco Calzolari (1521-1600?), author of one of the earliest local floras;[119] Andrea Cesalpini (1519-1603) of Arezzo; Ulisse Aldrovandi (1522-1605) of Bologna; Castor Durante of Gualdo in Umbria (he was at the Sapienza of Rome in the second half of the sixteenth century) ; Giovanni Battista della Porta (1538-1615) of Naples; Prospero Alpini (1553-1617) of Maròstico (Vicenza), whose *De plantis Aegypti* (Venice: Franciscus de Franciscis, 1592) is one of the great books of the century; Fabio Colonna (1567-1650) of Rome.

In the Hispanic peninsula we could not expect to find as many distinguished men as in the Italian, yet five must be named, three of whom were Portuguese. The first was Amatus Lusitanus (1511-after 1561) of Castelo Branco. The second was Garcia da Orta (*c.* 1490-1570) of Elvas, whose *Coloquios dos simples e drogas he cousas medicinais da India . . .* (4to. 217 fol.; Goa: J. de Endem, 1563) contained the first descriptions of Indian plants and was one of the first books to be printed in India.[120] A Portuguese book printed in Goa could not attract much attention outside of the Portuguese world, but happily for Garcia da Orta his book was soon epitomized in Latin by Clusius (Antwerp: C. Plantin, 1567; reprinted 1574, 1579, 1593, 1605). Not only were those many editions printed but they were generally available. A book issued by Plantin, especially at this time a book on natural history, on simples and drugs, could be depended upon to reach the whole Republic of Letters. Italian and French translations of Garcia da Orta plus Acosta and Monardes (see below) appeared soon; they were made not from the Portuguese text, however, but from Clusius' abbreviation of it. The Italian translation by Annibale Briganti was first printed in Venice, 1576 (reprinted Venice, 1582, 1615-16). The French translation of "Garcie du Jardin" made by Antoine Colin was printed by J. Pillehotte (Lyon, 1602; again, 1619).

The third Portuguese was Christoval Acosta (died at Burgos, 1580).[121] Garcia da Orta had spent thirty-six years of his life practising physic in India; Acosta was born at the end of the fifteenth century in Mozambique. These two and their illustrious contemporaries, St. Francis Xavier[122] (1506-52) and Luis Vaz de Camões (1524-80), symbolize the extention of the Portuguese empire. The four men were connected with Goa, and remain to this day her main glory. Acosta's treatise was written in Spanish, however: *Tractado de las drogas y medicinas de las Indias Orientales, con sus plantas debuxadas al bivo* (Burgos: M. de Victoria, 1578).

This was also translated by Clusius (Antwerp: C. Plantin, 1582), and the Latin was translated into Italian and French as indicated above. There was also a translation made directly from Spanish into Italian (Venice: F. Ziletti, 1585). Christoval Acosta's book was largely plagiarized from the one by Garcia da Orta but had the great advantage of being well illustrated (46 plants), while Garcia's text was not.[123]

The two Spaniards were Nicolas Monardes of Seville and Francisco Hernández of Toledo, both of whom dealt mainly with natural history in America.

Nicolas Monardes (1493-1588) was a very learned physician, mineralogist, and botanist, whose most famous work is a Spanish one published in three installments, each with a very long title. The whole is generally given an abbreviated title: *Cosas que se traen de las Indias Occidentales* (Sevilla: S. Trugillo, 1565). *Segunda parte* (Sevilla: A. Escrivano, 1571). *Primera y segunda y tercera partes* (*ibidem,* 1574; reprinted Sevilla: F. Diaz, 1580). Latin abbreviation by Clusius (Antwerp: C. Plantin, 1574. Reprinted Antwerp, 1582, 1605). Collected edition of Clusius' translations of Orta, Acosta, and Monardes (461 pp., ill.; Antwerp: Plantin and Moretus, 1593). Italian translations from the Latin by Annibale Briganti (Venice, 1576; reprinted Venice, 1582, 1615-16). French translation from the Latin by Antoine Colin (Lyon: J. Pillehotte, 1602; again, 1619).

In addition to writing this book which advertized the existence of a number of American herbs, he took the initiative in organizing in Seville a museum where specimens of them were on exhibition. This was not the first museum, but certainly the first museum of American products.

Francisco Hernández was born in Toledo in 1517 and died in 1578. He was physician to Philip II, who sent him on a mission to Mexico to investigate the flora and fauna. He accumulated a large amount of materials, Latin text and drawings, none of which could be published before his death. The first publication was a Spanish translation by Francisco Ximenez (Mexico, 1615). This Mexican imprint of 1615 may be called the first printed account of American nature even as the Goa imprint of 1563 was the first of Indian nature. Hernández's original MSS were kept in the Escorial and destroyed in the great fire of 1671.[124] An abbreviated Latin edition was prepared by Nardo Antonio Recchi (950 pp.; Rome, 1628). A more elaborate edition of Recchi's text was prepared under the direction of Prince Federico Angelo Cesi, duca d'Acquasparta (1585-1630), founder of the Accademia dei Lincei.[125] That edition was the first great gift of that Academy to the world of letters (5 parts in one vol. folio; Rome: V. Mascardi, 1649-51). It was enriched with notes and additions by Lincei members, Johann Schreck (or Terrentius),[126] Johann Faber (1570-1640) of Bamberg, professor of medicine and botany in Rome, and Fabio Colonna whose acquaintance we have already made.

The publication of Hernández's magnum opus has taken us out of the Renaissance, but the work itself was a fruit of it. Hernández died as early as 1578.[127] Before the end of the sixteenth century, the flora and fauna of a large part of the world, including parts of India and of America, had been explored, described, and illustrated.

The French herbalists and students of botany form a large group, many members of which we have already met. Jean Ruel (1474-1537), Pierre Gilles (1490-1554), Pierre Belon (1517-64), Guillaume Rondelet (1507-66), Jacques Dalechamps (1513-88), Olivier de Serres (1539-1619), author of the *Théâtre d'agriculture et Mesnage des champs* (folio, 1004 pp.; Paris: Jamet-Métayer, 1600), Antoine Mizault, Geoffroy Linocier, Jacques Le Moyne de Morgues.

The most important of the authors not yet dealt with before is Olivier de Serres, [128] whose great book closed the French Renaissance but was reprinted many times in the following centuries either in full or in abbreviation or extracts. The part which had the greatest success, concerning the education of silk worms, had been published separately before the whole work: *La cueillette de la soye par la nourriture des vers qui la font. Echantillon du Théâtre d'agriculture* (130 pp.; Paris: Mettayer, 1599).

Le Moyne de Morgues is much less important, but claims our attention for two reasons. He joined the French expedition sent by Admiral de Coligny (1519-72) in 1564 under René de Laudonnière to establish a Protestant colony in Florida; the French Protestants were driven out by Spanish Catholics. After his return, he settled in London; he was primarily an artist and his *Clef des champs pour trouver plusieurs animaux* (London: Blackfriars, 1586) was beautifully illustrated. The book was dedicated to Lady Mary Herbert, Countess of Pembroke; many of the original drawings and water colors made by Le Moyne are preserved in the Victoria and Albert Museum. His account of the Florida expedition·was edited in French by Theodore de Bry and Latinized by Clusius (folio; Frankfurt a.M.: T. de Bry, 1591). This Frenchman thus provided a double connection, with America and with England.

Inasmuch as we ended the French section with Olivier de Serres, we may well begin the English one with Fitzherbert,[129] whose *Boke of husbandry* was the first English book of its kind. It was first printed by R. Pynson in London in 1523, and often reprinted during the sixteenth century. It was a small, rudimentary, and medieval book which cannot be compared with Olivier's monumental one, but the latter appeared three quarters of a century later, and the French Renaissance was incomparably more sophisticated than the English Renaissance. Fitzherbert's book may stand here as a symbol of the husbandry books of the English Renaissance.

Let us now enumerate briefly the authors of other books on natural history: Edward Wotton (1492-1555) of Oxford, zoölogist; William Turner (1510-68), botanist, dean of Wells; John Caius (1510-73) of Norwich, Hellenist, physician, zoölogist, writer of a book on dogs; Thomas Penny (d. 1589) of Trinity, Cambridge, botanist and entomologist; Thomas Moffett[130] (1553-1604) of London; John Gerard (1545-1612), also a Londoner, herbalist.[131]

9. THE ENCYCLOPEDISTS

THERE IS ANOTHER ASPECT OF NATURAL HISTORY DURING THE RENAISsance, the one which might be symbolized by the term "encyclopedism." But was that a true Renaissance feature, or was it more general? Have not encyclopedic tendencies always existed in various degrees? Have not some men always tried to understand and to describe the cosmos, and to accumulate all the information available to them? These tendencies became stronger when knowledge increased, and when the accumulation of it was facilitated; one might make a synthesis at various levels, the high level of Aristotle (IV-2 B.C.) or the lower level of Pliny the Elder (I-2), but the fundamental desire was the same. There were many natural encyclopedists during the Middle Ages, such as al-Masʿūdī (X-1), Bartholomew the Englishman (XIII-1), Thomas of Cantimpré (XIII-1), Albert the Great (XIII-2), Vincent of Beauvais (XIII-2), Conrad von Megenberg (XIV-1). Few tried to reach the Aristotelian level; none came anywhere near to it. The invention of printing gave a new life to the medical encyclopedias[132] and to the scientific ones, such as the *Specula*.[133] The Renaissance encyclopedists could work on a larger scale and, what is more important, their knowledge of the ancient naturalists was incomparably more precise. They could easily refer to well-indexed, printed editions of Aristotle, Theophrastos, Dioscorides, Pliny, Aelian (III-1), and others. They could make full use themselves of the two great inventions, typography and engraving, and did so.

The main characteristics of these Renaissance encyclopedias is an astonishing combination of erudition and realism, the latter being largely the fruit of the drawings and engravings or more exactly of the observations which these implied. Another characteristic is an enormous enlargement of experience due to the discovery of new continents and of their floras and faunas.

The new encyclopedic spirit as evidenced in the illustrated descriptions of nature was best represented in the sixteenth century by four men: the German, Adam Lonicer; the Englishman, Edward Wotton; the Swiss, Conrad Gesner; and the Italian, Ulisse Aldrovandi. These men were contemporaries, but the youngest of them (Lonicer) was thirty-six years younger than the oldest (Wotton).

Though Adam Lonicer (1528-86) was the last of them to be born, his encyclopedia was the first to be printed. He was the son of the more famous Johann Lonicer (1499-1569), Augustinian monk in Wittenberg and later one of the foremost Lutheran polemists, translator of Luther into Latin and Professor of Greek and Hebrew in Marburg where he died. Adam was born in Marburg and devoted himself to arithmetic, medicine, and scientific studies of many kinds. In 1553, he was professor of mathematics in Marburg and in 1554 professor of medicine. He then married Magdalena, daughter of the printer Christian Egenolph of Frankfurt, was appointed town physician in that city, and was literary adviser and proofreader(?) to his father-in-law. He died in Frankfurt in 1586.

He wrote an arithmetic (Frankfurt, 1551) and a *Kreuterbuch* (Frankfurt: Egenolph, 1557) very often reprinted until as late as 1783 (Augsburg). He edited the *Aphorisms* of Hippocrates (Frankfurt, 1554) and the *Hebammenbüchlin* of Eucharius Röslin (Frankfurt, 1582).[134] His main work, however, was an illustrated encyclopedia of natural history: *Naturalis historiae opus novum, in quo tractatus de natura et viribus arborum, fructicum herbarum animantiumque terrestrium, etc.* (the title is very long). Printed by his future father-in-law, C. Egenolph (folio, 352 l., fig.; Strassburg, 1551).

He was primarily a botanist, or at any rate, the botanical part of his knowledge was better than the rest of it; Linnaeus gave his name to a large genus of shrubs, the honeysuckles (*Lonicera*).

The oldest of the four, Edward Wotton (1492-1555) of Magdalen, Oxford, a Padovan M.D., was a zoölogist and his masterpiece was the *De differentiis animalium libri decem* (folio; Paris: Michel de Vascosan, 1552).

In his dedication to Edward VI, he explains his first intention of compiling an encyclopedia of natural history for the use of physicians, but the Frenchman, Jean Ruel, has described the plants so well, and the German, Georg Bauer (Agricola, 1494-1555), the minerals, that he may restrict himself to the animal kingdom. The ten books are subdivided as follows: 1-3. generalities; 4. man; 5. quadrupeds that bear young; 6. quadrupeds that lay eggs; 7. birds; 8. fishes; 9. insects;[135] 10. squids, crustaceans, molluscs. It is a compilation mainly derived from ancient writers, but also to some extent from "modern" ones. It is the work of a bookman rather than a genuine naturalist; it is not illustrated.

Lonicer and Wotton indicated a trend, the encyclopedic trend caused by a large accumulation of new knowledge, and they satisfied it as well as they could, but their activities were dwarfed by those of the two men whom we shall now try to evoke. We can hardly do more; Gesner and Aldrovandi were the two giants of the Renaissance in their field. They have not yet received their full reward.

Conrad Gesner was born in Zürich in 1516. His father was a furrier and could not help him much, but Conrad's precocious intelligence and his hunger for knowledge were so clear that relatives and strangers united to give him the education which he deserved more than any other Züricher of his time. He began his studies in Zürich, continued them in Strassburg and Paris. His studies were mainly philological, because these were the highest studies of his time. He mastered Greek, Latin, and Hebrew and, returning to his native city, he married and began his career as a teacher. He taught in Zürich and Lausanne, and then, like other ambitious philologists of his day, he realized the need of positive science. This was generally interpreted as medicine with natural history as a side show. Gesner went to Montpellier where his new kind of enthusiasm was fired by Rondelet; he completed his medical studies in Basel in 1541. From that year on, until his death, he held the chair of philosophy in Zürich; he practised medicine and was appointed town physician in 1554. When a plague desolated Zürich in 1564, a special commission, of which he was a member, was established by the city fathers to fight it as well as they could. Most of his time was devoted to his scientific and literary labor. He fell gravely ill in 1565, asked to be transported to his study, where he died on the night of 13/14 December. He was then a little over forty-nine years and nine months.

His main writings can be divided chronologically into groups as follows: (1) 1541-42, botanical writings of his philological period; (2) universal bibliography, 1545-55; (3) polyglottism, 1555; (4) the masterpiece, *Historia animalium,* 1551-58; (5) his best botanical work, published posthumously. Our main concern is the *Historia animalium,* but we cannot illustrate his gigantic personality without referring, however briefly, to his other writings.

Yet, before dealing with any of them, we must make a kind of excursus on Alpinism to give the reader some idea of Gesner's originality. Learning was a fashion and a passion of his age; there were many men of learning in the sixteenth century, and when we realize that they did not yet have at their elbow the astounding tools which we have, their erudition is almost unbelievable. The key to the mystery was the prodigious diligence of these men, who worked literally day and night, in a way which has become almost impossible to the men of our own generation. They had little time for pleasure, no time for travel (except the necessary translations from one university to another), and certainly none for mountain climbing. Very different in that respect from the Buddhists of India and the Far East, the Christians had never taken to the high mountains.[136] Indeed, they were afraid of them, assuming that the Alps were the resorts and refuges of evil spirits. The exploration of high mountains is one of the most remarkable innovations of the Renaissance.[137] Petrarca gave the first example when he ascended Mount Ventoux near Avignon in 1336. Leonardo da Vinci explored some of the Italian Alps (Monte Bo, 1511) and, thanks to the ambivalence of his extraordinary genius, he observed them from the scientific as well as from the artistic point of view. Vadianus reached one of the summits (Gnepfstein) of Mount Pilatus near Luzern in 1518. Like Gesner, Vadianus (Joachim von Watt of St. Gall) had the advantage of being born in Switzerland, where the mountains surround one on every side and almost cry to him who stands in the middle of them, "Come up! Come up!" One of the earliest writings of young Gesner was a letter on the admiration of mountains (*De montium admiratione*) to his learned friend, Vogel (Jacobus Avienus), dated "Tiguri, mense Junio, anno salutis humanae 1541" (Zürich, 1541) and signed "Conradus Gesnerus medicus." Gesner had just obtained his M.D. in Basel.[138] He declares to his friend that as long as God permits him he will climb a few mountains each year for the health of his body and of his soul. This is the first document of its kind in world literature[139]—a declaration of enthusiastic Alpinism, and in contrast with the cloistered habits of scholars, a declaration of freedom.

On 20 August 1555, Gesner ascended one of the peaks of Mount Pilatus near Luzern and his account is again one of the first of its kind.[140] It was his habit to climb mountains at the time of flowering, and he was abundantly rewarded on Mt. Pilatus, the flora of which is exceptionally rich. His description does not deal with particular flowers, however; it is like many other descriptions of alpine expeditions, but mixed with it there is a new hymn to the beauty and glory of the Alps and a restatement of man's privilege and duty to visit them.

The first treatise on the Swiss Alps, and we might say the first treatise on any Alps, was published in 1574 by another Züricher, Josias Simler (1530-76), together with his description of the Valais.[141] It is a very elaborate treatise dealing with the Alps in general and various districts, early crossings, main roads, difficulties and dangers, population, hydrography, crystals and metals, flora and fauna. Simler had put together all the facts that could be derived from Greek and Latin books and added the more abundant and detailed information given by Renaissance authors. His work marked the end of a period, for the remarkable achievements of sixteenth-century Alpinism almost stopped during the seventeenth and eighteenth centuries and did not begin again in full earnest until the coming of another Swiss, but a French one this time, Horace Bénédict de Saussure.[142]

The thing to remember is that Alpinism was one of the glories of the Renaissance, and its two coryphaei were two men of Zürich, Gesner and Simler.

It was well to begin with Gesner's Alpinism, because that reveals the most attractive aspect of his personality. The amount of scientific and literary work which he managed to crowd into less than twenty-five years is so enormous that a survey of it, as rapid as ours must be, is almost forbidding. Good men are at their best when they are idle, but a scholar as ambitious as Gesner was, had no time for relaxation except the annual visits to his beloved mountains.

There is no point in enumerating all of his works, but we shall give a few specimens of each kind and speak a little longer of the more important.

His earliest botanical activity was rather of the humanistic type, as the titles of the two following items suggest: *Enchiridion historiae plantarum ordine alphabetico, ex Dioscoride sumtis descriptionibus, et multis ex Theophrasto, Plinio et recentioribus Graecis* (Basel: Rob. Winter, 1541; reprinted in Venice and Paris within the same year); and *Catalogus plantarum (Namenbuch aller Erdgewächse) nomina latine, graece, germanice et gallice* . . . (332 pp.; Zürich: Froschauer, 1542).[143]

In spite of his botanical vocation (Gesner had a genuine interest in living plants such as he might discover in the mountains or examine in his garden), he was primarily a humanist. His perusal of ancient botanical literature had obliged him to handle many old volumes and he realized the need of a key—of a bibliography. Don't we feel that need at every step? And yet we are fortunate to have many bibliographical tools which were nonexistent in his time. He decided that the bibliographic urgency was the highest, and ten years of his short life were largely devoted to it. His bibliographical works follow:

Bibliotheca universalis sive Catalogus omnium scriptorum locupletissimus in tribus linguis, latina, graeca et hebraica, extantium et non ex-

tantium, veterum et recentiorum in hunc usque diem, doctorum et indoc-
torum, publicatorum et in bibliothecis latentium (1492 pp., folio; Zürich:
Froschauer, 1545). This was an alphabetical list of all the books published in Latin, Greek, and Hebrew within the first century of printing.
To increase its usefulness he prepared another work wherein all books
were classified according to subject and divided into nineteen categories:

Pandectarum sive partitionum universalium libri XXI (folio; Zürich, 1548). In spite of its title, there are only nineteen books, for Book XX
on medicine remained unpublished, and Book XXI on theology was issued
separately in 1549:

Partitiones theologicae, pandectarum universalium liber ultimus
(356 pp.; Zürich, 1549).

Appendix Bibliothecae Conradi Gesneri (Zürich, 1555).

These four volumes—folios, two columns, all printed by Froschauer—
constitute a tool which was of supreme value in the mid-Renaissance and
is not negligible today.[111]

It is worth while to see how Gesner had "partitioned his Pandects."
There were to be twenty-one partitiones or books, as follows. The figures
between parentheses give the number of two-column leaves occupied by
each book.

I.	Grammar	(42)	
II.	Dialectics	(6)	
III.	Rhetorics	(10)	
IV.	Poetics	(14)	
V.	Arithmetic	(4)	
VI	Geometry	(4)	
VII.	Music	(6)	
VIII.	Astronomy	(8)	
IX.	Astrology	(4)	
X.	Divination, Magic	(8)	*Divinatio cum licita tum illicita*
XI.	Geography	(10)	
XII.	History	(48)	
XIII.	Mechanics	(16)	*De mechanicis et aliis illiteratis* *artibus*
XIV.	Natural philosophy	(56)	*De physicis*
XV.	Metaphysics	(24)	*De prima philosophia*
XVI.	Ethics	(42)	
XVII.	Economics	(8)	
XVIII.	Politics	(18)	Ending with peace and war *De re militari*
XIX.	Law	(46)	*De jure civili et pontificio*
XX.	Medicine		(not realized, except as far as included in XIV)
XXI.	Theology	(157)	

Theology was the largest book (157 leaves), one third of the whole.

The next in size is Natural philosophy (56), less than a third the length of Theology, and yet it includes not only physics but the whole of natural history with which Gesner was exceptionally well acquainted. Then came in order of decreasing size: History (48), Law (46), Grammar and Ethics (each 42), Metaphysics (24), Politics (18), Mechanics (16), Poetics (14), Rhetorics and geography (each 10). The remaining eight books cover less than ten leaves each.

The book which interests us most, Natural philosophy, was subdivided into twelve sections: generalities, heaven and earth, four elements, generation and corruption, meteors, nature of things in general, and first, nature of stones and gems, metals, plants, souls, parva naturalia, animals, natural magic and miracles. Note that the final part and also Books IX and X deal with astrology and with divination and magic. There was always a background of occultism to Renaissance science.

He had dedicated his *Bibliographia universalis* of 1545 to an imperial councilor, and the *Appendix* of 1555 paid tribute to another. This was probably expedient for the success of the immense opus and the welfare of its publisher, the ambitious Christopher Froschauer. The latter lived almost as long as Gesner (he died in 1564), and kept Gesner busy almost until the end. It was probably upon his suggestion that each book of the *Pandectae* (except the first) was handsomely dedicated to a contemporary typographer, each dedication including a list of the main publications of that particular printer. The Basel printers obtained the lion's share of these dedications, seven out of nineteen, and these seven dedications celebrated nine printers, to wit, Joannes Bebelius and Michael Isengrinus, Joannes Oporinus, Nicolaus Brylingerus, Henricus Petrus, Hieronymus Curio, Joannes Hervagius, Hieronymus Frobenius, and Nicolaus Episcopius. Gesner's familiarity with the Basel printers was natural, but no book was dedicated to a Züricher!

The German printers in the Gesnerian list of honors were Joannes Petreius (Hans Peterlein) and Joannes Montanus with Ulrich Neuber of Nürnberg, Wendelin Richelius of Strassburg, Joannes Gymnicus of Cologne. The French were Robertus Stephanus (Robert Estienne) and Christian Wechel of Paris, Joannes Frellonius and Sebastianus Gryphius of Lyon. The Venetians were Paulus Manutius Aldi, Vincentius Valgrisius, Hieronymus Scotus, and the Juntae.

In spite of partiality for the Basel printers, as against those of Lyon and other cities, the list established by a polyhistor of Gesner's experience is a very interesting document. There were not enough *partitiones* in the *Pandectae* to do justice to many other printers who deserved the same honor, but the interest of Gesner's dedications lies not so much in the choice as in the fact that Gesner wanted to recognize in the best manner the great importance of the role played by the publishers of his time. These publishers were not simply businessmen and money-makers, but collaborators of the scholars whose works they so gladly and proudly revealed to the public. Like the scholars they were distinguished members of the Republic of Letters.

For the sake of curiosity, a brief mention may be made of his *Mithridates: Mithridates, sive de differentiis linguarum, tum veterum tum quae hodie apud diversas nationes in toto orbe terrarum in usu sunt, observationes* (158 pp.; Zürich, 1555. Reprinted in Zürich, 1610).

Gesner's activities were generally those of a naturalist dominated by humanistic traditions and habits. His *Mithridates* reveals a philologist inspired by the methods of natural history. Even as the naturalists were engaged in the enumeration, description, and differentiation of plants and animals, Gesner tried to enumerate and differentiate the languages used by men. He dealt with no less than 130 languages, quoted the *Pater noster* in twenty-two of them, and provided a gypsy vocabulary. Gesner was interested not only in languages but also in dialects, and encouraged his friend Josua Mahler to investigate the German ones. He wrote a preface for Mahler's German-Latin dictionary[145] which is, next to Paracelsus' writings, one of the best monuments of the Schweizerdeutsch of the sixteenth century.

One hundred thirty languages may have seemed a lot at about that time; that number would be judged very small by modern philologists.[146] In the same way, the numbers of birds or fishes which he described were so large that they astonished the contemporary readers, and yet modern zoölogists could not help being amused by their smallness. His *Mithridates* was a baby, yet a promising one.

After this linguistic excursus, we may now approach Gesner's main work, the work which has immortalized his name. He had been collecting for years an immense mass of information on plants and animals—their names, descriptions, characteristics, medical properties, habits, etc. Not only had he excerpted all the printed books, but he had enlisted the help of some fifty correspondents—German, French, Italian, English, Polish—who added their observations to his own, and he had accumulated a large number of drawings. Though he was more of a botanist than a zoölogist, he decided to begin with the animal kingdom. The first folio volume appeared in Zürich in 1551, when Gesner was thirty-five years old (Aldrovandi's first volume appeared when he was seventy-seven). I shall now give the titles of the first edition of each volume of Gesner's *Historia animalium*. All the volumes are folios. The title of the first volume is quoted more fully than the others.

1. *Historiae animalium liber primus qui est de quadrupedibus viviparis cum figuris ad vivum expressis. Opus philosophis, medicis, grammaticis, philologis, poetis et omnibus rerum linguarumque studiosis, utilissimum, simul jucundissimumque futurum* (1156 pp., woodcuts; Zürich: Froschauer, 1551).

2. *H. a. liber secundus de quadrupedibus oviparis* (144 pp., ill.; Zürich, 1554).

3. *H. a. liber tertius, qui est de avium natura* (813 pp.; Zürich, 1555). A posthumous edition by Cambier (Frankfurt a.M., 1589) contains many addenda prepared by Gesner.

4. *H. a. liber quartus qui est de piscium de aquatilium animantium natura* (1338 pp., ill.; Zürich, 1558). This volume included the writings of Rondelet and Belon on the same subjects.

Volumes 1-4, plus 3 volumes of *Icones* containing only the illustrations with legends (1553-55-60), were the only zoölogical ones issued within his life time; the *Liber quintus* was published twenty-two years after his death.

5. *H. a. liber quintus, qui est de serpentum natura, adjecta est ad calcem scorpionis insecti historia* (204 pp., ill.; Zürich, 1587).

The five folio volumes of the *Historia animalium* extend to some four thousand pages and include many hundreds of woodcuts. A great mass of this was a rearrangement of ancient knowledge. Not only was part of the text old (some of it as old as Aristotle), but many of the illustrations were borrowed from printed books. Nevertheless, there was also a large body of new knowledge, and Gesner's *Historia* is an encyclopedia of zoölogy as known in the second half of the sixteenth century; modern zoölogists hardly need it, but for the humanist and the historian of zoölogy it is one of the greatest monuments of the Renaissance.

Gesner's ambitious purpose concerned not only the animal kingdom, but also the two other kingdoms of nature.

The part dealing with minerals and fossils could have been published by himself, under the title *De omni rerum fossilium genera, gemmis, lapidibus, metallis, et hujus modi libri aliquot plerique nunc primum editi* (Zürich, 1565). This includes his own treatise plus others contributed by some of his assistants.

The botanical part could not have been completed by himself, though he had accumulated a large amount of data including nearly one thousand drawings of plants. It is noteworthy that the data which he had gathered included the plants living in his own botanical garden, the drawings already mentioned, and enough natural objects to constitute a little museum of natural history, located in his own house.[147]

A year after Gesner's death, his friend, Caspar Wolf, announced the publication of the botanical part, but failed to accomplish it. In 1580, he committed the materials to the care of Joachim Camerarius of Nürnberg, who used them for his own purposes. They were purchased in 1744 by another Nürnberg naturalist, Jacob Trew, and were finally edited by Casimir Christoph Schmiedel, professor of botany in Erlangen, the publication being finally completed 206 years after Gesner's death: *Opera botanica* (2 vols., folio; Nürnberg: I. M. Seligmann, 1751-71).

The name *Gesneria* was given by Plumier to a large genus of tropical American herbs, and the name *Gesnerus* (in 1943) to the journal of the Swiss history of science society (*Horus,* 216).

A life of Gesner was published soon after his death by his friend and fellow Alpinist, Josias Simler: *Vita Conradi Gesneri* (Zürich, 1566; German translation, Leipzig, 1711). A longer biography was written in German by Johannes Hanhart (Winterthur, 1824).

Many unpublished writings and letters of Gesner have been edited, and many documents concerning him have appeared in *Gesnerus* and other journals; many more exist in MS in European libraries, chiefly in Zürich. There is thus an abundance of biographical information, the marshaling and publication of which would add considerably to our knowledge of Gesner and his time.

A small biography was published by Willy Ley: *Konrad Gesner, Leben und Werk* (162 pp., 6 ill.; *Münchener Beiträge zur Geschichte und Literatur der Naturwissenschaften,* Heft 15/16, München, 1929). Gesner deserves a full biography, but the preparation of it would require the life-long devotion of a competent scholar.

Ulisse Aldrovandi was born in Bologna in 1522. His family was noble, but not rich. They first thought of preparing him for business, but Ulisse escaped, making a long pilgrimage with a friend through Italy, parts of France and Spain.[148] He returned home in 1539 but his wanderlust was not yet appeased, for he wanted to make a pilgrimage to the Holy Land. Instead of that, he was persuaded to attend courses in the University of

Bologna; he studied law, philosophy, medicine, and much else. About 1548, he was continuing his studies in Padova. His restlessness caused him to be accused of heresy and he was obliged to go to Rome in 1549 for examination. He was finally absolved by the new pope, Julius III (1550-55). During his stay in Rome, he became acquainted with Rondelet, and probably with Salviani, and this fired his enthusiasm for natural history. He then returned to Bologna, and his acquaintance with Luca Ghini increased his interest in botany.

It is important to note that though Aldrovandi was primarily a scholar, a student of antiquity, he was also a genuine naturalist. He started the collection of a vast herbarium, for the sake of which he traveled considerably in Italy, herborizing with friends. He even visited Monte Baldo and other Italian Alps to study their flora. He obtained his M.D. in 1553 and began teaching in Bologna soon afterwards. The senate of Bologna decided to imitate the example given by Pisa and Padova (1545) and to provide the medical school with a botanical garden; this was done in 1567-68 and Aldrovandi was the first director. He died on 4 May 1605.

Aldrovandi's activities as a naturalist, and especially as a botanist, were such that he published nothing of importance before 1574 (*aet.* 52). In that year appeared his *Antidotarii Bononiensis sive de usitata ratione componendorum miscendorumque medicamentorum epitome* (Bologna: Giov. Rossi, 1574).

This was often reprinted and augmented until the end of the eighteenth century. Aldrovandi's *Antidotarium* is sometimes called the first pharmacopoeia, but that is misleading. The earliest book deserving that name is very probably the *Dispensatorium* of Valerius Cordus (Nürnberg: Joh. Petreius, 1546); the second prototype was the *Enchiridion Dispensarium* (Lyon: Theobaldus Paganus, 1556); the third appeared in Augsburg and was also called *Enchiridion sive . . . dispensatorium* (Augsburg, 1564); the fourth appeared in Cologne, 1565; and the fifth in Augsburg, 1573. This was the first to be entitled *Pharmacopoeia seu medicamentarium pro Rep. Augustana* (Augsburg, 1573). It is generally called *Pharmacopoeia augustana.*[149] Thus, Aldrovandi's *Antidotarium* is not the first book of its kind, but the sixth; and Bologna was preceded by Nürnberg, Lyon, Augsburg, and Cologne. Before the end of the century, such books had become commonplace; they were regarded as prime necessities for every doctor and pharmacist.

Aldrovandi's main work, however, was not that, but the preparation of a gigantic natural history in folio volumes abundantly illustrated (the publication began only in 1599):[150] *Ornithologiae hoc est de avibus historiae libri XII* (fol., more than 900 pp., ill.; Bologna: Giov. Bat. Bellagamba, 1599). Two other volumes on birds were published by the same printer in 1600 and 1603, and in the meanwhile, *De animalibus insectis libri septem* (same printer, 1602).

These four volumes were the only ones of the collection to appear within Aldrovandi's life. In spite of their size and their expensiveness, they were reprinted at least five times during the seventeenth century in Bologna and Frankfurt. Many other volumes appeared posthumously, thanks to the devotion of the senate of Bologna and of various collaborators. Here is a very brief list of them:

5. *De reliquis animalibus exsanguibus libri quatuor, nempe de Mollibus, Crustaceis, Testaceis et Zoophytis (ibidem, 1606).*

6. *De piscibus libri V et de cetis liber unus (ibidem, 1612/13).*

The following items were first printed in Bologna but by other printers:

7. *De quadrupedibus solidipedibus volumen integrum* (Bologna, 1616).

8. *Quadrupedum omnium bisulcorum historia* (Bologna, 1621).

9. *De quadrupedibus digitatis viviparis libri tres et de quadrupedibus digitatis oviparis libri duo* (Bologna, 1637).

10. *Serpentum et draconum historiae libri duo* (Bologna, 1639).

11. *Monstrorum historia cum paralipomenis historiae omnium animalium* (Bologna, 1642).

12. *Musaeum metallicum in libros IV distributum* (Bologna, 1648).

13. *Dendrologiae naturalis scilicet arborum historiae libri duo* (Bologna, 1667/68).

Thus, did the publication of the giant's work continue for sixty years after his death. Each of these big volumes was reprinted, and they served the naturalists of the seventeenth century as well as the earlier volumes had served their Renaissance ancestors. In fact, they continued to be used throughout the eighteenth century and were then gradually replaced by new compilations which were more technical and included a much larger variety of natural objects.

Aldrovandi was a great collector not only of ancient words, like the majority of Renaissance doctors, but also of natural objects, plants, and animals. He spent his vacations herborizing, accumulating a herbarium and a whole museum of objects which he bequeathed to the University of Bologna, where many of them can be seen to this day. He has been accused of lacking originality and critical sense; he has even been accused of mixing the cetacea with the fishes. That is obviously untrue; the cetacea were described in the same volume as the fishes (no. 6 in my list above), but carefully separated. It is true that his scope was far too large, but one had to begin that way. As knowledge increased (in quality as well as quantity), the need of specialization would increase too. At the end of the Renaissance, the main need was a vast survey such as was provided by Gesner and Aldrovandi. The task which those men accomplished was gigantic. It is remarkable that both of them were primarily botanists, and yet their main works were devoted to zoölogy. When we compare them, we should always remember that Gesner died at forty-nine and Aldrovandi at eighty-three; that is, the active creative life of the latter was more than twice as long as that of the former.

There is no full bibliography of Aldrovandi in any language. This is due less to the paucity of materials than to their forbidding abundance. In addition to the objects collected by him and preserved in the University Museum of Bologna, there are so many MSS of his in the University Library that a catalogue of them was published by Lodovico Frati (Bologna: Zanichelli, 1907).
Giovanni Fantuzzi: *Notizie degli scrittori bolognesi* (Bologna, 1781), vol. 1, pp. 165-90. Giovanni Battista de Toni (1864-1924), notice in Aldo Mieli: *Gli scienziati italiani* (Rome: Attilio Nardecchià, 1923—*Isis 4*, 112-14), vol. 1, pp. 328-36. G. B. de Toni has written a series of investigations called "gleanings," *Spigolature aldrovandiane,* the first of which appeared in Milano, 1907, the last seen by me, no. 19, in Venice, 1922.
At the time of the third centenary of Aldrovandi's death, a collection of studies was published, *Intorno alla vita e alle opere di U. Aldrovandi* (223 pp.; Bologna: Treves, 1907). There was also published a de luxe volume *Onoranze a Ulisse Aldrovandi nel terzo centenario dalla sua morte celebrate in Bologna nei giorni XI, XII, XIII, giugno MCM VII* (432 pp., Imola: P. Galeati, 1908). The first and humbler of these volumes contains valuable information which a biographer should take into account. The second is almost worthless.

The name *Aldrovanda* was given to a genus of floating plants represented by a single species. This is an amusing contrast with his encyclopedic genius.

10. THE ANATOMISTS

WE HAVE REFERRED MANY TIMES TO ANATOMY IN THE FIRST LECTURE because anatomy was considered a part, an essential and fundamental part, of medicine. So was botany. Yet, in both cases, anatomy as well as botany, these studies tended to become more independent in the very measure of their growth.

Students of Renaissance anatomy have the advantage of a landmark of such pregnancy, Vesalius' *Fabrica* of 1543, that the history is much simplified. It can be divided into three natural groups: (1) before Vesalius, (2) Vesalius, (3) the remainder of the sixteenth century. These groups are not mutually exclusive; yet, they are very tangible.

The general scheme of evolution was the same as for other sciences; yet, perhaps clearer. In the fifteenth century, the medieval tradition was generally accepted; but scholarly physicians were beginning to realize the value of the Greek anatomical writings, and their main task was then the recovery of these writings in their original state and the cleaning up of the text: translations, commentaries, supercommentaries, indices, dictionaries. In the meanwhile, genuine anatomists were continuing their own dissections and autopsies. The predilection for direct observations over textual references steadily increased. Public dissections were organized in the medical schools and students were obliged to attend some of them. The respect for ancient authorities was shaken but not by any means destroyed, nor even compromised. Not only was Vesalius anxious to conciliate the Galenists, but even Harvey was, when the Renaissance had already completed its cycle.

Medieval anatomy was derived from Galen, Avicenna, and the school of Salerno; and its leading representatives in the Christian West were the surgeons Guglielmo da Saliceto (XIII-2), Lanfranchi of Milano (XIII-2), Henri de Mondeville (XIV-1), Guido da Vigevano (XIV-1), Mondino de' Luzzi (XIV-1), and Guy de Chauliac (XIV-2). The writings of these men, except those of Mondeville and Vigevano, were well represented in the incunabula, not only in Latin but in sundry vernaculars,[151] and they were frequently reprinted in the sixteenth century. Saliceto, Lanfranchi, Mondeville, Chauliac were translated into English before the invention of printing but not printed until later. A short text of Chauliac translated by R. Coplande was printed in London, 1542 (revised edition, 1579). A translation of Lanfranchi and Mondeville was published in 1548 under the title *The anatomie of the bodie of man* and the name of Thomas Vicary (d. 1561), surgeon, member of the Barbers' Company of London. No copy of that edition is extant, and we know the text only from a reissue by the surgeons of St. Bartholomew in 1577.[152] The *Chirurgia parva* of Lanfranchi was Englished by John Halle (London, 1565).

So much to illustrate medieval anatomical traditions in Renaissance England. Similar stories might have been told for other countries. For example, the Hessian Johann Eichmann, called Dryander (1500-1560), studied mathematics, astronomy, anatomy in Paris. He was acquainted with Johann Günther and with Vesalius, and became an anatomist probably because of their influence. He obtained his M.D. in Mainz, 1533, and two years later was called to the University of Marburg. He is said to have dissected two human bodies; he redacted the anatomical demonstrations which he gave in the University of Marburg and a few years later published a new edition of Mondino. Here are the titles of these books:

Anatomia capitis humani in Marpurgensi Academia publice exhibita (Marburg, 1536).

Anatomiae, hoc est corporis humani dissectionis pars prior . . . Item anatomia porci ex traditione Cophonis, infantis ex Gabriele de Zerbis (Marburg, 1537).

Anatomia Mundini (Marburg 1541).

Note these titles and the typical mixture of ideas which they represent. The first two were published to help the student attending public

117

dissections. Yet, the second shows that Dryander was continuing the tradition of Copho of Salerno (XII-1) and the more recent one of Gabriele de Zerbis.[153] His edition of Mondino appeared just two years before Vesalius' *Fabrica;* it was well illustrated from nature and, it is said, from Vesalius' unpublished drawings.

It may serve to represent one of the tendencies of the age, anatomical realism, growth of dissections; two other tendencies were the medieval tradition (to which we have just referred) and the revival of Greek anatomy, the rediscovery of the ancient texts from which the medieval anatomists from Avicenna to Mondino had derived much of their knowledge. The question was—Had they derived it correctly, without debasement?

These three developments occurred within the same century, and it is especially difficult to describe each of them without repetitions, because they coexisted to some extent within the same individuals, the proportion of medievalism, Hellenism, and autopsy varying for each of them.

We have already outlined some aspects of the medieval tradition, and other aspects may be indicated later. As to the humanists who rescued Galen, we have spoken of them in the first lecture; his anatomical writings were reëdited and reëxplained at the same time as his medical ones. We may recall the work done by Johann Günther of Andernach; his *Anatomicarum institutionum secundum Galeni libri quatuor* was published in Basel, 1539. Galen's outstanding anatomical contribution, the *De anatomicis administrationibus* (we might call it a manual of dissection), was translated from Greek into Latin by Günther (Lyon: G. Rouillé, 1551) and from Greek into French by Jacques Dalechamps (Lyon: Rigaud, 1572). Günther was aware of the conflict between ancient and modern medicine and discussed it in *De medicina veteri et nova tum cognoscenda tum faciunda commentarii duo* (Basel, 1571). This was something different, however; for the conflict he dealt with was not the one between learning and experience (as the anatomists understood it), but rather the conflict between traditional medicine and Paracelsism.

To return to the new pre-Vesalian anatomy, it was characterized (like the new herbals) by illustrations which departed more and more from the medieval schemes and became more and more realistic. The images of the *Fasciculus medicinae* were still medieval. Material progress was accomplished by Giacomo Berengario da Carpi (d. 1550), professor of surgery in Bologna, in his commentary on Mondino: *Carpi Commentaria cum amplissimis additionibus super anatomia Mundini una cum textu ejusdem in pristinum et verum nitorem redacto* (quarto, 428 1.; Bologna: Hieron de Benedictis, 1521).

According to Singer[154] "this is the earliest anatomical treatise that can properly be described as having figures illustrating the text." Some of the figures are excellent, better than his Latin. Another treatise of his *Isagogae breves*, prepared for his teaching in the medical school of Bologna, was even more remarkable: *Isagogae breves, perlucidae ac uberrimae in anatomiam humani corporis a communi medicorum academia usitatam* . . . (quarto, 80 leaves; Bologna, 1523).

Another edition of Mondino by Dryander (Marburg, 1541) has already been mentioned; it brought us very close to Vesalius, extremely close indeed since some of the illustrations are supposed to have been pinched from the latter's MSS.

Giovanni Battista Canano (1515-79) of Ferrara published in 1541 his "illustrated dissection of the muscles,"[155] but did not continue, being probably discouraged by the preparation and appearance of the *Fabrica*.

Another immediate precursor was Charles Estienne (1504-64), third son of Henri I Estienne (d. 1520), founder of the illustrious family of Parisian typographers. His treatise, *De dissectione*,[156] was posterior to the *Fabrica* in appearance but had been on the stocks for at least fifteen years.

The case of Estienne suggests that of Sylvius (Jacques Dubois of Amiens, 1478-1555), for Sylvius was also pre-Vesalian though his main work, the *Isagoge*,[157] appeared only in 1555. Sylvius had been Vesalius' teacher in Paris and became his main adversary and his enemy. His book was an introduction to Hippocrates and Galen, yet it contained many novelties and helped to clarify the anatomical nomenclature.

A new stream of anatomical knowledge was opened by the study of morbid conditions, and the initiator was Antonio Benevieni (d. 1502) of Florence who made about twenty autopsies, the account of which was posthumously published and is considered the first treatise of pathological anatomy: *De abditis nonnullis ac mirandis morborum et sanationum causis* (quarto, sign. a-g; Florence: Juntae, 1507).

Benevieni was not the first to carry out a post-mortem. The first autopsy on record is that of Bartolommeo da Varignana (XIV-1), made in Bologna, 1302; but it is probable that others were made before that, but remained unrecorded. When Pope Alexander V (Peter of Crete) died suddenly at Bologna in 1410, Pietro d'Argelata made a post-mortem and described it.[158] One would expect a post-mortem to be ordered whenever the death of an important person aroused suspicions. However, such a procedure was made difficult, if not impossible, because of superstitions and social taboos. The first code of criminal law, the C.C.C. (*Constitutio criminalis carolina*) formulated in 1521 and 1529 and sanctioned by the emperor Charles Quint in 1533, did not permit post-mortem examinations. The first legal post-mortem in France was made by Ambroise Paré in 1562. There were many cases, however, when post-mortem examinations were natural enough and could not be forbidden; if a man's death was caused by an outside material cause and his body was ripped, the surgeon could and did make anatomical observations. It is for that simple reason that military surgeons (like Paré) were able not only to make autopsies but also to observe accidental vivisections and thus improve their anatomical knowledge.

Another cause of anatomical progress which I have not yet referred to was more deeply typical of the Renaissance than any other—artistic reverence for the human body, and appreciation of its beauty. This was not absolutely new—there is nothing new under the sun—but the medieval climate had not favored these feelings; on the contrary, good Christians had been trained to consider the human body as a source of evil, which it was their duty to hide.[159] The Renaissance artists rediscovered the nude statues of the ancient world and resolved to emulate them. This implied the study of the body and even some knowledge of its superficial anatomy. Many artists drew from the nude and some went further and attended anatomical dissections. Think of the works of such men as Donatello, Luca della Robbia, Antonio Pollaiuolo, Verrocchio, Leonardo da Vinci, Michelangelo, Albrecht Dürer, and many others. It is difficult if not impossible to determine the extent of the anatomical studies of each of them, except in the case of Leonardo.

Leonardo became so interested in anatomy that "artistic anatomy" could not satisfy him any longer; he undertook elaborate dissections, and recorded them in drawings some of which have never been equaled. We need not expatiate on this, because Leonardo's anatomical knowledge and his artistic power are discussed at great length in excellent books.[160] In spite of the fact that he had received no medical training whatsoever, Leonardo was an anatomist of genius, one of the greatest of all times. He also was a forerunner of Vesalius, but "hors concours." His notes and drawings were unpublished and remained practically unknown until the end of last century; hence, he played no part in the progress of anatomy. He came before Vesalius but did not prepare the way for him.

The fruits of "artistic anatomy"—of the artists' interest in male and female bodies—were more tangible, for they are illustrated in many paintings, even in religious ones. For example, St. Sebastian gave the artists a good pretext for painting the nude body of a handsome man; as a source of inspiration, we may consider him as the Christian epiphany of Apollo.[161]

Leonardo died in Amboise in 1519, five years after the birth of Andreas Vesalius in Brussels. There is no more need of describing the latter's life in this book than in retelling Leonardo's. Both men are so great that sufficient knowledge of them may be taken for granted.[162]

Vesalius' masterpiece is the *De humani corporis fabrica libri septem* (Basel: Joannes Oporinus, 1543. Reprinted *ibidem,* 1555; and again, Venice: Francisco Senense, 1568).

Soon after the publication of the *Fabrica,* Vesalius resigned his professorship at Padova to become physician to Charles Quint (1544); he remained in Spain in Charles' service and later in the service of Philip II until 1564. In that year, he made a pilgrimage to the Holy Land and died on his way back in the island of Zante (Zacynthos) in the Ionian Sea.[162a]

Though the publication of the *Fabrica* is one of the main landmarks in the whole history of science, one should not imagine that the anatomical books which appeared after 1543 were all of them derived from it. As we have shown above, some had been prepared and written before the *Fabrica.* However, a number of anatomical (and physiological) discoveries were made, and treatises published, by men who followed in his footsteps: for example, the Spaniard Miguel Serveto (1511-53); the Italians Matteo Realdo Colombo of Cremona (1516-59), Gabriele Fallopio of Modena (1523-62), Bartolommeo Eustachi of San Severino, Marche (*c.* 1520-74),[163] Costanzo Varoli of Bologna (1543-75), Leonardo Botallo of Asti (1530-   ),[164] Archangelo Piccolòmini of Ferrara (1525-85), Giulio Cesare Aranzi of Bologna (1530-89), Fabrizio da Acquapendente (1537-1619), Giulio Casserio of Piacenza (1545-1616); the Dutchmen Volcher Coiter of Groningen (1534-1600)[165] and Peter Paauw of Amsterdam (1564-1617); the Frenchmen Ambroise Paré of Laval, Mayenne (1517-90) and André Dulaurens of Arles (d. 1609); the Swiss Caspar Bauhin of Basel (1560-1624); the Englishmen Thomas Geminus[166] (fl. 1540-60), John Caius of Norwich (1510-73), John Banister (1540-1610).

As always happens, when a subject becomes standardized, some of the professors, and not the least influential, are simply or chiefly lecturers and textbook writers. For example, Piccolòmini, professor in Rome, is best known because of his textbook, *Anatomicae praelectiones explicantes mirificam corporis humani fabricam* (folio, 414 pp., index; Rome: B. Bonfadini, 1586). And Dulaurens (or du Laurent; Laurentius in Latin) is known because of another textbook: *Historia anatomica humani corporis et singularium ejus partium multis controversiis et observationibus novis illustrata* (Erfurt, 1595. Often reprinted: Frankfurt, 1599; Paris, 1600; Hanau, 1601; etc. Translated into French, Lyon, 1621).

These two textbooks were used by Harvey, but that does not mean much, except as an indication of their popularity at the end of the century. Dulaurens' book was somewhat antiquated and included many superstitions. On the other hand, Piccolòmini, who was less popular, made a number of new observations.

Some of the anatomists, we might perhaps say all of them, dissected animals as well as men. Sylvius (Jacques Dubois, 1478-1555) carried out public dissections of animals as a part of his teaching in Paris and a little treatise *ad hoc* was published under his name soon after his death: *Observata in variis corporibus secandis* (Paris, 1555).

That book must be very rare; I have not yet seen it. Vesalius had attended Sylvius' lectures in Paris. It was impossible for any intelligent man to dissect various animals without making comparisons between them. The zoölogists like Guillaume Rondelet and Pierre Belon could not help comparing, say, the fishes which they were dissecting; but they went further than that, and Belon published a drawing illustrating a comparison bone by bone between the skeleton of a bird and that of a man.[167]

The master of comparative anatomy (as well as of embryology) was the Dutchman Volcher Coiter, but his works appeared a generation later than Belon's. He was a great admirer of Gabriele Fallopio and edited the latter's comparative studies of various human skeletons and later he published illustrated comparisons between the skeletons of various animals. His investigations of the bones of foetuses and of babies remained unpublished until 1659. Here is a list of his works:

Externarum et internarum principalium humani corporis partium tabulae atque anatomicae exercitationes observationesque variae (fol., 125 pp., pl., Nürnberg: Dietrich Gerlach, 1573).

Lectiones Gabrielis Fallopii de partibus similaribus humani corpori ex diversis exemplaribus a Volchero Coiter collectae (2 parts in 1 vol., folio; Nürnberg: Dietrich Gerlach, 1575).

Diversorum animalium sceletorum explicationes iconibus artificiosis et genuinis illustratae (Nürnberg, 1575; reprinted in 1595). This includes comparisons between the skulls of men, apes, etc.

Tractatus anatomicus de ossibus foetus abortivi et infantis dimidium annum nati. Included in Henricus Eyssonius: *Tractatus anatomicus et medicus de ossibus infanti* (Groningen, 1659).

LECTURE II: NATURAL HISTORY

In the meanwhile a jurist of Bologna, Carlo Ruini (d. 1598),[168] prepared a very elaborate study, magnificently illustrated, of equine anatomy. There had been many veterinary treatises in Greek, Arabic, Latin, and vernaculars, but nothing on this scale.[169] Ruini was standing on the shoulders of Vesalius and others and applying their methods to the horse. His remarks on the heart and blood were such that he was sometimes quoted as the discoverer of the circulation of the blood (the veterinary school of Bologna put up that claim on a monumental tablet, but that does not justify it). Ruini's book was one of the latest fruits of the Renaissance, such a late one that its influence could be felt only in the seventeenth century. It was originally published in Italian and was never translated into Latin, but only into French. The lack of a Latin translation is partly due to its lateness, partly to the ignorance of the veterinary doctors. The title of the book is *Dell' anatomia e dell' infermità del cavallo* (2 vols., folio, ill.; Bologna, 1598). Second edition augmented (2 vols., folio, ill.; Venice: O. Blndoni, 1602). Reprinted, Venice, 1618. A French translation appeared in Paris, 1647, 1654, 1655.

It is clear that by the end of the sixteenth century the new teaching of anatomy with public dissections was practised in every respectable school of medicine.

The best examples had been given first in Paris by Sylvius, and later more fully in Padova. An anatomical theatre had been established in that city as early as 1490 by Alessandro Benedetti of Legnago (d. Venice, 1525).[170] The school of anatomy of Padova was illustrated by Vesalius, Colombo, Fallopio, Fabrizio, Casserio, and by disciples all over Europe, including Harvey. Its greatest glory was in the period which began with Vesalius' appointment on St. Nicholas day, 1537, and ended with that of another Bruxellois, Adriaan van den Spieghel, or Spigelius (1578-1625). He and his predecessor, Casserio, take us already out of the Renaissance.

The anatomical theatre of Padova must have been one of the first. To give a list of the earliest ones would be difficult, because the matter is not sufficiently tangible. Any hall where anatomical demonstrations were made was *ipso facto* an anatomical theatre, however poor its appurtenances and equipment. The name was probably given to the more ambitious kind of set-up. Strangely enough, after Benedetti's no new ones are mentioned in the first half of the sixteenth century. Rondelet established one in Montpellier in 1556, Casper Bauhin another in Basel in 1589, Peter Paauw one in Amsterdam in 1597. Public dissections were carried out in many other places, e.g., in England, though no definite reference is made to a special theatre.

The list could probably be lengthened. Such as it is, it suffices to confirm the statement made above that the teaching of anatomy in the Vesalian manner was introduced in many countries of western Europe before 1600.

11. CONCLUSIONS

THE PSYCHOLOGICAL CLIMATE OF THE NATURALISTS WAS NOT VERY different from that of the physicians, and no wonder, because most of them were M.D.'s and derived their main sustenance from medical practice. The elite was driven asunder by two passions which had been close enough at the beginning, but tended to diverge more and more: the love of ancient learning and the love of nature. It had been very easy at first to love flowers and be anxious to know what Dioscorides had to say about them, but gradually the lovely flowers were insisting upon more attention to themselves. It is as if a man had courted a lady because of her noble ancestry, but after having gained her discovered that she had a personality of her own, wanted to be loved for her own sake and won.

The botanic profession had emerged at the beginning of the sixteenth century and was growing in importance: there were professors of botany in every medical faculty, the botanical standards of the herbalists and pharmacists were gradually raised, new opportunities were created by the botanical gardens and the botanical explorations.

The two professions, botanic and medical, were often intermingled; yet, there were notable differences between them. The appeal of nature was not by any means of the same kind in both cases. New medical problems arose every year, if only because of new plagues or of old plagues which had a new complexion: smallpox, measles, lead poisoning, scurvy, yellow fever, typhus, Hungarian disease, diphtheria, whooping cough, ergotism, the sweating sickness, influenza. Each of these "new" diseases invited descriptions, but the diagnosis was generally difficult, if not impossible. Fevers of different origin might easily be confused; while similar ones would be differentiated. Clinical pictures were unclear; nosological entities vague. On the other hand, a new plant or a new animal was something very tangible which even an imperfect description would help one to recognize at once.

There were two Renaissance diseases, however, which were sufficiently characteristic to be recognized: the doctors recognized the first almost at once; very few of them were capable of recognizing the other.

The first was syphilis; we would hesitate to call it a fruit of the Renaissance, but it was certainly the Renaissance disease par excellence. It began explosively at the end of the fifteenth century in Italy and the earliest printed documents concerning it date from 1495, but from that year on syphilis literature has never stopped.[171] Syphilis treatises were among the first printed medical books written by contemporary authors. The new disease was given its name by the humanist Girolamo Fracastoro (1484-1553) of Verona who devoted a Latin poem to it, *Syphilis sive morbus gallicus* (Verona: Stefano Nicolini da Sabbio, 1530).[172] It is a poem of 1346 verses divided into three books and of such outstanding quality that it was compared with the *Georgica* (the meter and rhythm recall Virgil) and is considered one of the greatest Latin poems of the Renaissance. The comparison with Virgil was almost unavoidable, for every poetaster imitated him. It is perhaps more to the point to say that Fracastoro's poem was at least as good or not worse than the master-piece of Jacopo Sannazzaro (1458-1530) of Naples, *De partu Virginis* (1526), or the many poems of Marco Gerolamo Vida (*c.* 1480-1566) of Cremona, such as *De bombyce, De ludo scacchorum, De arte poetica* (1527), and his *Christiad* (1535). The good bishop of Alba has often been called "the prince of modern Latin poets" but "modern readers" do not find it more painful to read Fracastoro's *Syphilis* than the poems of Sannazzaro or of Vida himself. Note that these three poets were close contemporaries and that their main works appeared within a decade. The poetical taste was not then the same as ours and Fracastoro's poem was very popular, no less than twenty editions appearing within seventy years of its first appearance. The new disease had the double distinction of being the only disease with a poetic name, and the only one which inspired a poet and is celebrated in a special epic. These two distinctions are typical enough of Renaissance paganism.

The other disease was a mental one, the fear of witchcraft. That fear was very ancient, but it had remained latent; it was awakened at the very end of the Middle Ages, and was revived more completely by the bull *Summi desiderentes* of Innocent VIII in 1484 and by the *Malleus maleficarum* of the two Dominicans, Jacob Sprenger and Heinrich Kraemer (Institoris), first printed soon afterwards. After that, it was like a monster let loose and claiming innumerable victims. The first person to realize that the fear of witchcraft was a delusion and a disease was the Dutch doctor, Johann Weyer, and he had the great courage to print his views in 1563.[173] Before the end of the century, his treatise was reprinted five times plus twice in German translations and twice in French. There were thus ten editions in the century, but in the meanwhile, the witchcraft terror was propagated by innumerable books.[174] The very few people who accepted Weyer's point of view were talking "like rational beings to the inmates of a gigantic insane asylum and with the same success."

The witchcraft delusion and the mass psychosis which it caused were undoubtedly stirred up and aggravated by religious intolerance and by the cruelties and the disgraces of the religious wars. It was tempting for propagandists to confuse heretics with witches. When people are unbalanced by irrational fears, it is easy to make them suspect each other; they mistake jealousy and hatred for love. Men of good will were persuaded to help uproot the imaginary evils. We can understand that situation, because we are witnessing similar ones, except that the present hallucinations are centered upon something else.

That delusion was the main plague of the sixteenth century, and it was the more pernicious because so few men were capable of recognizing it as such. A disease cannot be fought unless it is known. Instead of fighting the conflagration, most people (even the "best people") were willing enough to fan it.

During the Renaissance, syphilis could hardly be called a "secret" disease, but the fear of witches was so secret that the very people who were afflicted were unaware of their illness.

We need not describe the exploration of the American continent and the circumnavigation of Africa. Everybody knows the great deeds of Bartholomeo Diaz (1487), Columbus (1492), Vasco da Gama (1498), Amerigo Vespucci (1499-1502), Magellan (1519-21), and many others. The navigators and explorers accomplished the discovery of an entirely new world: new continents, thousands of islands, new climates, new plants, new animals, new peoples. Everything was new, as it were a new creation. This happened then and can never happen again except on a much smaller scale.

The motive of these discoveries was greed rather than curiosity; yet, curiosity was excited. And greed itself had many roots. One of those roots was botanical. Indeed, one of the main causes of colonial expansion was the need of spices most of which were growing in tropical regions: cinnamon, ginger, benzoin, nutmeg, mace, cloves, sandalwood, aloes, camphor, China root, rhubarb, and above all, pepper.[175] It was thus necessary to take botanists to Asia and America, and some botanists were very eager to go. This was drawing them far away from Theophrastos and Dioscorides. They still carried the old books in their baggage, yet were obliged to observe the new landscapes with new eyes and fewer prejudices.

Let us forget the political vicissitudes of the new colonial empires which disgraced humanity and think only of the scientific aspects. Naturalists were getting so used to explorations that they began to reëxplore their own countries. We have already referred to the sudden growth of Alpinism; the discovery of the flora and fauna of high mountains was as exciting as the discovery of the American ones. Everywhere, at home and outremer, prospectors were looking for minerals, precious ores or precious gems, herbs and roots, animals of every kind. The first motive was the satisfaction of needs, but scientific curiosity was soon added to that. The speedy accumulation of plants and animals which were either new or somewhat unlike the familiar ones increased the necessity of better descriptions and classifications; these tasks were too difficult and too complex to be carried out during the Renaissance, but they were fairly well begun as is witnessed by the many herbals which have been enumerated above.

The necessary descriptions were facilitated and stimulated by an increasing number of engravings; one always wanted more of them and better ones. A good drawing implies careful analysis. Unfortunately, the cost of engravings was great and there was a great temptation to use and abuse old ones. Such was the competition between rival printers that there was also sometimes a temptation to complete drawings on the basis of insufficient models. For example, so good a man as Gesner published the drawing of an ostrich with ornamental feathers covering the whole body!

Another result of explorations was the attempt (not always successful) of importing exotic plants and animals and acclimatizing them to home conditions. The task was facilitated by the existence of botanic gardens of which many were established within the century: Pisa and Padova, c. 1545;[176] Firenze, 1550; Zürich, 1560; Bologna, 1568; Leyden, 1577; Leipzig, 1579; Montpellier, 1592; Paris, 1597 (called Jardin des Plantes in 1635; subordinated to the Muséum in 1794).

The list might probably be lengthened, and some dates modified. Indeed, the dates vary somewhat, according to one's conception of the beginning. The formal inauguration, if any, may be preceded by informal gropings. The dates of foundation are often determined long afterwards with unavoidable arbitrariness.

The botanical gardens were not absolutely new. There had been such gardens in the Middle Ages and even in Athens and Alexandria, but they were organized in a new way.[177] They were always associated with medical schools and their main purpose was to facilitate the botanical education of medical students. The directors (who were generally the professors of botany) were anxious to exhibit as many plants as were available to them; there was some emulation between the gardens of various universities with regard to novelties. Some gardeners may have tried to cultivate useful plants more extensively. That is, it is possible that the acclimatization of exotic plants was attempted in some of the gardens.[178] The most significant event in that direction was the project which was submitted by Pierre Belon to the king of France about 1550 but remained unrealized.

The most pregnant vegetal importation in the Renaissance was that of cacao (cocoa, chocolate) by the Spaniards from Peru or Mexico. They did not import the plant itself, but its seeds, which were used to make a stimulating beverage. This was the first Western example of the use of a xanthine, a kind of drug which excites the nervous system and is in great demand because of the need of that excitation. Other beverages of the same kind, such as tea and coffee, obtained even more popularity but were introduced only after the Renaissance.[179]

There were also menageries or zoölogical gardens, but these were less different from their ancient or medieval models. Popes, kings and lords, city magistrates loved to exhibit wild and exotic animals which were living symbols of their power and opulence. The taste was perhaps stronger in Muslim than in Christian lands, and the renewal of interest in the West during the Renaissance was much increased by the descriptions of the menageries of Constantinople by Pierre Gilles, Pierre Belon, and André Thévet. During the sixteenth century, there were menageries and various collections of living animals at the papal court in Rome, and also in Florence, Ferrara, Milano, Naples; in London; in many cities of the Netherlands and Burgundy, Lorraine, Savoy, Anjou; in Germany; in France where the kings kept wild animals in Chinon, Plessis les Tours, St. Germain, the Louvre and Tuileries. Some animals were taken around by businessmen to be shown at the fairs. The Spaniards had their traditional bull fights and under Charles Quint new fights were organized between bulls and other animals. The Swiss had their bear pits. The ambassador Busbecq traveled back from Turkey in 1562 with a whole menagerie. And so on.[180]

The main point is that the people of the sixteenth century, especially those living in the neighborhood of the greater cities, had some opportunities of seeing unfamiliar animals. Botanical gardens and menageries opened new horizons for the relatively few people who had eyes to see them.

The main interest of naturalists exploring new countries was to find better drugs. Among the many superstitions, there was one according to which God had placed appropriate remedies close to the evils which they would cure, antidotes in the neighborhood of poisons, etc. Thus, it was natural to hunt in the West Indies for drugs to cure syphilis; the fact that such a hunt was made proves that the doctors living at the turn of the fifteenth century believed that the disease was of American origin. The drug was duly found—*guaiacán*[181]—and as long as it was new enough, a number of people were cured by it, or at least believed so. Fracastoro's poem was written in part for the glorification of the wonder drug, and one of the patients who was saved by its use, the German knight Ulrich von Hutten, wrote a special treatise, *De guaiaci medicina et morbo gallico* (Mainz: Johann Schoeffer, 1519), which was frequently reprinted in Latin, German, and French. The book was dedicated to Albrecht, cardinal and archbishop of Mainz. A fine Renaissance touch was provided at the end of the book when, addressing his noble and venerable patron, Ulrich von Hutten declared something to this effect: "If Your Grace or members of its household got the French pox (which heaven forbid! but one can never tell) here is a sure remedy which might be of use. . . . "[182]

Other drugs were introduced into the pharmacopoeia—in 1525, the China root (*Smilax china*), which attracted Vesalius' attention;[183] in 1536, *sarsaparilla* (an American kind of *smilax*); *sassafras; lignum nephreticum* (Monardes, 1565); etc.—and each of them raised high hopes, but the really important natural drugs were not brought to Europe until the following century: *ipecac* from Brazil and *cinchona* from Peru. These were wonder drugs, indeed, especially the second one. If the ancients had known cinchona, they would have made a god of it.

In the meanwhile, the iatrochemists were trying to develop mineral drugs. Such drugs had been used in medieval times and even in antiquity,[184] but the use was systematized and generalized by Paracelsus and his followers. For example, mercurial ointments had been successfully applied to the alleviation of various skin troubles; it was natural to apply them to syphilis. Mercurial fumigations and inunctions proved more efficacious than guaiac.[185] Other experiments were made with mineral drugs but none was very fortunate. Nevertheless, the passion for alchemy and magic was steadily increasing. The sixteenth century was a golden age for occultists and impostors, but it is impossible to speak here of that aspect of the Renaissance, the most backward and repulsive aspect of it. Alchemists and astrologers were protected by popes and sovereigns and by lesser lords; one of their greatest patrons, Rudolph II of Hapsburg (1552-1612), ruled the Holy Roman empire from 1576 to his death, but we should remember to his credit that he was the patron not only of quacks but also of such men as Tycho Brahe and Kepler. The history of alchemy is a jungle which I prefer not to enter. Let us end this section simply with the *Alchemia* of Andreas Libavius (1597);[186] this is not yet the end of alchemy, nor the beginning of modern chemistry, but it is one of the monuments marking the end of the Renaissance. Libavius was born in Halle, Saxony, in 1540; he obtained his M.D. and became professor of history and poetry at Jena, later director of the gymnasium of Coburg where he died in 1616. Note the curious ingredients of his personality: medicine, poetry, history—more might be added—but his main writings were devoted to alchemy or chemistry. The greatest, his *Alchemia* of 1597, was a survey of contemporary knowledge wherein he tried to explain chemical reactions in plain language. This *Alchemia* has been called the first textbook of chemistry. It deserves that name to the extent that it was a reaction against Paracelsism, against occultism and extravagance. It was textbook-like in its matter-of-factness and moderation. Libavius was really a chemist (rather than alchemist) and various chemical discoveries are to his credit (e.g., stannic chloride, *liquor fumans Libavii*). Yet, two more centuries had still to elapse before the chemical darkness was to be ended.

A more pleasant aspect of the Renaissance is the love of nature, in the form not of herbals and other such books, but rather in the form of art and poetry. We have already spoken of the artists who opened their eyes to the wonders of the world, Flemings like the Van Eyck brothers in the first half of the fifteenth century; Italians like Botticelli, Leonardo, and many others; Germans like Dürer. We may assume that some of the travelers and Alpinists were prepared to admire the flowers, the insects, and the birds which they came across. It is more difficult to estimate the share of poets, though we might almost rule out those who wrote in Latin, for the use of an "artificial" language instead of the mother tongue was sufficient to discourage genuine inspiration and to nip spontaneous poetry in the bud.[187]

The painters and musicians had more freedom to express themselves than the Latin poets, and some of them did so beautifully and helped in their own sweet ways to liberate the human mind from many unnecessary shackles.

In spite of all these novelties, of all the free winds which were refreshing the atmosphere, the men of science were overwhelmed by a mass of learning which was top-heavy and often irrelevant. Even such a man as Garcia da Orta, whose privilege it was to see the plants of India, to be the first European botanist to do so, could not shake off Dioscorides and Pliny. The scholars of the Renaissance had carried their love of antiquity so far that some of them had become half-pagan or wholly so; they had carried out the rediscovery of ancient wisdom as if to achieve thereby their own liberation and were enthralled in a new kind of bondage.

The struggle for the defense of Hellenic science did not occur quite in the same way as it did in medicine. Some of the Renaissance physicians had thought it necessary to attack al-Rāzī and Ibn Sīnā in order to vindicate Hippocrates and Galen. There was no need of an anti-Arabic crusade in natural history. Great books on husbandry in Arabic were not available to the West, except in Spain, and even in Spain, the tradition was chiefly manual and oral rather than written. Some Arabic treatises on husbandry had been put into Castilian but as far as I know that had not been the case for the most important one, the *Kitāb al-falāḥa* of Ibn al-'Awwām (XII-2) of Seville; we must bear in mind, however, that a translation was not absolutely necessary, for there remained in Spain until the beginning of the Renaissance a goodly number of people who could read Arabic, and chiefly because Ibn al-'Awwām had put together agricultural traditions which were still alive.[188] It has been said in that spirit that the gardens and the orchards of Spain were the best part of her Arabic heritage. There could be no conflict about that, but only, insofar as the Spaniards were conscious of their inheritance, gratitude.

Moreover, there were plenty of opportunities for quarreling about medical theories, not only the more philosophical but also the more practical ones, such as the theory of venesection. The Muslim physicians taught that bleeding should be "revulsive," that is, at a distance from the ailing part of the body. The Hippocratic method on the contrary was "derivative," that is, blood should be let on the same side of the body and as near the seat of inflammation as possible. The controversy was particularly hot concerning pleurisy. In Paris in 1514, many cases of pleurisy were treated "revulsively" with disastrous results; the "derivative" (Hippocratic) method seemed more helpful. Pierre Brissot (1478-1522) of Fontenay-le-Comte, Poitou, took up the cudgels for Hippocrates and a battle royal ensued between the two parties. Strangely enough, the Arabists had the advantage for a while and Brissot was obliged to leave Paris and go to Evora in Portugal. He was supported by the medical school of Salamanca, but his enemies insinuated to the young emperor, Charles Quint, that his ideas were as scandalous as Lutheranism! Brissot died in 1522 and his "apology" was edited posthumously by one of his Evora colleagues in 1525. Clement VII (pope, 1523-34), Vesalius, and many others took part in the dispute which lasted throughout the century and was envenomed by irrelevant arguments and by verbal ambiguities.[189]

This story has been told at some length, because it is a good example of medical controversy. Such controversies would not have been impossible in the field of natural history—quarrelsome and jealous people are capable of disputing about anything—but the opportunities were fewer than in medicine, which was overloaded with dialectics.

The Renaissance was like all ages a kind of Middle Ages. It was a period of transition. One had tried very hard to purify and to bolster the medieval traditions by appealing to the Ancients; the appeal had been fruitful in many ways, but in spite of it, the medieval traditions were slowly disintegrating. The enemies were not the Arabs, nor anybody else in the past; by 1600, the real enemies were in the offing. The scientific travail of the Renaissance was the slow metamorphosis of ancient and medieval traditions into modern ones.

LECTURE III

MATHEMATICS AND ASTRONOMY

THERE WAS AN ESSENTIAL DIFFERENCE BETWEEN THE HUMANISTS who were mathematically minded and those who were interested in natural history or medicine. If the latter restricted themselves to the study, however rigorous, of the Greek classics, they condemned themselves to sterility. The mathematicians who were editing or translating Euclid, Archimedes, or Ptolemy might discover fragments of the eternal truth, for mathematical truth is to a large extent independent of nature. In order to find new truth, they would have to throw off the yoke of the written word, but they would not be obliged to explore the real world. Mathematical truth could be extracted from their own minds with little reference to reality.

When we dealt with medicine or natural history, we had to take into account not simply Greek writers but also Latin ones, Celsus and Pliny, whose influence was considerable. The mathematical heritage was exclusively Greek and Arabic (not Latin). There is no need of reviewing the whole of it. We shall limit our survey to Plato, Euclid, Archimedes, Apollonios, and Ptolemy and then outline very briefly the work done in algebra, trigonometry, and astronomy.

1. PLATO AND ARISTOTLE (IV-B.C.)

THE PLATONIC TRADITION IS FULL OF SURPRISES AND PARADOXES. Its importance cannot be denied, but it was to a large extent the result of misunderstandings. When we think of the Renaissance we cannot help visualizing Plato at the beginning and the center of it.

133

Thanks to the Platonic Academy of Florence and especially to the efforts of Marsilio Ficino (1433-99), Plato was considered the supreme teacher. For all the virtuosi of the Medici circle who were artists and men of letters rather than men of science, Plato, not Aristotle, was the guide and master. Strangely enough, the Platonic supremacy, which was established in Florence, had been prepared a generation earlier by a German, Nicholas of Cues (on the Moselle, 1401-64), who was one of the greatest personalities of the century. Nicholas was not simply a theologian of unusual generosity, one of the leading members of the Council of Basel (1431-49), but he was deeply interested in Platonic and Neoplatonic philosophy and in the mathematical and physical sciences. He was created a cardinal in 1448 and died at Lodi, in Umbria, in 1464. He thus preceded the Renaissance (as we defined it) and anticipated some of its achievements; he was a forerunner of Simon Stevin and of Giordano Bruno. Being a prince of the church and an international statesman, Nicholas influenced the Neoplatonists of Florence, including Leonardo da Vinci. The Florentine Academy had been founded by Cosimo de' Medici, that is, before Nicholas' death (Nicholas and Cosimo died in the same year); the light of the Academy was Marsilio, who translated Plato and Plotin into Latin. His translation of Plato was published by Laurentius Venetus in Florence in 1483-84, that of Plotin in the same city by A. Miscominus in 1492. The Platonic tradition was full of ambiguities and of prevarications; these were increased by Marsilio when he tried to reconcile Plato with Christianity. The comedy of errors and the tragedy of lies which that tradition implied were not started by Marsilio, far from it, but he intensified them and he stimulated Platonic studies and dreams not only in Florence but in the whole Republic of Letters.

Plato was not a creative mathematician; the real mathematical work of his school was done much less by himself than by others, above all, Eudoxos of Cnidos, one of the greatest mathematicians of all times. Yet, Plato's influence upon the progress of mathematics could hardly be exaggerated; he did not create mathematics, but he created mathematicians, which was better. His own contributions were of a dubious nature. To illustrate his tendency it will suffice to consider the case of the regular solids. He did not discover them and we cannot even credit him with the astounding realization of their limited number. While an infinity of regular polygons is conceivable, the regular polyhedrons are restricted to five. Was this proved by Theaitetos, or even before? The proof is easy enough, but one had to think of it. Plato, the mystic, could not stop there, however. The existence of five regular solids and no more must have a cosmological meaning which it was his business to bring out and to exploit. He identified them with the elements. But there are only four elements? Never mind that, the fifth solid would symbolize the whole universe. The theory of the four elements was as gratuitous as could be; from the scientific point of view, it was nonsense; the dovetailing of that theory with the five Platonic figures was compounded nonsense. Nevertheless, this invention was accepted and regarded as an achievement of the very first magnitude. Nonmathematicians accepted it as a kind of mathematical truth; the authority of the philosopher was immeasurably increased by belief in his mathematical genius. This is not a unique case in the history of philosophy; many philosophers have tried to bolster up their metaphysics with mathematical arguments, or their authority has been fortified by mathematical deeds whether real or spurious. Think of Spinoza, Leibniz, Berkeley, and closer to us, Russell and Whitehead. One of the leading mathematicians of the Renaissance, the Franciscan Luca Paccioli (*c.* 1445-after 1509), published an Italian treatise entitled *Divina proportione* (Venice: Paganinus, 1509), wherein he explained the golden section (the divine proportion of his title), that is, the division of a straight line in extreme and mean ratio, and the application of mathematics to architecture, the arts, artistic anatomy, and the canon of the human body. Leonardo da Vinci is said to have worked with Paccioli, made the drawings and perhaps the engravings. At any rate, Leonardo's manuscripts prove that he was deeply concerned with such matters. The third and final part of Paccioli's book was devoted to the five regular solids, but that part was a verbatim translation of the Latin treatise by the painter Piero della Francesca (*c.* 1416-92), who hailed like himself from Borgo San Sepulcro in Umbria. The point is that the knowledge of the golden section and of the five regular solids had reached the artists of the quattrocento as well as the philosophers and the mathematicians and was exciting their imagination. Neoplatonic arithmetic or numerology was causing another kind of fermentation which was equally evil, if not more so, but it would not be fair to blame Plato too much for that, for he did not initiate that kind of folly, but simply transmitted it from the Pythagoreans to the Neoplatonicians.

The mathematical influence of Aristotle was more discreet.[1] The most fruitful teachings of the Lyceum during the Renaissance were in the field of natural history, as set forth in my second lecture. It is significant that an anti-Aristotelian movement was already shaping itself, at the very time when Platonic extravagances were more popular than ever. The protagonist of that early revolt was the French mathematician, Pierre de la Ramée (1515-72) or Ramus,[2] who hailed from the Vendômois (like Ronsard) and was murdered in the St. Bartholomew purge. In spite of a violent anti-Aristotelian thesis defended in 1536 and of an early condemnation, he became professor at the Collège Royal (now Collège de France). He wrote a good many textbooks on logic, grammar, and mathematics, edited Euclid, and was a great educator, perhaps the greatest of his age. The anti-Aristotelian revolt which he had the temerity to lead was continued in the following century by

135

Gassendi; it was gradually completed by the steady progress of experimental science.

2. EUCLID OF ALEXANDRIA[3] (III-1 B.C.)

ONE OF THE GLORIES OF THE GREEK RENAISSANCE WHICH BLOSSOMED in Alexandria during the Ptolemaic dynasty was the textbook of geometry put together about the year 300 B.C. by Euclid. No mathematical book has enjoyed a greater popularity, a popularity so great indeed that the words Euclid and geometry became almost interchangeable. It does not follow, of course, that Euclid and his *Elements* were always known in the best manner.

Of the man Euclid we know practically nothing and, what is worse, he was confused in the Middle Ages and the Renaissance with the philosopher, Euclid of Megara, one of Plato's disciples. In the early printed editions, he is generally called Euclides Megarensis; that is true until the end of the sixteenth century.[4] A deeper mistake which lasted almost as long[5] was the idea that Euclid had provided only the theorems, and that Theon of Alexandria (IV-2) had been the first to prove them. Such a mistake reveals a complete incomprehension of Euclid's task, for the order of his theorems was conditioned by logical necessities; without knowing the proofs of each and every one it would have been impossible to put them in any logical sequence.

Not only were the proofs available in Euclid's time, it is certain that many of the theorems had been proved before it. If Euclid had been able to write the *Elements* without knowledge of the proofs, he would have been a magician. He was not by any means the inventor of geometry, but his achievement is nevertheless immense. He it was who put together all of geometry in a single orderly sequence. He realized the need of postulates and his selection of them was so clever and economical that it was not improved upon until the nineteenth century. One of them, the parallel postulate, resisted the attempts made by mathematicians of many nations during more than two millennia to prove it, and Euclid's uncanny wisdom was justified, when it was finally shown that the rejection of that postulate implied the establishment of non-Euclidean geometries. That is, one had to choose between keeping the postulate as such, or rejecting the geometry which is familiar to us.

Euclid's work was so deep that the Romans were unable to appreciate it and the early Latin tradition was weak, incomplete, and capricious. The Greek tradition was strong, however, and the most philosophically minded of the Romans studied Euclid in Greek if they studied him at all. The Greek text was reëdited by Theon of Alexandria (IV-2) and MSS of it fell early into the hands of Arabic writers. If the translation of Books I and II of the *Elements* ascribed to Boetius (VI-1) was actually made by him or by one of his contemporaries, it was necessarily made from the Greek.[6] The most popular Latin versions, however, were made from the Arabic, the best known being those of Adelard of Bath (XII-1), of Gerard of Cremona (XII-2), and of Giovanni Campani (XIII-2). It is possible that those translations were not independent of each other; every translator will use earlier translations if available to him (it is his duty to do so); it has been claimed, for example, that Campani used Adelard, and that his own contribution was more in the nature of a commentary than of a translation pure and simple. At any rate, it is Campani's text which was immortalized by the first printed edition, produced by Erhard Ratdolt[7] in Venice on 25 May 1482 and reprinted without modifications by Leonardus Achates and Guglielmus of Pavia at Vicenza in 1491.[8] The first edition is a typographical monument of considerable interest, being the first mathematical book illustrated with diagrams.[9] In the meanwhile, various scholars had tried to translate Euclid directly from the Greek. The first such translation to be printed was made by Bartolommeo Zamberti and printed by Joannes Tacuinus (Venice, 1505; again, 1510). Zamberti's version was materially different from Campani's and superior to it, yet Luca Paccioli found it necessary to publish a revision of Campani's text, with a few additions of his own (Venice: Paganinus, 1509). Then, Jacques Lefebvre[10] published a new Latin version together with the commentaries of Hypsicles (II-1 B.C.), Theon of Alexandria (IV-2), and Campani (Paris: Henri Estienne, 1516).

The honor of producing the Greek princeps was shared by the editor, Simon Grynaeus, and the printer, Johann Herwagen (Basel, 1533); it included the commentary of Proclos (V-2) on Book I. The princeps was dedicated to Cuthbert Tunstall,[11] whom Grynaeus had probably met in England. The same printing house published a few years later (1537) a new edition of Zamberti's Latin version with a preface by Philipp Melanchthon.

Among other early editions we must still mention two Latin ones, the very elaborate one by Federico Commandino, with ancient scholia and commentary (Pesaro: Camillo Francischini, 1572), and the one by Christopher Clavius (Rome: Vincenzo Accolti, 1574), because of their intrinsic value and of the eminence of their editors. Federico Commandino of Urbino, born in 1509, was in the service of Clement VII, after whose death (in 1534) he went to Padova to study Greek, philosophy, and medicine (a good Renaissance combination). He obtained his M.D. at Ferrara, but being far more interested in mathematics than in physic he devoted his life to the translation and interpretation of the Greek mathematical classics. He translated not only Euclid but also Archimedes, Apollonios, and ancient scholia relative to them. His main original work was a treatise on the center of gravity of solids, *Liber de centro gravitatis solidorum* (Bologna: Benatius, 1565). He was one of the dominating figures of Renaissance mathematics; he died in his native city in 1575.

As to Clavius (1537-1612), he was a German Jesuit,[12] born in Bamberg. He was assigned to a post in Rome, taught mathematics in the Jesuit college of the eternal city for a great many years, and died there. His teaching was crystallized in a long series of textbooks dealing with arithmetic, algebra, geometry, gnomonics, the astrolabe, the computus, trigonometrical and astronomical tables. These textbooks were published in Latin, some of them also in Italian. They were widely used in all the Jesuit colleges, then the best in Europe, and were the vademecum of the Jesuit missionaries delegated to China.[13] When Gregory XIII (pope, 1572-85) decided to realize the calendar reform which was long overdue, he naturally applied to Father Clavius for scientific help. The reform of 1582 is rightly called Gregorian, but we should remember that Clavius was the engineer of it; this increased his popularity, but it also increased his worries, for he had to suffer the brunt of the objections made not only by Protestants but also by Catholic mathematicians; the adversaries of the reform included such eminent men as Vieta, Joseph Scaliger, and Michael Moestlin. Clavius wrote polemical treatises in defense of the reform, chiefly the *Calendarii romani gregoriani explicatio,* given by order of Clement VIII (pope 1592-1605) and published in Rome, 1603. The fame of Clavius was considerable but not quite deserved. It was partly the fame of a teacher whom ignorant students mistake for an inventor; as to the reform of the calendar, many educated men considered it a prodigious achievement, while it required only elementary knowledge of astronomy and arithmetic, plus common sense. His mathematical intelligence may be judged from his continued misunderstanding of decimal fractions twenty-three years after Stevin's explanation of them.[14] That was bad for a good teacher. To return to his Latin edition of Euclid (Rome, 1574): it was reprinted by Bartolommeo Grassi (Rome, 1589), by Giov. Batt. Ciotti (Cologne, 1591), and many times afterwards. His contemporary glory is witnessed by the publication of his collected works, *Opera mathematica* (5 vols., folio; Mainz: A. Hiérat, 1611-12); that edition was prepared by himself, but vols. 4 and 5 are probably posthumous.

Euclid's appeal extended beyond the domain of Latin scholarship, because there was a growing class of men who needed geometry more than Latin. Therefore, Euclid was translated into no less than five vernaculars before the end of the sixteenth century. Let us deal with the languages in chronological order of their first Euclid. The leading vernacular into which Euclid was translated by Niccolò Tartaglia was Italian (Venice: Venturino Roffinelli, 1543); reprinted by other Venetian printers in 1565, 1569, 1585. Tartaglia's Italian version was made "secondo le due Tradottioni" (meaning Campani and Zamberti, or from the Arabic and the Greek). The better text of Commandino was

Italianized and published by himself (Urbino, 1575).

A German translation by Wilhelm Holtzmann, i.e., Xylander, of Augsburg appeared in 1562 (Basel: Jacob Kündig). It is restricted to Books I-VI.

The pioneer in French was Pierre Forcadel of Béziers, whose translation of Books I-VI appeared in 1564 (Paris: Marnef et Cavellat), and of Books VII-IX in the following year (Paris: Charles Périer, 1565). Forcadel translated other Greek mathematical books into French and composed elaborate arithmetics; thanks to Ramus' help he was elected professor of mathematics in the Collège Royal; he did not survive his protector very long, for he died in 1574, in Paris.

The first English translation came a few years later; we owe it to Sir Henry Billingsley (London: John Day, 1570). It was made from Campani's version, that is, from the Arabic. It included a "fruitfull preface" by the singular John Dee, whom my readers know well onough. Sir Henry was an alumnus of St. John's, Cambridge, but learned mathematics in Oxford; he was so successful as a merchant that he was elected Lord Mayor of London; he died in 1606. He is a negligible person in the history of mathematics, but we are safe in claiming that he is the greatest mathematician in the distinguished group of London Lord Mayors.

The first Spanish translation was made by Rodrigo Zamorano,[15] astrologer, mathematician, and professor of cosmography in Seville. It is restricted to Books I-VI (Seville: Alonso de la Barrera, 1576).

When one bears in mind that the Arabic version was the basis of the Euclid incunabula, and of many early editions including the first English one, it is amusing to bring the sixteenth-century procession to a close with the first printed Arabic text, *Tahrīr usūl li Uqlīdis,* as revised by Nāsir al-dīn al-Tūsī (XIII-2). This is a magnificent folio printed by the Tipographea Medicea in Rome in 1594 (454 pp.).[16] The *Qānūn* of Avicenna had been published by the same press in the preceding year. These two splendid volumes cannot be put to the credit of the Arabic people; they were published without their knowledge and interest for the sake of Western and Catholic propaganda. The Arabic Euclid was reprinted in Constantinople in 1216 H (= 1800/1); that was an Islamic production, but very late and derivative.[17]

To sum up, the first printed editions of Euclid in various languages occurred in the following order: Latin (Venice, 1482), Greek (Basel, 1533), Italian (Venice, 1543), German (Basel, 1562), French (Paris, 1564-65), English (London, 1570), Spanish (Seville, 1576), Arabic (Rome, 1594); but those who have read my account of them will realize that such a summary is (like every summary) oversimplified and treacherous. One would have to discuss the merits of those translations, their origin and scope, even their size (the German and Spanish ones contain only Books I-VI). At any rate, by the end of the sixteenth century,

Euclid was available to the whole Republic of Letters, including its Arabic section.

Modern edition of Euclid in Greek by J. L. Heiberg and H. Menge (8 vols.; Leipzig: Teubner, 1883-1916); vols. I to IV (1883-86), edited by Heiberg, contain the *Elements*. English readers have an excellent translation with all necessary notes by Sir Thomas Heath: *The thirteen books of Euclid's Elements* (3 vols.; Cambridge University, 1908; 2nd ed., 1926—*Isis 10*, 60-62).

3. ARCHIMEDES OF SYRACUSE (III-2 B.C.)

A RCHIMEDES WROTE MANY IMPORTANT TREATISES, GENERALLY SHORT, of the size and nature of what would be called today "monographs." He could not enjoy the popularity of a man like Euclid who had provided a general textbook covering the whole of elementary geometry. The situation is not very different in our time; the author of special mathematical papers is not at all as well known to the mass of students as the author of popular textbooks. Moreover, Archimedes' reputation as a mathematician, the greatest of Antiquity and one of the greatest of all times, was eclipsed by his popular fame as an inventor. Various machines were ascribed to him, and he was said to have destroyed by means of burning mirrors the Roman ships which were besieging Syracuse. He was not able to prevent the fall of Syracuse, however, and was himself killed by a Roman soldier during the sack of the city in 212 B.C. In 75 B.C., when Cicero (I-1 B.C.) was quaestor in Sicily, he discovered Archimedes' tomb and restored it; the tomb is lost again; according to Cicero, it bore a geometrical drawing illustrating one of his discoveries.[18] During the Middle Ages, he was remembered as an engineer and wizard and in later times when one wanted to celebrate a mechanical inventor, it was usual to call him a new or a second Archimedes.[19]

Considering the very special and abstract nature of his writings, the astonishing thing is not that a few were lost, but rather that so many are extant. The Greek MSS of most of them escaped the vicissitudes of war and peace and were preserved in Byzantine libraries either long enough to be copied or to be translated into other languages, chiefly Arabic. Some Greek MSS must have reached Baghdād early in the ninth century or before, because in the second half of that century no less than four scholars (al-Māhānī, Thābit ibn Qurra, Yūsuf al-Khūrī, Isḥāq ibn Ḥunain) were engaged in the writing of Arabic translations and commentaries. During the rule of Leon VI (the Wise), emperor from 886 to 911 and restorer of the University of Constantinople, a new Greek MS was prepared which was almost the only source of Archimedean knowledge up to recent times.

Another source was the Arabic tradition. The treatise on measurement of the circle was translated from the Arabic into Latin by Gerard of Cremona (XII-2).[20]

To return to the Greek MS written for Leon VI. After various transfers, it reached the papal library and remained there from 1269 to 1311. The Flemish Dominican, Willem of Moerbeke, studied it and translated the treatise on floating bodies at the papal court in Viterbo in 1269. From 1311 on, the MS passed into private hands and was finally lost about the middle of the sixteenth century, but in the meanwhile, it had been well used. About the middle of the fifteenth century, it was translated into Latin, at the instance of Nicholas V (pope, 1447-55), by Jacopo of Cremona;[21] his translation was not printed until a century later, but there is evidence that it was read by Nicholas of Cusa.

There are no incunabula and the first text to appear in print was in the *Tetragonismus, id est circuli quadratura, per Campanum, Archimedem Syracusanum atque Boetium*[22] (32 ff.; Venice: G. B. Sessa, 1503), edited by Luca Gaurico.[23] The first important publication appeared only forty years later;[24] that was the Latin edition by Niccolò Tartaglia, *Opera Archimedis . . . per Nicolaum Tartaleam* (Venice: V. Rubinus, 1543).

The Greek *princeps* was published the following year by Thomas Gechauff, called Venatorius (3 parts in 1 vol., folio; Basel: J. Hervagius, 1544). This included the Latin translation by Jacopo da Cremona. A new Latin edition, *Archimedis Opera nonnulla* (2 parts in 1 vol., folio; Venice: P. Manutius, 1558) was prepared by Federigo Commandino of Urbino on the basis of the Basel edition and MSS. The treatise on hydrostatics was edited, reconstructed, and commented upon by the same Commandino (Bologna: A. Benatius, 1565). The two treatises on statics were published in Latin by Guido Ubaldo marchese Del Monte Santa Maria of Pesaro (Pesaro: Geronimo Concordia, 1588; colophon dated 1587). It should be noted in this respect that Simon Stevin's statics and hydrostatics had appeared in Leiden, two years before (1586—*Isis 21*, 250, 292-93).

The statical treatises were translated into French by Pierre Forcadel of Béziers (2 vols.; Paris: C. Périer, 1565). These are the only vernacular editions of the Renaissance; they precede the Latin edition of G. U. Del Monte and also Stevin's original work. As Stevin read French easily, it is highly probable that he was acquainted with Forcadel's translation.

To complete the account of Renaissance editions, we may add the *Liber de numero arenae* edited and commented upon by Paschasius Hamellius[25] (Paris: G. Cavellat, 1557), the discussion of *De quadratura circuli* by Johannes Buteo[26] (Lyon: G. Rovillius, 1559), and another treatise on the same subject by the Belgian mathematician, Adrian Romanus: *In Archimedis circuli dimensionem expositio et analysis. Apologia pro Archimede* (Würzburg, 1597).[27]

Still one more item. The mathematician and optician, Francesco Maurolico of Messina (1494-1575),[28] wrote in 1548 a book to celebrate Archimedes, but it was published only toward the end of the following century and hence could not exert any influence on Renaissance mathematics. The title reads *Admirandi Archimedis Syracusani monumenta ex traditione D. Francisci Maurolici* (Palermo, 1685).

Another Italian, Marino Ghetaldi (1566-1627), published in 1603 the *Promotus Archimedis,* a study of specific gravities, said to be the first book containing a list of them.[29]

For most people, scholars included, Archimedes was remembered as an engineer and wizard. The mathematician in him was studied by Jacopo da Cremona, Gaurico, Tartaglia, Venatorius, Hamel, Jean Borrel, Adrian Romanus; the mechanician by Nicholas of Cusa, Commandino, Forcadel, Del Monte, Ghetaldi, and finally by his first equal after eighteen centuries, the Fleming Simon Stevin (1548-1620).

Many a man was called the Archimedes of his time, but Stevin is the only one who would have deserved that title and, as far as I know, he did not receive it. It would be tempting to speak here of him at greater length, but that would disrupt the frame of the present book.[30] His main achievements date from the end of the sixteenth century, to wit, his explanation of the decimal system in 1585, his hydrostatics (completing Archimedes) in 1586, his algebra in 1594. Nevertheless, he is less a man of the Renaissance than one of the annunciators of modern science; his fame was eclipsed by that of his younger contemporaries Galileo (1564-1642) and Kepler (1571-1630), and it was built up slowly after the Renaissance had bloomed and faded.

As compared with the tradition of other Greek men of science, the Archimedean was relatively poor, but that was due to the depth and abstractedness of his thought. This shows once more that greatness and popularity are very different things, which may be and often are incompatible. The glory of Archimedes was not generally understood by the learned public before the nineteenth century.

Modern edition of Archimedes in Greek and Latin by J. L. Heiberg (3 vols.; Leipzig: Teubner, 1880-81; new edition, 3 vols., 1910-15). English translation by Sir Thomas Heath (Cambridge University Press, 1897); translation of the *Method* of Archimedes by the same (Cambridge University Press, 1912).

4. APOLLONIOS OF PERGA (III-2 B.C.)

THERE WERE TWO OTHER OUTSTANDING MATHEMATICIANS IN Archimedes' time, though a little younger than himself: Eratosthenes of Cyrene (*c.* 274-193) and Apollonios of Perga (*c.* 262-190). We shall not deal with the first of these because his writings are known only in fragments or through indirect references, and the Renaissance scholars were not concerned about him.

The story of Apollonios is on the contrary very instructive and helps us to complete our account of Renaissance geometry. Apollonios did most of his work in Alexandria where he could commune not with Euclid but with the latter's pupils in the third quarter of the third century. He traveled to Ephesos and to Pergamon where he befriended Eudemos. We shall concentrate our attention upon his main work, the treatise on conics (*Cōnica*), which is one of the outstanding books in the whole history of science. It completed Euclid's textbook and the investigations of other Greek mathematicians and gave a general theory of those curves to which he gave the names with which we are familiar (ellipse, parabola, hyperbola). His treatise was divided into eight books (387 propositions) of which the first four only were preserved in Greek and known before 1661. The first edition of his work was dedicated to one Naucratis, who had suggested the writing of it; later, after his travels to Asia, he prepared a new edition and dedicated the first three books to his new friend, Eudemos of Pergamon. Books IV and following were dedicated to Attalos I Soter (King of Pergamon from 241 to 197).

There are no incunabula of *Cōnica*, and the first appearance in print was a poor Latin translation of Books I-IV by the Venetian patrician, Giov. Batt. Memo, printed by Bernardinus Bindonus (Venice, 1537).[31] This was superseded by a much better translation by Federico Commandino (Bologna: A. Benatius, 1566), to which were added the lemmas of Pappos of Alexandria (III-2) and the commentaries of Eutocios of Ascalon (VI-1). Commandino's edition was a good one but unavoidably restricted to the first four books because the others were unavailable. Though seventeenth-century editions are out of bounds, it would be a pity not to say a few words explaining the recovery of the other books. In my first lecture, I had occasion to speak of the academy of Hellenists and translators established in Baghdād by Ḥunain ibn Isḥāq (IX-2). Ḥunain and his collaborators were making the whole body of Greek medicine available to Arabic readers. The same kind of work was done at the same time by another team of translators headed by Thābit ibn Qurra (IX-2). Books I to IV were Arabicized by Hilāl al-Ḥimsī (IX-2) and Books V to VII, by Thābit himself. A century later the whole Arabic text was revised and Book V commented upon by Abūl-Fatḥ Maḥmūd ibn Muḥammad al-Iṣfahānī (X-2). Thus were Books I to VII completely available in Arabic under the title *Kitāb al-makhrūṭāt*. The first Latin edition of Books V to VII was translated from the Arabic by the Maronite father Abraham Ecchellensis (= Ibrāhīm al-Ḥaqilānī, 1605-64) and Giacomo Alfonso Borelli (Florence, 1661). The English astronomer, Edmund Halley, published in Oxford in 1710 a splendid folio containing the Greek princeps of Books I to IV, a Latin translation from the Arabic of Books V to VII, and a reconstruction of Book VIII lost in Arabic as well as in Greek.

Though the sixteenth-century mathematicians knew Apollonios' *Conics* they did not know the very best of it, for Books I to IV were only an elementary introduction to the rest, while Books V to VII discussed special problems. Book V dealing with maxima and minima and with normals was perhaps the most important; it included problems leading to the determination of the evolute[32] of any conic.

Among the other (much shorter) treatises of Apollonios only one

143

seems to have attracted the attention of sixteenth-century mathematicians. That is the one on tangencies (*epaphai*). It contains a problem which became famous: how to draw a circle tangent to three given circles. This was discussed by the French Viète (1540-1603), by the Belgian Adrianus Romanus (1561-1615),[33] and later by Newton. Another text, *De inclinationibus,* was edited by Marino Ghetaldi (1566-1627) of Ragusa but published only in the following century.[34]

It is interesting to note that some knowledge of conics was published before the existence of any printed edition of Apollonios. I am referring to the treatise of Johann Werner (1468-1528) of Nürnberg.[35] Werner's work was carried much farther by Francesco Maurolico (1494-1574) of Messina who tried to reconstruct Book V of Apollonios, then unknown, on the basis of Pappos' commentary.[36] Thanks to Apollonios, Maurolico, and Commandino, the mathematicians of the sixteenth century had a sufficient knowledge of conics for various applications, and the outstanding application was Kepler's to the trajectory of the planet Mars (*Astronomia nova,* 1609). This marks the beginning of a new astronomy and of a new interest in conics. To Kepler's discoveries, published in 1609 and 1619, must be added on the mathematical side Pascal's amazing broadside of Paris, 1640.[37]

Modern edition of Apollonios in Greek and Latin by J. L. Heiberg (2 vols.; Leipzig: Teubner, 1891-93). For Books V to VII one must still refer to Halley's edition (Oxford, 1710); English translation by Sir Thomas Heath (Cambridge University Press, 1896).

5. PTOLEMY OF ALEXANDRIA (II-1)

NOW, LET US JUMP FROM THE THIRD CENTURY B.C. TO THE SECOND century after Christ. The new world was Roman, but science, the living science, was Greek. The second century was dominated by two giants, the greatest men of science of the Roman age, both Greeks, Ptolemy of Alexandria in the first half, Galen of Pergamon in the second. Euclid's *Elements* remained for two thousand years the main textbook of geometry. Ptolemy's fame was even greater because he bequeathed us (in addition to many other writings) two major textbooks: the *Almagest,* which was the astronomical bible until the middle of the sixteenth century; and the *Geography,* which was geography itself for as long a period. Ptolemy was not only an astronomer, a geographer, but also an astrologer, a physicist, a chronologist. In this lecture we must restrict ourselves to astronomy.

The first point to remember is that Ptolemy's astronomy was very largely a reëditing of the works of another Greek, Hipparchos of Nicaia (II-2 B.C.), who had flourished in Rhodes and Alexandria three centuries before him. The main astronomical work of Hipparchos is lost, largely because it was superseded by that of his successor Ptolemy, who was not a better astronomer but a more efficient teacher and textbook maker.

LECTURE III: MATHEMATICS AND ASTRONOMY

Ptolemy's *Mathematical Treatise* (that was the original title of the *Almagest*) was carefully preserved in Greek MSS which were commented upon by Pappos (III-2), by Theon (IV-2), the latter's daughter Hypatia (V-1), and Proclos (V-2). All these men flourished in Alexandria, but the last-named ended his life in Athens, where he was one of the last directors of the Academy. Try to imagine the astronomical (and mathematical) activities continuing in Greek Egypt from the third century B.C. to the end of the fifth century after Christ, a stretch of eight centuries, Greek pagan astronomy flourishing in the midst of a world which was increasingly Roman and Christian.

Christianity finally overcame paganism; the Academy of Athens was irrevocably closed by order of Justinian in 529. Greek astronomy could survive only by moving eastward from Alexandria to Baghdād. It reappeared in Arabic dress in the writings of al-Ḥajjāj ibn Yūsuf (IX-1), of al-Khwārizmī (IX-1), and especially of al Farghānī (IX-1), and then continued its development in other Arabic treatises. Three centuries later, Greek-Arabic astronomy was translated into Latin. Strangely enough, this new transmission occurred at almost the same time in two countries, Sicily and Spain. These two countries, by the way, were the only ones where it could happen with relative ease, because there coexisted in both of them a sufficient number of good scholars, some of whom were Arabic-speaking while others were Latins. By contrast, little work of that kind was done in the Near East, for the Crusaders were not interested in science, and Arabic-Latin communications did not exist except on the political and vulgar level. The conditions were even better in Sicily than in Spain, for in the first country there were not only Arabic and Latin scholars but also Greek scholars, who had a native knowledge of the Greek language. And thus it happened that the first Latin translation of the *Almagest* was made in Sicily (in Catania or in Palermo), not in Spain, and what is more extraordinary, not from the Arabic but directly from the Greek. Aristippus (XII-2), archdeacon of Catania, an officer of the Sicilian court, *c.* 1160, had brought a Greek MS of Ptolemy's astronomy from the library of Manuēl I Comnēnos (emperor of Byzantium from 1143 to 1180). That Greek text was translated into Latin in Sicily, *c.*1160; the translators are not known, but Eugenios of Palermo (XII-2), Eugene the Amīr, was probably one of them. Fifteen years later, in 1175, a new translation was made from the Arabic by Gerard of Cremona (XII-2) or by another member of the school of Toledo. Such was the prestige of the Arabic language in the twelfth century that the translation made previously from the Greek in Palermo was superseded by the one made in Toledo in 1175. Gerard's translation accredited the title *Liber Almagesti* or *Almagest,* a hybrid word[38] which is as symbolic of Arabic hegemony as the words algebra, astrolabe, admiral, and countless others. It is very significant that the two scientific bibles of the Middle Ages and the Renaissance were known under names of Arabic

145

filiation, the *Canon* of Avicenna and the *Almagest* of Ptolemy.

The story of the medieval commentaries on the *Almagest,* in Greek, Arabic, Latin, and Hebrew is too complicated to be told here and would sidetrack us. We might say that that story is continually intermingled with the history of pre-Copernican astronomy.

The Latin *Almagest* was not included among the incunabula, but Ptolemaic astronomy was represented indirectly, first by the *Compilatio astronomica* of Alfraganus (Ferrara: Belfortis, 1493; Klebs 51.1), second by the *Epitoma in Almagestum* of Regiomontanus (Venice: Hamman, 1496; Klebs 841.1). The first of these, the astronomy of al-Farghāni (IX-1), had been translated from Arabic into Latin by John of Seville (XII-1), then again by Gerard of Cremona (XII-2); the text printed in 1493 was John's version, but both versions circulated in MS from the twelfth century to the fifteenth century. Gerard's version was paraphrased in Hebrew by Jacob Anaṭoli (XIII-1) about 1232;[39] it was translated into French and from French into Italian by Zucchero Bencivenni (XIV-1) in 1313. Alfraganus was Dante's main source of astronomical knowledge.

Regiomontanus' *Epitoma,* published posthumously in 1496, was more important because he was very familiar with the *Almagest* (as I shall show presently) and was a practical astronomer, the greatest of the third quarter of the fifteenth century.

The first Latin translation of the *Almagest* to appear in print was the one made from the Arabic by Gerard of Cremona (XII-2); it was edited and published by Peter Liechtenstein (Venice, 1515).[40] The first Latin translation from the Greek was made by George of Trebizond and revised by Luca Gaurico (Venice: Juntae, 1528).[41] The honor of publishing the Greek princeps fell to the Basel community; it was prepared by Simon Grynaeus (Basel: J. Walderus, 1538).

These two editions deserve a few additional remarks. The knowledge of the original text of the *Almagest* is truly a fruit of the new Greek Renaissance, which was caused by the agony and fall of Constantinople. We owe it to the efforts of two Greeks, one Italian, and three Germans.

The so-called George of Trebizond (he was really born in Crete in 1396) flourished in Rome and Naples, and died in Italy in 1486. He translated the *Almagest* with Theon's commentaries from Greek into Latin. His translation was very imperfect and was criticized by Jacopo of Cremona, a pupil of Vittorino da Feltre, who flourished in Mantova and Rome.

Now appears the other Greek, Bessarion[42] (Trebizond, c.1400; Ravenna, 1472), an orthodox archbishop who came to Italy to discuss the reunion of the churches, became an Italian and a Catholic, was elected a cardinal and in 1463 (Latin) titular patriarch of Constantinople. He had a perfect knowledge of Latin as well as Greek, and was the greatest patron of the Greek revival.[43] He obtained a good number of Greek MSS, which he bequeathed to Venice and which were the nucleus of the San Marco Library. Among those MSS was one of the *Almagest*. As he was not competent to deal with an astronomical text, he intrusted that task to a German (or rather Austrian) mathematician, Georg Peurbach (born near Linz in 1423; died Vienna, 1461), whom he met in Italy. I do not know how much of the *Almagest* was actually translated by Peurbach; the task was done or completed by one of his students, Regiomontanus (1436-76). Regiomontanus' career is typical of the international atmosphere of that time. He studied under Peurbach in Vienna, flourished in various Italian cities, at the court of Matthias Corvinus in Buda, then in Nürnberg where a wealthy friend enabled him to establish an observatory and a printing press. That press might be called the first scientific press, for it was created for the exclusive printing of mathematical and astronomical books.[44] He would have remained in Nürnberg and might have lived longer, but he was called to Rome by Sixtus IV in 1475 to reform the calendar,[45] and died there in June 1476, at the age of forty.[46]

The text of the Greek princeps (Basel, 1538) was established by Simon Grynaeus on the basis of the very MS which had been obtained by Cardinal Bessarion and had been used by Peurbach and Regiomontanus. The edition of 1538 is made of two volumes, the first of which contains the *Almagest* edited by Grynaeus, the second the commentaries by Pappos and Theon edited by Joachim Camerarius. According to the latest editor, Canon Rome of Louvain, those editions were done very carelessly.[47]

My account of the Ptolemaic tradition may seem to be complicated and yet it was restricted to the *Almagest,* his greatest work but the least popular. The *Cosmographia* was more popular: witness the existence of seven incunabula in Latin, plus one German abstract.[48] The most popular of his works, unfortunately, were those dealing with astrology, the *Tetrabiblos* or *Quadripartitum* and the *Carpos* or *Fructus* or *Centiloquium*. These two books, the first of which is probably genuine and the second certainly apocryphal, were transmitted together in the MSS and prints, in the original and translations. The Latin translation by Plato of Tivoli (XII-1)[49] was printed by Ratdolt (Venice, 1484) and reprinted by Locatellus (Venice, 1493); both editions include various other astrological writings (Klebs 814.1-2). The Greek princeps was published with the Latin translation by Joachim Camerarius (Nürnberg: J. Petreius, 1535). A second Greek-Latin edition was edited by no less a person than Philipp Melanchthon (Basel: Oporinus, 1553). Catholic writers might be tempted to say, "Look here, Melanchthon, the scientific collaborator of Luther, helping to diffuse the superstitions of Antiquity," but it is better to be forbearing and humbly to remember that to this day the astrological works of Ptolemy are the only ones available in English translations.[50]

Modern edition of the *Almagest* by J. L. Heiberg (2 vols.; Leipzig: Teubner, 1898-1903). *Opera astronomica minora* by the same (*ibidem*, 1907). Greek and French edition of the *Almagest* by the Abbé Nicolas Halma with notes by J. B. J. Delambre (2 vols.; Paris, 1813-16) ; facsimile reprint (Paris: Hermann, 1927).

6. THE MIDDLE BOOKS

AS STATED ABOVE, THE ORIGINAL TITLE OF THE ALMAGEST WAS *Megalē syntaxis* (the second word means *the putting together in order,* as in a treatise or collection; the title might thus be translated *The great treatise* or *The great collection*). As opposed to the great collection, there was soon formed a smaller one, *Micros astronomumenos* (*topos*), or little astronomy, which included tracts by Euclid, Apollonios, Archimedes, and Ptolemy, and also treatises by other mathematicians: Autolycos of Pitane (IV-2 B.C.), Aristarchos of Samos (III-1 B.C.), Hypsicles (II-1 B.C.), Theodosios of Bithynia (I-1 B.C.), and Menelaos of Alexandria (I-2). These many writings remained unknown in Western Europe until very late, but were eagerly translated by Arabic mathematicians. As often happens when a number of treatises have clustered together, they generally remain so in the MSS and are translated together by the same translators or the same group of translators. Thus, the "little astronomy" began a new collective life in Arabic MSS, but other writings of Arabic origin were gradually added to the original ones.

The Arabic name of the collection was *Kitāb al-mutawassiṭāt* which I translated in the title of this chapter "the middle books." They probably meant the books which had appeared between the two great monuments, the *Elements* and the *Almagest,* a description which applies to all of them except to those of Autolycos, which may have been anterior to Euclid's. To the Greek texts translated into Arabic were added new ones written directly in Arabic by the Banū Mūsā (IX-1), by Thābit ibn Qurra (IX-2), and by Nāṣir al-dīn al-Ṭūsī (XIII-2). There is a MS of the whole collection as edited by Nāṣir al-dīn in Aya Sophia (no. 2760), but his work was done too late to influence the Latin tradition or even the Arabic one.[51] Most of these books have come to us in smaller clusters and without the Arabic accretions, Hypsicles with Euclid, Theodosios and Menelaos with Autolycos.

Aristarchos of Samos and Hypsicles were the only ones to attract the attention of the early typographers. A Latin translation of Aristarchos' treatise on the sizes and distances of Sun and Moon was included in the very heterogeneous *Collectio* edited by Giorgio Valla, a learned physician of Piacenza (1447-1500), whose work was based upon Greek MSS. The title (which is a table of contents) begins *Georgio Valla Placentino interprete Hoc in volumine hec continentur Nicephori logica* . . . . The book was published by Simon Bevilaqua (Venice, 1498).[52] The first independent Latin edition of Aristarchos was given by Federico Commandino (Pesaro: Camillus Franciscinus, 1572), who added to it

Pappos' commentary. Commandino's Latin version was reprinted with the Greek text by John Wallis (Oxford, 1688). This was the Greek princeps.

Modern edition in Greek and English of Aristarchos' *Treatise on the sizes and distances of the Sun and Moon* by Sir Thomas Heath, with notes (Oxford: Clarendon Press, 1913).

As to Hypsicles (II-1 B.C.), the text of his so-called fourteenth book of Euclid was translated into Latin by Valla and included in his collection (1498). Euclid XV was written in the sixteenth century by a pupil of Isidoros of Miletos, the architect of Hagia Sophia. Many sixteenth-century editions of Euclid, Greek or Latin, contain the fifteen books and hence Hypicles' text was often reprinted.

Modern Greek edition in Heiberg's Euclid (vol. 5) and English translation in Heath's Euclid (vol. 3).

The three other authors—Autolycos, Theodosios, and Menelaos— dealt with spherical geometry or spherics (the kind of geometry which astronomers needed before the existence of trigonometry); therefore, it is natural enough that their writings clustered together. That was especially the case for the first two, Autolycos and Theodosios; the tradition of Menelaos involved more vicissitudes, as we shall show presently.

The three authors were united in the Latin translation by Maurolico (1558), but before speaking of it, let me mention earlier editions of Autolycos and Theodosios.

The two treatises of Autolycos were translated from the Greek by Giorgio Valla and included in Book XVI of his encyclopedia *De expetendis et fugiendis rebus,* published posthumously through the care and at the expense of his adopted son, Gian Pietro Valla Cademosto (Venice: Aldus Romanus, 1501).[53] As to Theodosios, a Latin translation of Books I-II of his *Spherics* was published with the *Sphere* of Joannes de Sacro Bosco (XIII-1) and other writings on the same subject by H. de Nuciarellis (Venice: heirs of Octavianus Scotus, 1518), and a separate edition of his *Spherics* was prepared by Joannes Vögelin (Vienna: Joannes Singrenius, 1529). These editions were completely superseded by the one of Francesco Maurolico including Autolycos, Theodosios, and (for the first time in print) Menelaos. This was a folio volume printed in Maurolico's native city (Messina: Petrus Spira, 1558). The translations were made from the Greek by Maurolico, who had a fluent knowledge of the language. As Autolycos tucked in the middle of a bulky encyclopedia would be easily overlooked, we may say that it was Maurolico's famous book of 1558 which revealed for the first time the whole of Greek spherics to the mathematicians of Western Europe.

In 1572, Conrad Rauchfuss (1532-1600), better known under the name Dasypodius, published the *Sphaericae doctrinae propositiones graecae et latinae nunc primum in lucem editae* (Strasbourg: C. Mylius,

1572); the book was dedicated to Ramus and appeared in the year of the latter's cruel death. It is a very incomplete edition in Greek and Latin of Autolycos and Theodosios, together with the *Phaenomena* of Euclid and astronomical writings of Barlaam (XIV-1). It is too incomplete to be considered the Greek princeps of the authors dealt with.

In the same year Pierre Forcadel of Béziers published a French translation of Autolycos and Theodosios (Paris: Marnef et G. Cavellat, 1572). This is also a summary, not a complete translation; yet, it is independent of Dasypodius. Christopher Clavius, whose acquaintance we have already made, published the Latin text of Theodosios' *Spherics*, together with his own trigonometry (Rome: D. Basa, 1586). A complete Latin translation of both Autolycos and Theodosios was issued by Giuseppe d'Auria of Naples (Rome: heirs of Antonius Bladius, 1588). The Greek princeps of Theodosios' *Spherics* was edited by Jean Pena with Latin translation (Paris: Andreas Wechel, 1558).

The Greek princeps of Autolycos edited by Friedrich Hultsch, with Latin version, appeared only three centuries later (Leipzig, 1885). Greek text of Autolycos edited by Joseph Mogenet (Louvain, 1950—*Isis 42*, 147).

Greek-Latin edition of Theodosios' *Spherics* by J. L. Heiberg (Berlin, 1927 —*Isis 11*, 409). French translation by Paul Ver Eecke (Bruges, 1927); Ver Eecke's translation, which appeared just before Heiberg's edition, is based upon the earlier Greek edition by Ernest Nizze (Berlin, 1852).

Extracts from Autolycos and Theodosios translated into German by Arthur Czwalina (*Ostwalds Klassiker*, Nr. 232; Leipzig, 1931).

As to Menelaos, there is no Greek princeps, because the Greek original has long been lost.

The pre-Renaissance tradition of Menelaos is so curious that we cannot resist the temptation of describing it briefly. Like the others, he was translated into Arabic, and according to the latest editor (Max Krause), there were five Arabic translations: (1) by al-Ḥajjāj ibn Yūsuf (VIII-1), (2) by al-Māhānī (IX-2), (3) by Isḥāq ibn Ḥunain (IX-2), (4) by an anonymous translator who prepared a new text, (5) by Abū Naṣr Manṣūr ibn 'Alī (X-2).[54]

The anonymous translation (no. 4) was the source of the Latin translation by Gerard of Cremona (XII-2) and of the Hebrew translation by Jacob ben Maḥir ibn Tibbon (XIII-2). The first appearance in printed form was the Latin version in Maurolico's book of 1558. The great astronomer, Edmund Halley (1656-1742), Newton's friend and patron, prepared a new translation derived from the Arabic and Hebrew MSS and had it printed as early as 1706-10. The 112 pages printed for him remained unpublished, however, and were published only in 1758, sixteen years after Halley's death, together with the preface provided by the Orientalist, George Costard (1710-82), one of the early historians of astronomy.[55]

The improved Arabic version of Abū Naṣr was edited recently with a German translation by Max Krause.[56] Menelaos was known to Renaissance mathematicians only through Maurolico's imperfect Latin version.

7. ARITHMETIC[57]

IT HAS BEEN SHOWN IN THE PRECEDING CHAPTERS THAT BEFORE THE end of the sixteenth century a good part, but not by any means the whole, of extant Greek mathematics was available to Western scholars in Greek and Latin. It will be interesting to complete our survey by the consideration of four branches of mathematics: arithmetic, algebra, trigonometry, and astronomy. Geometry is left out, because it was covered in the previous chapters, chiefly the one on Euclid.

Arithmetic was a medieval novelty, very different from the arithmetic of the Greeks, which was the beginning of the theory of numbers, and from the crazy numerology of the Neoplatonists and their followers. Of course, plain arithmetic had always been used for the computations of ordinary life and of business, but the ancient mathematicians had taken it for granted and had not found it necessary to explain it. We may assume that all the computations, some of which (in the great business houses and banks) might be very complex, were made with the help of some kind of abacus. Our numerals and the use of zero were invented by the Hindus and transmitted to us by the Arabs (hence the name Arabic numerals which we often give them).[58] Together with the new numerals came the new arithmetic explained to the Western people by Leonardo of Pisa (XIII-1) and others. The transmission ought to have been speeded up by the enormous mercantile and banking development of the thirteenth century and later, but it was incredibly slow. The slowness was due to inertia and to reliance upon manual methods.

Professor Robert Sabatino Lopez has shown that the Renaissance[59] was on the whole a period of economic regression, yet the shopkeepers established in a great many cities had abundant arithmetical needs. Think only of the printing presses and the bookshops, which were particularly numerous in university towns. Those shops sold books (printed and MS), woodcuts, engravings, stationery.[60] For example, in Salamanca at the beginning of the sixteenth century there were already fifty-two printing presses and eighty-four bookshops.[61] The situation was very much the same in other university towns, and the number of merchants of every kind must have been considerable. The business of most of them was small, yet no business is so small that it does not require computations. Those petty merchants were not interested in the theory of numbers, but they needed practical guidance for their accounts. The earliest practical arithmetic was printed in Italy relatively early; that was the anonymous *Arte dell' abbaco* (Treviso, an., 1478). The second Italian arithmetic, far more elaborate, by Pietro Borghi, was called *Arithmetica* (Venice, 1484).[62]

The second printed arithmetic, anterior to Borghi's, was composed by Francesch Sanct Climent in Catalan: *Suma de la art de arismetica* (Barcelona: Posa, 1482).[63] Another arithmetic was written by a Hispanic mathematician, Pedro Sánchez Ciruelo, but it can hardly count as a Spanish arithmetic, for it was written in Latin, *Tractatus arithmetice practice qui dicitur Algorismus,* and printed by Marchant in Paris, 1495.[64]

The German Rechenmeister, Balthasar Licht, composed an *Algorithmus linealis* (Leipzig: Lotter, s.a. 1500), which is a short treatise on the line abacus.[65]

Note the word *algorismus* in the titles of Ciruelo's book and Licht's. It is an ambiguous word, sometimes used for an old-type arithmetic, sometimes for a new-type. For example, in the introduction to his *Cyrurgia* Henri de Mondeville (XIV-1) explained the "doctrine of algorism," meaning the new arithmetic. It may refer to practical arithmetic and yet be opposed to abacus arithmetic. It is, I believe, correct to say that every algorismus used Hindu-Arabic numerals rather than Roman; on the contrary, the many books called *compotus,* dealing with the church calendar, used Roman numerals.

There are a number of anonymous incunabula bearing such titles as *Algorismus, Ars numerandi, Regula falsi.* It would be worth while to examine them and make a comparative study of them; this would not be easy, because these books are rare and scattered in a great many libraries.[66]

During the sixteenth century, arithmetics were printed in many countries, covering the whole field from the most theoretical (Boetian) to the practical, commercial, military handbooks. The theoretical books, written for university students or for clerics, were generally in Latin, the more practical ones in vernaculars, but the classifications by subjects and by languages (Latin *vs.* vernaculars) do not always tally. It would take too much space to enumerate them all, even in the briefest manner, but we shall give a few examples illustrating the kind of efforts made in the leading countries: Italy, England, France, Germany, Spain, Mexico, Portugal, and the Netherlands.

Italy.—As Venice was the most prosperous city of Italy and had become the greatest printing center of Europe, we are not surprised that the new arithmetics issued mostly from Venetian shops. Girolamo and Gian Antonio Tagliente (not brothers, but members of the same family) wrote together a commercial arithmetic, the *Opera che insegna a fare ogni ragione de mercantia* (Venice: anon., 1515), of which thirty editions appeared in the sixteenth century. The *Libro de abaco* of

Francesco Feliciano da Lazisio (Verona) was also very popular; first printed by Nicolo Zopino (Venice, 1518), it was reprinted at least thirteen times within the century. Another type of book was the *Tariffa perpetua* by the Venetian merchant Giovanni (or Zuane) Mariani (Venice, 1535); a dozen editions appeared within the century. It is a collection of mercantile tables for Venetian usage; it is perhaps the first printed collection of its kind.

The most elaborate Italian arithmetic and perhaps the most elaborate published anywhere during the Renaissance was composed by Niccolò Tartaglia and appeared under the title *La prima parte del general trattato di numeri e misure* (Venice: Curtius Troianus, 1556). The whole work consists of six volumes generally bound in three (1556-60); vol. 1 contains the arithmetic. Says D. E. Smith,[67] "There is no other treatise that gives as much information concerning the arithmetic of the sixteenth century, either as to theory or application. The life of the people, the customs of the merchants, the struggles to improve arithmetic, are all set forth in an extended but interesting fashion." Tartaglia's arithmetic was reprinted in Venice, 1560, 1592-93. There was also an abridgment, *Scelta di abbaco ridotto dal famosissimo Nicolò Tartaglia* (Venice, 1596). A French translation by Guillaume Gosselin of Caen was published by Gilles Beys (Paris, 1578).

The most important books published in Italy in the Latin language were the *Practica arithmetice et mensurandi singularis* by Girolamo Cardano (Pavia, 1501; Rome, 1576), printed by Jo. Antonius Castellioneus (Milan, 1539), and the *Epitome arithmeticae practicae* by Father Clavius, S. J. (Rome: Dominicus Basa, 1583).

England.—The first English arithmetic was the *De arte supputandi* of Cuthbert Tunstall, dedicated to Thomas More (London: Richard Pynson, 1522), a good book but very prolix. The first English book in English we owe to Robert Recorde (1510-58):[68] *The grounde of artes, teachyng the worke and practise of arithmetike* (London: R. Wolf, 1542), reprinted at least seventeen times before 1601. Leonard and Thomas Digges (father and son) wrote the *Arithmeticall militare treatise called Stratioticos* (London: Henrie Bynneman, 1579). Was an earlier edition printed in 1572? The book was reprinted in 1585 and 1590. It was an arithmetical (and geometrical) introduction for military people.

France.—The more old-fashioned arithmetics written in Latin are represented by the first section of the *Protomathesis* of Oronce Finé (1494-1555). Finé was professor of mathematics at the Collège Royal of Paris from 1532 on, and he enjoyed a great reputation, perhaps greater than he deserved. His *Protomathesis* was first printed by Gerard Morrhius and Joannes Petrus (Paris, 1530-32); it was reprinted five times in Paris and once in Venice before 1601. The other outstanding Latin writer was Pierre de la Ramée, better known as Ramus. Ramus was Finé's colleague at the Collège Royal, but he was professor of eloquence and philosophy. His *Arithmeticae libri tres,* dedicated to Charles, Cardinal of Lorraine, was first printed by Andreas Wechelus (Paris, 1555) and before 1601 it had been reprinted at least twice in Paris, and once in Basel. In 1569, Ramus published another treatise, *Arithmeticae libri duo* (Basel: Eusebius Episcopius, 1569), which is a little more practical than the first, though it would have been hardly suitable for a business office. It was reprinted (before 1601) in four cities at least eight times, and was translated into English by William Kempe under the title, *The art of arithmeticke in whole numbers and fractions* (London, 1592).

The French arithmetics are more numerous and more interesting. The first noteworthy one was *L'art d'arythmétique contenant toute dimention . . . tant pour l'art militaire que pour autres calculations,* by Claude de Boissière (Paris: Annet Brière, 1554). Note the mention of the military art in the title, many years before the Digges' English treatise. Far more important are the books written by Pierre Forcadel (d. 1574), Finé's successor[69] as professor of mathematics at the Collège Royal: *L'Arithmétique* (Paris: Guillaume Cavellat, 1556-57), *L'Arithmétique par les gects* (Paris: G. Cavellat, 1558),[70] *Arithmétique entière et abrégée* (Paris: Charles Périer, 1565), *Arithmétique démontrée* (Paris[?], 1570). Jan Trenchant wrote *L'arithmétique départie en troys livres. Ensemble un petit discours des changes avec L'art de calculer aux Getons,* published by himself (Lyon, 1558).[71] This was a very good treatise, rich in contents, very often reprinted before 1601, at least eleven times in Lyon, once in Paris, three or four times in Rouen. To these French books may be added the *Invention nouvelle et admirable pour faire toute sorte de compte . . .* by "Monte Regal Piedmontois, professeur de mathématique en l'Université de Paris" (Lyon: la Sphère, 1585). This is a collection of tables, mostly for multiplication. The author, Monte Reale Piemontese, is otherwise unknown to me.

Germany.—A number of arithmetics appeared in Germany, some of them rudimentary for the use of children or very simple people. This was partly a result of the Reformation. Luther had declared, "Wenn ich Kinder hätte und vermöchte sie müssten mir nicht allein die Sprachen und Historien hören, sondern auch singen und die Musika mit der ganzen Mathematika lernen."[72] Every child must learn how to read, write, and count. Let us begin with the books in German which were written for the simpler people, though not exclusively for them.

Jacob Köbel (1470-1533) of Heidelberg published a *Rechenbiechlin* (Augsburg: Erhart Öglin, 1514), and *Mit der kryden od' Schriebfedern durch die zeiferzal zu rechen* (Oppenheim, 1520). The first book was often reprinted and the second published with the first in and after 1520. Note the title of the second book. The purpose is to teach how to solve arithmetical problems in writing, that is, without counters. Adam Riese (*c.* 1489-1559) wrote a whole series of arithmetical books which enjoyed so much popularity that his name became proverbial.[73] The first edition of each kind appeared in 1518; Erfurt, 1522; Leipzig, 1533; Leipzig: Jacobus Berwalt, 1550. The bibliography of these books, frequently reprinted, is the more difficult because some items are exceedingly rare, and there are many variations in the German titles. No German arithmetic of the sixteenth century exceeded Riese's in popularity.

The two other German arithmeticians, Rudolff and Stifel, were more sophisticated. Christoff Rudolff published an algebra *Die Coss* (1525), *Die künstliche Rechnung* (1526), and the *Exempel Büchlin,* a collection of problems (Augsburg: Heynrich Stainer, 1530). Michael Stifel (Esslingen, 1487; Jena, 1567) wrote three arithmetics and an algebra in German, and one arithmetic in Latin. The title of his first book is significant: *Ein Rechenbüchlein vom End Christ. Apocalysis in Apocalisim* (Wittenberg, 1532). He was very learned, but his mind was disordered by number mysticism and religious fanaticism.

A few examples of German arithmetics in Latin will now follow. We might begin with Stifel himself whose *Arithmetica integra* was prefaced by Philipp Melanchthon, published by Johann Petreius (Nürnberg, 1544), and reprinted four times before 1601. It is a very scholarly book comparable to those published in Italy by Cardano and Tartaglia. We must mention the other examples more briefly:

Johann Scheubel: *De numeris et diversis rationibus seu regulis computationum* (Leipzig: Michaël Blum, 1545) and *Compendium arithmeticae artis* (Basel: Joannes Oporinus, 1549).

Jacobus Micyllus (Strassburg, 1503-58), *Arithmeticae logisticae libri duo* (Basel: Ioannes Oporinus, 1555). Very learned; never reprinted.

Christopher Clavius (Bamberg, 1537; Rome, 1612), *Epitome arithmeticae practicae* (Rome: Dominicus Basa, 1583). Often reprinted; translated into Italian in 1586. This might be counted as an Italian book; it was really as international as the Jesuit order. The book was a good compromise between theory and practice.

Spain.—We shall mention first two Latin treatises, then two Spanish ones:

Joannes Martinus Blasius: *Liber arithmetice practice astrologis phisicis calculatoribus admodum utilis* (Paris: Jehan Lambert, 1513), written for the use of astrologers, physicians, and computers. Reprinted thrice, the third edition was corrected with the utmost care by Oronce Finé (Paris: Henricus Stephanus, 1519).

Hieronymus Munyos: *Institutiones arithmeticae ad percipiendam astrologiam et mathematicas facultates necessariae* (Valencia: Joannes Mey, 1566). Very theoretical; not reprinted.

The first Spanish item was written by Juan de Ortega (Dominican from Aragon; still alive in 1567). It is a commercial arithmetic, practical and popular, often reprinted. The first edition appeared under the title *Tratado subtilissimo de Arismética y de Geometria* (Seville: Jacob Cronberger, 1512). Other editions (e.g., Rome: Stephanus Guillerus de Lorena, 1515) are entitled *Suma de arithmetica geometria pratica utilissima.* The book was published in Seville, Barcelona, Granada, Messina, Rome, Lyon, Paris. The book was translated from Spanish into French by Claude Platin, who calls the author "Jehan de Lortie": *Oeuvre très subtille et profitable de l'art de science aristméticque et géométrie* (Lyon: Estienne Baland, 1515). This was the first commercial arithmetic in French and in France.

A more ambitious treatise, *Arithmetica practica y speculativa,* was composed by Juan Perez de Moya (Salamanca: Mathias Gast, 1562). As the title indicates, this is a combination of practical with theoretical arithmetic, such as was needed by the students. It was dedicated to the unfortunate Don Carlos de Austria (1545-68), who was then a student in Salamanca. D. E. Smith calls it "the most noteworthy book on mathematics published in Spain in the sixteenth century." It was reprinted only twice before 1601, but at least thirteen times in the following century.

Mexico.—The earliest mathematical book published in the New World was the *Sumario compendioso* of Brother Juan Diez, printed in Mexico City in 1556 (printing began there in 1536). Fraile Juan was a Galician, one of Cortès' companions. His book, being published chiefly to assist the buyers of gold and silver in their computations, included many tables *ad hoc;* it is thus comparable to the *Tariffa de pexi e mesure* of Ant. Bart. di Paxi (Venice: Albertin da Lisona, 1503) and to the *Tariffa perpetua* of Giovanni Mariani (Venice: heirs of Francesco Rampazetto, 1535).

A handsome facsimile copy of the arithmetical and algebraical parts of the Mexican book was published by D. E. Smith (Boston: Ginn, 1921 —*Isis 4,* 409). This was not an American book but a European one written in Spanish for Spaniards, but printed in Mexico for their convenience.

Portugal.—-The first arithmetic in Portuguese was written by Gaspar Nicolas (Lisbon: German Galharde, 1519). It was reprinted in Lisbon, 1530, 1541, 1559, 1594, and by the heirs of Arnold Byrkman in Antwerp, 1573. It is a practical book for the use of merchants.[74]

The leading Portuguese mathematician and astronomer, Pedro Nuñez (Petrus Nonius),[75] wrote in Spanish a *Libro de algebra en arithmética y geométrica* (Antwerp, 1567).[76] Nonius' international reputation is proved by the publication of his complete works in Latin (Basel: ex officina Henricpetrina, 1566). His writings were in Latin, except one in Portuguese (1537) and the Spanish arithmetic.

The Netherlands.—One of the most popular arithmetics of the Renaissance was composed by the Frisian or Dutchman Gemma Frisius

(1508; Louvain, 1555), happily not in Frisian but in Latin: *Arithmeticae practicae methodus facilis* (Antwerp: G. Bontius, 1540). It was printed some sixty times during the Renaissance. Being in Latin it was meant for students and clerks, yet did not overlook practical problems; its popularity was due to its clearness, brevity, and comprehensiveness.

The greatest arithmetician of the age and indeed one of the greatest of all ages was the Fleming Simon Stevin (Bruges, 1548; The Hague, 1620). Stevin's first work was a Dutch book containing "tables of interest together with their construction" (Antwerp: Christopher Plantin, 1582).[77] These were the first printed tables of their kind, though according to Stevin's own preface the inventor of them was Jean Trenchant, who gave a specimen of them in his *Arithmétique* (Lyon: author, 1558). Stevin was mistaken in ascribing the invention to Trenchant; it had been made a long time before (*c.* 1340) by the Florentine Francesco Balducci Pegolotti (XIV-1), and it is probable that Pegolotti was not the first, because bankers needed such tables very badly. At any rate, Stevin's were the first printed tables.

This is to Stevin's credit, but of very little importance as compared with his other achievements. His golden year was 1585; in that year, he published a large treatise, *L'arithmétique et la pratique d'arithmétique* (2 vols.; Leiden: C. Plantin, 1585). A very full arithmetic, practical and theoretical. It includes a translation of his tables of 1582, and a translation of Diophantos,[78] the former illustrating the practical purpose and the second Stevin's deep concern with theory.

His main achievement, however, is not that voluminous treatise but a very small one published in the same year by Christopher Plantin in Leiden (1585) in two editions, Dutch and French: *De Thiende* and *La disme*. Both are available in facsimile editions, the Dutch one edited by Father H. Bosmans (Antwerp, 1924—*Isis 7*, 543) and the French edited by myself in *Isis*.[79] The French text was really a part of the *Pratique d'arithmétique* (vol. 2 of the *Arithmétique*) but with an independent title page (many of Stevin's publications and other contemporary publications were like that, parts with separate title pages which might be sold apart or grouped in various ways).

This booklet (28 pp.) is the greatest arithmetical monument of Renaissance. It explains for the first time the meaning and use of decimal fractions and of decimal measurements. The innovation was as pregnant as it was simple; it was too simple for the more sophisticated mathematicians of its age. The decimal fractions did not immediately replace other fractions; the invention of common logarithms and the publication of tables *ad hoc* helped to diffuse the decimal idea, but the diffusion was very slow. As to the metric system, it was not accepted anywhere until two centuries later when it was established in France by the Convention (7 April 1795). Stevin's genius can be measured by the fact that there are still today a large number of civilized people who have not yet understood decimal ideas and their implications.

8. ALGEBRA

A S THIS BOOK IS NOT MEANT FOR A MATHEMATICAL AUDIENCE, IT IS not possible to deal as lengthily with algebra and trigonometry as we did with arithmetic. The history of algebra is exceedingly interesting and tantalizing, because it began very early (say, in the second millennium before Christ), then disappeared, reappeared in a different form in Hellenistic writings, disappeared again, and reached a new climax in the Islamic world; after many more vicissitudes, it began a new life in the sixteenth century and by the end of it had already attained a high degree of perfection. Algebra makes one think of those rivers in limestone districts which sink in a swallow hole, vanish underground and are forgotten, then come out again into the open, and repeat the same performance. Rivers which play hide and seek, as it were. Babylonian algebra disappeared into a sinkhole; more than a thousand years later one may find a few Babylonian ideas in Greek treatises; then algebra seemed almost forgotten until it was rejuvenated in Arabic dress. The first Arabic algebraist was al-Khwārizmī (IX-1); the greatest, the Iranian poet 'Omar Khayyām (XI-1), who classified cubic equations[80] and solved many of them. Some algebraical ideas reappeared in a Hebrew treatise on practical geometry written in 1116 by Abraham bar Ḥiyya[81] (XII-1). Latin translations of al-Khwārizmī by Plato of Tivoli (XII-1) and of Abraham bar Ḥiyya by Robert of Chester (XII-1) were completed in the same year, 1145, which might be called the birth year of European algebra. Other Arabic seeds were fructified a century later by the genius of Leonardo Fibonacci (XIII-1). These algebraic ideas were generally mixed with geometrical and arithmetical ones and they required three more centuries of incubation before they could acquire an independent existence. The authors of learned arithmetics (mentioned in the previous section) dealt sometimes with algebra or devoted special treatises to it. It is noteworthy that these algebraical or semialgebraical books were published not only in Latin but in various vernaculars, German, Italian, Spanish, English.

The Germans invented a special name for algebra, *die Coss* (*Coss* is the Italian *cosa* or the Latin *causa* used to designate the first power of the unknown quantity). The rules of *Coss* were explained by Henricus Grammateus (Heinrich Schreiber) in his *Rechenbüchlin* (Vienna, 1518); Christoff Rudolff devoted a special treatise to *Coss* (1525) and Rudolff's *Coss* was reëdited with amplifications by Michael Stifel (Königsberg i. P.: Alex. Behm, 1553). Stifel's *Deutsche Arithmetica* was divided into three parts: *Hausrechnung* (domestic accounts), *Deutsche Coss* (algebra, though most of it is really arithmetic), *Kirchrechnung* (computus). It was printed by Johan Petreius (Nürnberg, 1545). Another German,

Johann Scheubel (1494-1570), explained algebra in Latin; note the title of his book, *Algebrae compendiosa facilisque descriptio qua depromuntur magna arithmetices miracula* (Paris: Cavellat, 1552). Still another German, Marco Aurel, established in Valencia, included some algebra in his Spanish treatise, *Libro primero de arithmetica algebratica* (Valencia: Joan de Mey, 1552).

The first English algebra was *The Whetstone of witte whiche is the seconde parte of Arithmetike* by Robert Recorde (London: Jhon Kyngston, 1557).

The *Summa de arithmetica* of Francesco Ghaligai (1521) contained an account of algebra, and the other Italian arithmeticians did the same, more or less.

The true renaissance of algebra was begun by an astounding group of Italians, whom I cannot do more than evoke: Scipione del Ferro (*c.* 1465-1526) of Bologna, Niccolò Tartaglia (1506 57) of Venice, Girolamo Cardano (1501-76) of Pavia, and the latter's pupil Lodovico Ferrari (1522-60) of Bologna. All these efforts were brought to a climax by three outstanding men representing three nations, Rafaele Bombelli of Bologna, Simon Stevin of Bruges, and François Viète of Fontenay-le-Comte. Bombelli wrote *L'algebra parte maggiore dell' aritmetica* (Bologna: Giov. Rossi, 1572); Viète (1540-1603), *In artem analyticam isagoge* (Tours: Jamettus Mettayer, 1591), *Ad logisticam speciosam notae priores (ibidem,* 1591;), etc.; Stevin (1548-1620), the *Appendice algébraique contenant règle générale de toutes équations* (Leiden: Frans van Ravelingen, 1594).

The elaboration of algebra up to the level of Viète and Stevin is one of the greatest achievements of the Renaissance, and typical of it. Both men were very conscious of the superiority of Greek mathematics and anxious to do their share in its recovery. Stevin translated Diophantos, and Vieta discussed Apollonios. The former's enthusiasm for antiquity was tempered by ignorance;[82] on the other hand, Viète was a full-fledged humanist, a good Hellenist;[83] his mind harbored a strange combination of pedantic learning with mathematical genius; he was always showing off his learning by the invention of new Greek terms which mystified and discouraged his readers. He was a magistrate who cultivated mathematics as an exclusive form of recreation; he owed his prestige in high circles to the fact that he was able to decode cryptic messages sent by the Spanish court to the League; these messages were intercepted by Henri IV's officers and intrusted to him. That is, he was one of the first men to apply mathematical analysis to cryptography.[84] His writings were privately printed and their influence was further diminished by a forbidding terminology. He needed interpreters who appeared only after his death and do not belong any more to the Renaissance, but to a new age. They were I. L. de Vau-Lézard, who published the *Introduction en l'art analytic ou nouvelle algèbre de François Viète*

(Paris, 1630) and James Hume[85] in his *Algèbre de Viète d'une methode nouvelle, claire et facile. Par laquelle toute l'obscurité de l'inventeur est ostée et ses termes pour la plupart inutiles changez ès termes ordinaires des Artists* (Paris, 1636). The title is revealing.

Viète and Stevin were fin-de-siècle authors whose influence was felt only in the seventeenth century. Their fame was finally established when their works were collected and reprinted by competent mathematicians; it is curious that the opera of the Fleming, Stevin, were edited by the Lorrain, Albert Girard (Leyden, 1634), while those of the Frenchman, Viète, were edited by the Dutchman, Frans Van Schooten (Leiden, 1646). This has already brought us beyond the Cartesian revolution in the middle of the seventeenth century. At any rate, their own work was accomplished during the Renaissance and represents the mathematical climax of that age.

9. TRIGONOMETRY

UNTIL THE RENAISSANCE AND EVEN LATER, TRIGONOMETRY WAS CONsidered an introduction to astronomy. All the problems of mathematical astronomy are problems of spherical trigonometry. One might say that that relationship already existed before the birth of trigonometry proper, because the Greek astronomers used the methods of spherical geometry to solve the same problems. Trigonometry was like the new arithmetic, a Eurasian child; the mother was Hindu and the father Greek. The fundamental notion of sine (the first trigonometrical ration) was introduced in the *Sūrya-Siddhānta* (in the fifth century?)[86] and the idea was developed by Arabic mathematicians, too many to be listed here, the Arabic climax being reached by Nāṣir al-dīn al-Ṭūsī (XIII-2). The latter had begun his task by preparing a new edition of the *Spherics* of Menelaos of Alexandria (I-2); he then wrote an original treatise, the *Shakl al-qaṭṭāʿ*, which was probably the first textbook of trigonometry written for its own sake, independently of astronomy. Nāṣir al-dīn came too late, however, to be translated into Latin or Hebrew and the European tradition stemmed from earlier Arabic writings, the same which Nāṣir al-dīn had used. The earlier Arabic trigonometry had been fully exploited by the Jewish astronomers and translators working in Toledo for Alfonso X el Sabio (XIII-2). The results of Arabic efforts were transmitted to the West and the efforts were continued by Levi ben Gerson (XIV-1) writing in Hebrew *c.* 1321 in Provence and by Richard Wallingford writing in Latin in Oxford before 1327. Levi's treatise was Latinized by Peter of Alexandria in 1342. If 1145 was the birth year of European algebra, we might say in the same spirit that European trigonometry was born before 1343. The synchronism of Latin and Jewish endeavors is not as precise in the second case as it was in the first, yet it is very remarkable. The first great treatise on trigonometry to appear in print was the *De triangulis omnimodis* drafted by Regiomontanus in Venice in 1464. In spite of the fact that Regiomontanus was himself a printer, his trigonometry was not printed until a long time after his death. The explanation of that is simple. Regiomontanus had been provided with an observatory and a printing press by a generous patron, Bernhard Walther, and he made good use of them during his five Nürnberg years (1471-75). Then he was called to Rome by Pope Sixtus IV; he expected to return soon to Nürnberg and to continue there his studies and printing; that expectation was natural enough, because he was only thirty-nine years old when he started and he might look forward to at least twenty more years of work, but that was not to be; he died mysteriously in Rome in 1476. His trigonometry was finally edited by Johann Schöner: *De triangulis omnimodis libri quinque* (Nürnberg: Joh. Petrius, 1533). Regiomontanus' tables, *Tabulae directionum et profectionum, Tabella sinus recti,* had been printed within his lifetime by Ratdolt (Augsburg, 1490; Klebs 834), if not before by himself in Nürnberg (1475?). Many other tables of his were published in the sixteenth century with other texts by Peurbach, Schöner, Melanchthon, Luca Gaurico, etc. The bibliography of these tables is very intricate.

Regiomontanus' work was continued by Copernicus in the *De revolutionibus orbium coelestium* (Nürnberg: Joh. Petreius, 1543), but here trigonometry was again reduced to the needs of an astronomical introduction; and by Copernicus' disciple and collaborator, Georg Joachim Rhaeticus (1514-76) in the *Canon doctrinae triangulorum* (Leipzig: W. Gunter, 1551). Another capital book of the same time was composed by Johann Werner (1468-1528) of Nürnberg, the *De triangulis sphaericis,* first edited by Rhaeticus (Cracovia = Kraków: Lazarus Andreae, 1557).[87] Polar (or reciprocal) triangles had been used implicitly by Nāṣir al-dīn, but the first to give a clear explanation of them was Viète (1593). Rhaeticus' tables of 1551 (to every 10′ and to 7 places) were extented by Viète to every minute (Paris: J. Mettayer, 1579) and they were further extended in the *Opus palatinum de triangulis* by Lucas Valentinus Otho (Neustadt in Palatinate: M. Harnisius, 1596).

The Renaissance ends with the German Bartholomaeus Pitiscus (1561-1613), whose treatise was first to bear the word trigonometry in the title: *Trigonometria sive de dimensione triangulorum libri quinque* (Heidelberg, 1595).[88] The same Pitiscus had edited Rhaeticus' tables in his *Thesaurus mathematicus sive canon sinuum ad radium 10^{15} a Georgio Joachimo Rhaetico supputatus et nunc primum in lucem editus* (1593).

The work involved in the compilation of such tables must have been gigantic and it is tragic to think that those tables were useful only for a very short period, because the invention of logarithms necessitated the compilation of new ones. The first table of logarithms of trigonometric functions to the base 10 was compiled by Edmund Gunter (1581-1626): *Canon triangulorum sive tabulae sinuum et tangentium artificialium*

(London: Gul. Jones, 1620). This is already out of our period, however. In spite of a few adumbrations, the Renaissance was pre-logarithmic.

10. ASTRONOMY

AT THE BEGINNING OF THE RENAISSANCE THE ALMAGEST WAS STILL the standard treatise on astronomy. It could be read in Regiomontanus' *Epitoma* (1496), or in Latin translation (1515, 1528), or in the original text (1538). A short time after the publication of the Greek princeps, the new heliocentric astronomy was explained by Nicolaus Copernicus in the *De revolutionibus orbium coelestium* (Nürnberg: Joh. Petreius, 1543).[89] Even as Vesalius continued and corrected Galen, even so Copernicus was reviving Greek traditions, traditions which were much older than the *Almagest* and had been thrown into darkness and oblivion by Ptolemy's genius.

The new astronomy was accepted without demur by Paul III (Alessandro Farnese, pope 1534-49) to whom it was dedicated but was strongly objected to by the Lutheran church, especially by its scientific adviser, Philipp Melanchthon. Copernicus had died almost immediately after the publication of his masterpiece, but he was defended by his Protestant disciples Georg Joachim Rhaeticus (1514-76) and Erasmus Reinhold (1511-53), both of Wittenberg. The latter published the Copernican tables called *Prutenicae tabulae coelestium motuum* (Tübingen: heirs of U. Morhardus, 1551).

These tables were much better than the Alfonsine Tables of 1272, yet their accuracy was mediocre, because the astronomical observations upon which they were based were very insufficient in number and quality. One of the greatest astronomical observers of all times, the Dane Tycho Brahe,[90] devised better instruments and accumulated more precise observations, which did not tally with the Prussian Tables. As a result, being an honest scientist, he felt obliged to reject the Copernican theory and to accept a compromise between the new and the old astronomy.

Copernicus had been right to replace the sun in the center of our little universe, but he had continued to accept the old prejudice that every celestial trajectory is either circular, or a combination of circular motions. That fallacy was destroyed by the German Kepler in 1609; in the meanwhile, Brahe had been right to reject the Copernican system.

The astronomy of the Renaissance was a great confusion of Ptolemaic and Copernican doctrines, aggravated by Brahe's better observations which neither doctrine could account for. Add to that the theological controversies which became increasingly rancorous and finally caused the Protestants and the Catholics to outbid each other in their denunciations for propaganda purposes.

In spite of Copernicus' bold departure, the new astronomy is not his nor does it belong to the Renaissance; it was created by Kepler and

Galileo in the seventeenth century. As far as astronomy is concerned, the Renaissance was an age of disorder and futile compromises.

11. MATHEMATICAL ENCYCLOPEDIAS AND DICTIONARIES

IN THE FIRST CHAPTER, WE EXAMINED A NUMBER OF MEDICAL COLLECtions which were gathered more or less expertly to satisfy medical needs *grosso modo,* and also a few medical dictionaries without which the Renaissance doctors would not have been able to understand their Greek and Latin textbooks. The same needs existed in the mathematical field but were less acute, probably because mathematicians had more freedom than physicians in their choice of problems.

We shall consider only four encyclopedias compiled, respectively, by the Italian Pacioli, the German Reisch, the Swiss Dasypodius, and the French Ramus.

The Franciscan father, Luca Pacioli of Borgo San Sepulcro in Tuscany (*c.* 1445—after 1509), put together a collection which constitutes the largest mathematical incunabulum. It is the *Summa de arithmetica geometria proportioni et proportionalita* (308 leaves, folio; Venice: Paganinis, 1494).[91] It was the earliest great mathematical work to appear in print; the author had not hesitated to include in it earlier books (we would call that *plagiarize*) such as Giorgio Chiarini's *Libro che tratta di mercanzie*[92] and ideas derived from Leonardo Fibonacci (XIII-1) which were not printed *in extenso* until last century. Such as it was, original or stolen property, the *Summa* was very influential not only in Italy but in other countries of Europe. For example, the *De arte supputandi* of Cuthbert Tunstall (London, 1522) was partly derived from it.

An analysis of Smith's *Rara arithmetica* would reveal the existence of many sixteenth-century books built more or less on the same pattern as Pacioli's *Summa.* Arithmetic is generally put in the first place, but they deal as well with algebra and geometry, and are not restricted to theory but treat applications such as accounting, commercial usages, tables, etc. Some examples have been given above in Section 7. There is no need of considering them again; all of these books are very much alike in spite of linguistic and other superficial differences.

Instead of that, let us consider another kind of book, the *Margarita phylosophica* compiled by Gregorius Reisch, who hailed from Württemberg, studied at Freiburg im Breisgau, joined the Carthusian order, and became prior of the Breisgau monastery. He was a man of some importance, being at one time the confessor of Maximilian I (emperor, 1493-1519). He died in Freiburg in 1523.

The first edition of *Margarita* was long thought to be an incunabulum and I am ashamed to say I helped to perpetuate that mistake;[93] it was published only in Freiburg i. B. in 1503. It was reprinted at least fifteen times in the sixteenth century in Latin or in Italian. The edition printed in Paris, 1523, was prepared by Oronce Finé. The Venetian editions of 1594, 1599, 1600 are the Italian version by Giovanni Paolo Gallucci[94] and contain additions by Finé, Jacques Lefèvre, and by the Fleming Josse van Clichtove. This shows that the *Margarita* was taken very seriously. Its scope was much larger than that of Pacioli's *Summa,* for it covered the *trivium, quadrivium,* and much else. It is written in the form of a dialogue between Teacher and Student; much attention is paid to arithmetic and geometry.

The Swiss Conrad Dasypodius (1529-1600), professor of mathematics in Strasbourg, is perhaps best known because of his *Heron mechanicus* (Strassburg: N. Wyriot, 1580) wherein he described the famous clock of the Strasbourg Cathedral built in 1570 after his own specifications. He was primarily a mathematician and wrote an elaborate mathematical encyclopedia published by J. Rihelius (2 vols.; Strassburg, 1567): *Volumen primum mathematicum, prima et simplicissima mathematicarum disciplinarum principia complectens: geometriae, logicae, astronomiae, geographiae . . . Volumen II . . . complectens praecepta mathematica, astronomica, logistica.*

His French colleague Ramus published at the age of fifty-two the *Prooemium mathematicum ad Catharinem Mediceam, reginam, matrem regis* (Paris: A. Wechelus, 1567), divided into three books; it is a general introduction to mathematics, including a brief historical outline, one of the first of its kind. Ramus divided that history into four periods: 1. the Chaldaean period from Adam to Abraham; 2. the Egyptian, from Abraham on; 3. the Greek, from Thales (VI B.C.) to Theon of Alexandria (IV-2); 4. modern mathematics, the account of which Ramus hoped would be given by another scholar. It is rather amusing to us that for Ramus the modern period began in the fifth century. This *Prooemium* was considerably developed and its three books were the first three of the thirty-one books into which his *Scholae Mathematicae* were eventually divided: *P. Rami Scholarum mathematicarum libri unus et triginta* (Basel: E. Episcopius, 1569; reprinted in Frankfurt a.M., 1599, 1627).

Ramus had understood that history is an essential part of the mathematical propylaea. That way of thinking, new and pregnant, was shared by the Italian Bernardino Baldi (1553-1617) of Urbino. Baldi was a poet and learned dilettante; he was for a time abbot of Guastalla, and he was also librarian to the Duke of Urbino.[95] He wrote a *Cronica de' matematici* and *Vite de' matematici,* both of which come down to 1596. Unfortunately, these writings remained unpublished until much later. The first, the *Cronica,* an epitome of the second, was printed for the first time in Urbino, 1707. The composition of the *Vite* occupied him twelve years (1586-97). The MS of considerable size has not yet been completely edited, though various parts were included in Prince Boncompagni's *Bullettino*[96] between 1872 and 1887. Judging from those parts, Baldi's *Vite* are very prolix, yet must be taken into consideration, especially those dealing with Italian mathematicians.

To these two historians may be added the authors of historical monographs, such as those on *Arithmologia ēthicē* (Basel: J. Oporinus, 1551) and on the history of numbers (no place, date; 1557, rev. ed., 1569) both by Joachim Camerarius (1500-74) of Bamberg, and the one written on a similar subject by the numismat Matthaeus Host (Antwerp: Plantin, 1582). More important were the editors of Greek mathematical texts or of their Latin translations. Many of them have been mentioned apropos of the particular Greek or Latin treatises to which their learning was applied. That story constitutes an essential part of the history of mathematical thought during the Renaissance, but it is very long.

The only mathematical dictionary of the sixteenth century I have come across (but there are probably others) is the *Lexicon seu dictionarium mathematicum, in quo definitiones et divisiones continentur scien tiarum mathematicarum,* by Conrad Dasypodius (Strasbourg: N. Wyriot, 1573).

On the whole, the encyclopedic tendencies were rather meager (except for the natural sciences), but they took on immense development in the seventeenth century and later. A fin-de-siècle child of the Renaissance, Johann Heinrich Alsted (1588-1638) gave the first examples both in the mathematical field—*Elementale mathematicum* (Frankfurt a.M., 1611) and *Methodus admirandorum mathematicorum complectens novem libros matheseōs universae* (Herborn in Nassau, 1613)—and in the whole universe of knowledge in his *Encyclopaedia septem tomis distincta* (Herborn, 1630), this being the first modern encyclopedia.

The new interest in elaborate surveys was natural enough considering the mathematical revolutions which took place in geometry and analysis during the seventeenth century and later. From the point of view of modern mathematicians, the Renaissance was only the final period of the Middle Ages, an object of curiosity and learning; for real inspiration one had to go back to the Greeks or to wait for the new giants—Descartes, Pascal, Desargues, Newton, Leibniz, and many others.

These tendencies of mathematical encyclopedism found their climax in the *Encyklopaedie der mathematischen Wissenschaften* (Leipzig, 1904-35; new edition, 1939———) and its French translation which began to appear in 1904 but remained fragmentary.[97]

EPILOGUE

THE HISTORY OF SCIENCE DURING THE RENAISSANCE IS AN IMMENSE subject which the previous lectures do not profess to cover. I have tried simply to indicate some of the main aspects and to introduce a few of the main actors. If I had tried to deal with the Renaissance as I did with Antiquity and the Middle Ages in my *Introduction,* my summary would have required not a few hundred pages, but many thousands. A check list of men of science, inventors, explorers of the sixteenth century, which I compiled in 1929, included some fifteen hundred names. Not only was that check list incomplete to start with, but I know well enough from long experience that the investigation of each man's activities would necessarily uncover the activities of various others. Hence, if it had been my privilege to draw an intellectual map of the sixteenth century on the same style and scope as my map of the fourteenth, I would have been obliged to deal with at least five thousand men. A similar study of the period 1450-1500 would have required the investigation of another thousand. If I had been able to carry out that synthesis, it would have filled four or five thick volumes of my *Introduction,* doubling the size of the whole work, and I might have introduced it with the words, "This is the Renaissance, gentle Readers. . . ."

The present volume is hardly more than a glimpse of the subject. I cannot say, "Gentle Readers, this is the Renaissance"—but I can still say, "This is how I saw it, and I invite you to look at it for a moment from this particular point of view."

First, the importance of printing. Not simply the multiplication of books, though that was important too in many respects. Consider only the multiplication of Bibles, which became truly available to the multitude of clerks for the first time. In the MS age, a Bible was an exceedingly expensive volume which only very few men could acquire. A printed Bible was still an expensive volume in the year 1500, but most clerks could buy the New Testament, or the Gospels and the Psalms. It is true they had been permitted before to use the MS copies kept in the libraries of cathedrals or monasteries, but that was not the same as the possibility of using one's own book at any time of the day or night.

The multiplicity and cheapness of books were not, however, the main things. From the point of view of scientific progress the outstanding feature of typography was the production of hundreds of copies of a book, which were virtually alike, the production of standards texts. Another feature, which did not appear immediately but was already well developed before 1501 and was increasingly popular in the sixteenth century, was the publication of images illustrating the text, precising and amplifying it as only an image can do it. Those images were alike in every copy; they were standards to which one could easily refer.

It is because of these two features, the production of *standard texts* and of *standard illustrations,* that the twin inventions of typography and engraving may be said to have changed the intellectual face of the world. These inventions open the Renaissance, and their systematic use during the period 1450-1600 differentiate that period from the Middle Ages essentially.

The determination of the end of the Renaissance is more arbitrary, but the limit 1600 seems acceptable for the following reasons. The Renaissance was in many respects a continuation of the Middle Ages but with a deeper and fresher knowledge of Antiquity on the one hand, and an increasing tempo on the other. The tempo was increased by new machines, chiefly the printing presses. The early Renaissance was largely imitative of Antiquity, but original men of science appeared from time to time, with increasing frequency, whom it did not suffice any more to read the old books, Greek or Latin, but who were impatient to consult the Book of Nature. That attitude varied considerably from man to man; the consultation might be rare and incidental; at the other end of the gamut it might be exclusive. Great innovators like Copernicus and Vesalius were steeped in ancient literature; their learning was great but happily their genius was greater still. The same can be said of William Gilbert (1544-1603), whose *De magnete* (1600) marks the end of the period, and of Tycho Brahe (1546-1601), who improved immeasurably the art of astronomical observations. Now, consider some of their younger contemporaries—the Englishmen Francis Bacon (1561-1626) and William Harvey (1578-1657), the Italian Galileo (1564-1642), the German Johann Kepler (1571-1630)—all of them were children of the Renaissance, yet so revolutionary in their creations that they opened a new age. Their main work was done in the seventeenth century; yet they had been completely educated in the sixteenth century. Even the youngest of them, Kepler and Harvey, were respectively thirty and twenty-three at the beginning of the new century. Their achievements and their sayings, their best sayings at least, are radically different from those of the preceding age. They are no longer epigoni but rather heralds, initiators.

To return to the beginning of the Renaissance, the invention of typography was ambivalent. It helped the birth and diffusion of new ideas, but it gave a new lease on life to the old ones. I have proved that the incunabula represented a much larger proportion of ancient science than of a new science; a similar proof concerning the sixteenth century cannot yet be given because our bibliography of sixteenth-century books is still very incomplete, but my lectures show that the more popular scientific writers of the sixteenth-century presses were ancients like Hippocrates, Plato, Aristotle, Euclid, Pliny, Ptolemy, Galen; or medieval scholars like Avicenna, Sacrobosco, Albert the Great, Arnold of Villanova, Thomas Aquinas, Mondino, Chauliac, etc. Yet, they will also reveal the existence of a fairly large group of new authors—new in many degrees of novelty, from the meek and timid novelty of a faithful interpreter to the full-fledged novelty of men of genius like Belon, Rondelet, Gesner, Cardano, Stevin, Viète, and many others, or the iconoclastic ardor of a Paracelsus. The reader is asked to remember that my account of science in the Renaissance is exemplary and suggestive rather than complete.

In my first lecture, I made a distinction between two kinds of men of science, the imitative and the nonimitative or creative. The distinction is incomplete and in many cases unclear. At any rate, there was an intermediate type of men who were at one and the same time antiquarians and naturalists; they might be editors, translators, commentators most of the time and yet be capable of original reactions to natural problems. There was also a type of alchemist and occulist which became increasingly popular in the sixteenth century, but which I have preferred to leave out of the picture. The political wars, the more terrible religious wars, the economic difficulties, and other miseries drove some men into mysticism, others into superstition and magic. The former sought and found peace in submission and love, the others were impatient to the point of rebellion. Some tried to play both ends of the game. The alchemic and magic literature of the sixteenth century is enormous, but I did not spend much time in investigating it. There is not much that one could find in it except delusions and deceptions, pride and prejudice.

It has often been said that medieval thought was dominated by theologians; one could say with equal truth that the scholarship of the

Renaissance was dominated by philologists. This is particularly clear in the field of medicine. Medicine was taught by means of textbooks most of which were ancient Greek books in Latin translation or in the original. Medical discussions were often philological discussions, and ambitious doctors tried to know the Greek texts as well as possible. Indeed, the study of Greek was deemed to be the best preparation for higher medical investigations. If an M.D. had distinguished himself by the edition of a Greek medical text or of a Latin translation, he became a suitable candidate for a university chair or for the office of a royal or papal archiater. Even a man as fundamentally original as Rabelais had to follow that road, the only road to preferment, but he took his revenge later in an unforgettable manner.

My account is oversimplified and must be qualified in two ways. As explained in my second lecture, a new wind was blowing in at least two medical fields, anatomy and botany. The philological tendencies of the older anatomists were gradually overcome by the private and public dissections of naturalists, not only Vesalius, who was the most illustrious of them, but many others. The botanists had found it more difficult to emancipate themselves from Dioscorides, but they were helped by the artists illustrating the herbals, by the travelers finding new plants in exotic surroundings or in their own mountains, by the curators of botanic gardens. By the end of the sixteenth century, botany had become a natural science of great vitality; it had almost freed itself from philology and was beginning to become independent of medical purposes.

As to the medical sciences proper, pathology and internal medicine, they had too little vitality to be independent of the classics. A rebel like Paracelsus realized their shortcomings and denounced them, but could not do much to alleviate them. The average Renaissance physician accepted the wisdom of Hippocrates, Galen, and Avicenna with little if any hope of being able to increase it except in their own manner. New diseases, like syphilis, had to be dealt with in a new way, but this did not affect the general pattern of clinical thinking.

The other qualification is perhaps more important, but its value cannot be measured with any precision. In addition to the M.D.'s emerging every year from the medical schools, chock-full of classical learning, there was a large body of irregular practitioners. The surgeons were largely trained as the sons and apprentices of other surgeons; at their best, they were as good as could be in their age; they would not have been better if they had been more learned. The surgical writings of Antiquity were generally available in vernacular translations, and the new ones were often published in the vernacular. The practice of surgeons was not restricted to surgery proper (external surgery, hernia, lithotomy); it extended to skin diseases, swellings, abscesses, and other complaints. The irregular doctors were less learned than the noble M.D.'s;

but they might be more intelligent, more experienced, more skillfull, more helpful in emergencies. Many of them were quacks or had quackish habits, such as coarse methods of self-advertising (the poor devils were often driven to that extremity by circumstances); others were more honest and generous. We have no right to assume that they were necessarily inferior to their licensed colleagues. "The main difference between a charlatan and a scientific doctor did not lie so much in a diploma as in their mind and conscience."[1]

There is no possibility of estimating the number of irregular practitioners and of all the men and women who did medical work of one kind or another, but it must have been considerable. The medical schools were but few and small; the physicians were established in the cities; medical needs existed everywhere and had to be satisfied; it was hardly possible to detect and stop irregular practice unless it became too blatant, or private jealousies were involved.

Many of the surgeons were not entirely irregular. They had guilds of their own, at least in France. The Collège de Saint Côme had been established for them in Paris as early as the thirteenth century; that was not a college in the technical sense, but rather a guild.[2] It created an aristocracy of surgeons, whose social level was much below that of M.D.'s, yet superior to that of the great mass of country bone-setters. The most illustrious surgeon of the Renaissance, Ambroise Paré (1510-90), had been snubbed by the St. Cosmas guild, but he became a military surgeon. The greatest opportunities for new knowledge were open to the surgeons attached to an army in the field and Paré had the genius to improve them. His abundant writings were primarily in the French language.

Aside from the surgeons and a few independent doctors, the sixteenth century witnessed a hundred years' war between philology and medicine. It was a civil war in the deepest sense, for it created anxious dilemmas in the minds of every intelligent doctor. How much could he trust his own experience if that implied a denial of old authorities? The average doctor was too timid to make a stand, and at best he compromised. Meanwhile, all the prizes went to the Hellenists, the "philosophers," the learned physicians. Was it not safer to follow Galen and Avicenna than to try something new?

The statement that the Middle Ages were dominated by theology and the Renaissance by philology may suggest another objection. Was not the sixteenth century the age of the Reformation and of the Counter Reformation; did it not witness spiteful controversies, merciless persecutions, and religious wars? It was a golden age for theological pamphleteers, but in spite of that, or because of that, it was an age of growing disillusion and doubts, of intolerance. Many examples of religious intolerance as it obtained in France and England have been given above. In France, the persecution of the Protestants reached a climax in the night of St. Bartholomew (23 August 1572); in England, the situation was less simple but equally odious: Catholics were persecuted by Henry VIII (1509-47), Protestants by Mary (1553-58), Catholics by Elizabeth (1558-1603). We have finally learned from bitter experience that persecutions do not strengthen religion, but weaken it and may end in destroying it. Theological pamphlets failed to dominate public opinion, but helped to divide it. Intolerance is as different from religion as jealousy from love.

The Renaissance was an intolerant age, disgraced by persecutions and by religious wars.[3] It was a golden age of learning, art, music, and letters. Science had hardly won its independence; whatever prestige it obtained, it could obtain it only as a form of learning. To study geometry was to study Euclid; a geographical atlas was an edition of Ptolemy; the physician did not study medicine, he studied Hippocrates and Galen, and so on. On account of that fundamental confusion, it is not surprising that many authors passed easily from an edition of Plutarch to one of Apollonios, or from mythology to zoölogy. It was no longer theology which dominated the other sciences, but rather philology giving its methods or fashions to the writers of books on theology, law, Roman and Canonic, and other subjects. The arts were inspired by classical models; this was sometimes true even in the case of religious paintings, for the artists would easily mix the symbols of paganism with those of Christendom. Even poetry (and not only Latin poetry) was subjected to the mannerisms of the humanists. In a time of great religious susceptibility when clerics easily took umbrage at trivial matters, the Catholic church was repeatedly affronted by incongruous references to classical mythology.

There were great men of science during the Renaissance but even the main innovators, such as Copernicus and Vesalius, did not receive the praise which has come to them in later times. They were not by any means as great in 1543 as they are now four centuries later. It is true that neither of them was a complete innovator, but the history of science shows repeatedly that every great discovery is preceded by glimpses of it; that does not diminish its greatness, because there is an immense difference between the man who adumbrates an idea (he might do so absent-mindedly) and the man who devotes his life to its vindication. Both accomplished a revolution, each in his own field; neither was recognized without struggle, but that also is the rule rather than the exception.

The main point is that those men who have become in our eyes the incarnation of the scientific Renaissance were relatively inconspicuous in their own environment, Vesalius perhaps less than Copernicus, because he was a professor at the University of Padova and later physician to his imperial majesty. At any rate, they attracted less attention in the Republic of Letters than scholars like Erasmus, the Scaligeri, or Justus Lipsius, not to mention the more readable authors of that troubled age. Perhaps that was as it should be. Men of science do not need as much popularity, and the latter would not do them much good, but the point is that during the Renaissance their services were not appreciated, except on wrong principles.

It is a commonplace of historiography that the Renaissance was to a large extent the recovery of classical Antiquity, but some implications of that are not as generally understood as they should be. The Renaissance was the final integration of Western thought against the Orientals who had helped so powerfully to build up Western culture. During the Middle Ages, the part of the Orient best known in the West was the Islamic world, which was not purely Oriental but a kind of bridge between East and West. The author of these pages has proved in great detail that the Arabic writers led scientific thought for about three centuries (ninth to eleventh) and remained exceedingly influential for at least two more centuries (twelfth and thirteenth), but that after 1300 their influence declined, slowly at first, more rapidly later. The forerunners of the Renaissance, like Petrarca, gave to it a strong anti-Arabic twist, which was aggravated because of Christian distrust and hatred of Averroës. It is true, medical writers, chiefly Avicenna, had obtained so much credit among physicians that they could not be easily dislodged. In spite of its barbaric language and of many exotic outlandish phrases, European doctors read the *Canon medicinae* without thinking of its Arabic origin; in the same way, they read the Bible without realizing that it was an Oriental book.

Until the Renaissance, the Arabic East and the Greco-Latin West had worked together to a large extent, for the simple reason that Arabic science was a development of Greek science and that Greek science had first reached the Christian West through the Arabic detour. The Renaissance broke that coöperation and put an end to it; in the fifteenth century, East and West were finally divorced and, from then on, proceeded each along its own way—the West exploiting the experimental method and making possible the gigantic advance of modern science which would occur in the seventeenth century, the East refusing to follow the new roads of discovery and shutting itself up in a cocoon of orthodoxy and scholasticism. The West lost religious unity and peace but gained more knowledge; the East stiffened its thought and manner and resigned itself to its fate. As the West was going ahead with the seven-league boots of experimental science while the East stood still, the distance between them increased steadily.

The best symbol of their separation was provided by the invention of typography, which the Muslim East spurned, while the Christian nations developed it as much as they could and made of it the main instrument of Western progress.

From 1450 to the end of the eighteenth century, that is, throughout the Renaissance and two centuries beyond it, civilization was largely understood in the sense of Western civilization,[4] and humanism meant the knowledge of classical antiquities. The Bible, represented by the *Vulgate,*[5] was an essential part of Latin culture. A new Oriental renaissance occurred only by the end of the eighteenth century when Anquetil-Duperron and Sir William Jones discovered Zend and Sanskrit writings and the complicated pattern of Indic cultures.[6] This introduced a new kind of humanism, more catholic than the Renaissance humanism. Their discovery of a new spiritual world was infinitely more important than the discovery of a new material world by Columbus, Vasco da Gama, Magellan, *e tutti quanti,* but it attracted less attention, and to this day the great majority of the so-called humanists (meaning the teachers of Latin and Greek) are still on the Renaissance level or below.

Many historians have described the Renaissance as a period of expansion and discovery, the main discovery (or rediscovery) being that of the Ancient World. That description is not incorrect, but it is lopsided. Our humanists speak as if the scholars of the Renaissance had discovered all the humanities, while they discovered only those of Greece and Rome, a pretty small part of the world. Looking at it from the point of view indicated above, one might say that the Renaissance was a period of isolation.

After the Renaissance, the West was fully equipped to continue and complete its conquest of the material world. This implied colonial expansion and the subjection of Eastern peoples to Western needs and greed. The Western nations did not simply exploit and enslave their

173

Eastern brothers; they did much worse, they failed to appreciate their spiritual heritage and tried to deprive them of it; it was not enough for them to conquer their material goods, they wanted to conquer their very souls. We are today paying the cost of their greed and of their stupidity.

The Renaissance discovered or rediscovered the Western past, and carried out its investigation of Western humanities, including science, with great thoroughness. In spite of the fact that science was not excluded from their survey it was preëminently a literary survey; even the scientific investigations, or most of them at least, were textual investigations. The humanities dominated every field of endeavor and therefore the philologists were at the helm.[7]

The humanities are essentially historical: they represent the accumulated wisdom and poetry of past ages. Hence, we might say that the main peculiarity of the Renaissance was its negative orientation; its creative activities concerned the past. The true scientific spirit on the contrary is focused upon the future; it is not interested in things that have already been published, but rather on those which are as yet unknown.

Each of these opposite tendencies can be and has been carried too far. We must study ancient wisdom, Western and Eastern, but that is not enough. The best teacher is nature, reality. We must appreciate the work of our ancestors without whose efforts we would still be ignorant and graceless; we must revere the best of them but never follow them blindly. Reverence for the past is good, but reverence for the truth, whether old or new, is infinitely more important. Renaissance scholars had too much reverence for the past; we have far too little.

Ours is a golden age of science, which is fine, but it is also a golden age of technology, business, management, an age of overorganization and dehumanization, and that is ominous and degrading.

The Middle Ages were dominated by theologians, the Renaissance by humanists; we are dominated by technocrats and administrators. Is that better? Must it be the end? Whereto do the technocrats and the administrators lead us? They do not want war any more than other people, but the results of their greed and efficiency cannot be anything else. That is amply proved by the history of our own times.

Could we not make a new start? The quest for the truth should not be weakened in any way, but the struggle for efficiency and for profits might be moderated and slowed up. It would suffice to admit that material profits are not as desirable as many good people have been led to believe, and that there is infinitely more virtue and glory in creating beauty, justice, happiness than in creating wealth.

Will the leaders understand that? I am afraid not. Fortunately, whatever their greed for power and wealth may be, there will always be room for artists, philosophers, men of science, historians, humanists, if these be satisfied, as they should, to live in a bare competency or better still in blessed poverty.

APPENDIX

The Survival of Ancient and Medieval Men of Science in the Fourteenth and Fifteenth Centuries

A RAPID MEANS OF APPRECIATING THE SURVIVAL OF ANCIENT AND medieval authors in the second half of the fifteenth century is to consider the selections made by the early printers. We must not forget that MSS continued to be used and produced; yet, the printers were businessmen who were trying to meet the demands of their market. They were more likely to publish popular works than unpopular ones which would remain on their own shelves; we may be sure that they took pains to select the authors who would sell best. Such an investigation is greatly facilitated by Arnold C. Klebs' list, "Incunabula scientifica et medica," *Osiris 4,* 1-359 (1937), and by my own memoir, "The scientific literature transmitted through the incunabula," *Osiris 5,* 41-247 (1938.) In that memoir the scientific incunabula are classified in chronological order of their authors. It can be summarized as follows (the numbers indicate the number of authors represented in each centurial group):

VI	B.C.	1		I(1) B.C.	4	} 8
V	B.C.	3		I(2) B.C.	4	
IV(1) B.C.	2	} 7		I(1)	4	} 13
IV(2) B.C.	5			I(2)	9	
III(1) B.C.	4	} 4		II(1)	5	} 14
III(2) B.C.	—			II(2)	9	
II(1) B.C.	2	} 2		III(1)	4	} 8
II(2) B.C.	—			III(2)	4	

IV(1)	4	} 8
IV(2)	4	
V(1)	5	} 7
V(2)	2	
VI(1)	3	} 4
VI(2)	1	
VII(1)	3	} 3
VII(2)	—	
VIII(1)	1	} 3
VIII(2)	2	
IX(1)	6	} 11
IX(2)	5	
X(1)	3	} 7
X(2)	4	
XI(1)	5	} 9
XI(2)	4	
XII(1)	9	} 16
XII(2)	7	

XIII(1)	10	} 40
XIII(2)	30	
XIV(1)	39	} 64
XIV(2)	25	
XV(1)	51	} 429
XV(2)	378	

More briefly

B.C.	25		
I-VII	57	I-V	50
VIII-XII	46	VI-XII	53
			103

XIII	40
XIV	64
XV(1)	51
XV(2)	378
	661

Such a view is superficial, yet instructive *grosso modo*. The most significant feature is the largest number of authors classified in XV(2), more than half of the total. This is not surprising. They were the contemporaries of the invention and early development of printing. If we leave them out, we find that the 283 authors anterior to the invention of printing may be divided as follows:

Antiquity	(B.C., I-V)	75	} 168
Middle Ages	(VI-XIII)	93	
XIV, XV(1)		115	
		283	

In these lists all the incunabula, whether important or not, small or large (some are very small indeed, others enormous), popular or not, are considered as equal units.

In my memoir of 1938, I determined the chronological distribution of the most popular authors, and this yielded the following result:

B.C.	2	(Hippocrates, Aristotle)
I-VII	8	
IX-XI	4	(Arabic centuries)
XII-XIII	11	

177

XIV	13	XV(1)	12
XV	38	XV(2)	26
	76		38

Out of the 26 most popular authors who lived in the incunabula age, no less than 10 dealt with astrology or witchcraft.

The main point is that the 76 most popular scientific authors of the early printers may be divided into three groups almost equal in numbers:

Antiquity, Middle Ages (B.C., I-XIII)	25
XIV, XV(1)	25
XV(2), contemporaries	26
	76

Let us restrict our selection even more and consider only the 12 most popular authors. They are in chronological order:

V	B.C.	Hippocrates
IV(2)	B.C.	Aristotle
IX(2)		Rāzī
XIII(1)		Sacrobosco
XIII(2)		Albert the Great, Arnaldo da Villanova, Anianus
XIV(2)		Mandeville, Canutus
XV(2)		Wenzel Faber (astrologer) and Regio-montanus.

Only 3 out of 12 (one quarter) are contemporaries.

The artificiality of the list may be illustrated by the following facts. The most popular authors of all were Albert the Great (XIII-2) and Aristotle (IV-2 B.C.), represented respectively by 151 and 98 editions. The following illustrious authors had a much smaller number of incunabula to their credit:

Thomas Aquinas	25
Avicenna	21
Galen	19
Pliny	18
Averroës	14
Guy de Chauliac	14
Pier de Crescenzi	13
Ptolemy	10
Ramon Lull	10
Mondino de Luzzi	10

It is hardly necessary to comment upon that. One remark may suffice. If attention were paid to size, the *Qānūn* of Ibn Sīnā repeatedly printed in Latin and once in Hebrew was a gigantic work, equal in size to hundreds of other incunabula piled together. Vincent of Beauvais does not appear in the list of best sellers at all, because there were only three editions of the *Speculum naturale* and three of the *Speculum doctrinale,* but these two works were large folios of 698 and 404 leaves, respectively. Each of Vincent's volumes was comparable not to a single work but to a medieval library.

Here is another easy way of determining the popularity of ancient and medieval authors. Unfortunately, I cannot use it for the fifteenth or sixteenth centuries, but only for the fourteenth; the conclusions would have been essentially the same, however, if we had been able to deal with the later centuries.

The index to vol. 3 of my *Introduction* refers to all the authors dealt with in the three volumes; most of them were men of the fourteenth century, inasmuch as that volume deals with that century. Yet, the authors most often quoted are not those of that century, but earlier ones.

Here is the list of all the authors the references to whom in the index cover 5 lines or more (a few have been added who needed *almost* 5 lines).

The authors are arranged in chronological order.

(V B.C.)	*Hippocrates*	10*
(IV-1 B.C.)	Plato	6
(IV-2 B.C.)	*Aristotle*	23
(III-1 B.C.)	Euclid	a. 5
(I-1 B.C.)	Cicero	5
(I-2 B.C.)	Virgil	a. 5
(I-2)	Seneca	5
(II-1)	*Ptolemy*	15
(II-2)	*Galen*	13
(V-1)	St. Augustine	8
(VI-1)	Boetius	6
(IX-2)	Rāzī	a. 9
(XI-1)	*Ibn Sīnā*	17
(XII-1)	Abraham ben Ezra	6

* The figures indicate the number of lines in the index; "a. 5" means almost 5 lines. The names of the authors who cover in the index 10 lines or more are printed in *italics*.

(XII-2)	Ibn Rushd	10
	Maimonides	9
	Peter the Lombard	8
(XIII-1)	Sacrobosco	a. 5
(XIII-2)	Albert the Great	6
	Arnold of Villanova	9
	Giles of Rome	a. 5
	Marco Polo	6
	Naṣīr al-dīn al Ṭūsī	a. 5
	Raymond Lull	6
	Roger Bacon	a. 5
	St. Thomas	11
	Vincent of Beauvais	a. 5
(XIV-1)	Bernard of Gordon	a. 5
	Dante	8
	William of Occam	a. 5
	Petrarca	12
(XIV-2)	Boccaccio	9
	Chaucer	5
	Ibn Khaldūn	5
	Oresme	7
	Wycliffe	a. 5

The list based upon the index of a particular work is artificial; a list based upon another work would be different—that other work might include more references to Archimedes than to Euclid, or more references to Dante than to Petrarca—but who can doubt the general conclusion?

That conclusion forces itself upon us in so many ways that it is impossible to discard it. The most popular authors of the fourteenth century were ancient ones; their flesh had been corrupted and destroyed for centuries, but their spirit was alive, more alive indeed than that of the living men.

The most popular authors of the fourteenth century were, in order of importance, Aristotle, Ibn Sīnā, Ptolemy, Galen, Petrarca, St. Thomas, Hippocrates, and Ibn Rushd.

Close behind them came al-Rāzī, Maimonides, Arnold of Villanova, Boccaccio.

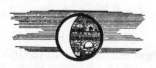

The procession of great men is steadily increasing, because each century adds its own while those of the past continue to live and to inspire us. Little men may gradually drop by the wayside, but the truly great go on forever. It is sometimes possible to silence living men, but it is impossible to restrain the dead.

NOTES

PREFACE

x—9

1. Comparison developed in an address to the American Council of Learned Societies, *Isis 25,* 6-8 (1936).
2. For more details, see my article, "The history of science in the Carnegie Institution," *Osiris 9,* 624-38 (1950).
3. The *Algorithmus de integris* was printed in Padova, 1483, printer unknown (Klebs 167 .1). Facsimile of *incipit* in *Osiris 5,* 158, 113. Gino Loria, *Isis 12,* 323.
4. Sarton: "Incunabula wrongly dated," *Isis 40,* 227-40, 18 fig. (1949).
5. For further discussion, see *Introd. 3,* 1914.

INTRODUCTION

1. *To Doctor R.* Essays here collected and published in honor of the seventieth birthday of Dr. A. S. W. Rosenbach, July 22, 1946 (302 pp.; Philadelphia, 1946). This includes a portrait and bibliography, but no biography, of the jubilarian.
2. One cannot conclude very much from the survival of a MS; it is too much a matter of luck. How many people used it? The MSS which were used most could hardly survive. On the other hand, when a book was printed, say, in 200 copies or more, it attracted the attention of scholars. It would not have been printed if it had not enjoyed a modicum of popularity to begin with. Of course, a book might fall flat then as now, but it could not remain completely unnoticed. In the course of time, the 200 copies put in 200 different places would find some readers and even critics or friends. It may be objected that some incunabula and later books did get lost; yet 200 copies of a book had a better chance of survival than a few MSS.
3. It even happened that printed texts were copied by hand. Nearly every old library contains a few MSS derived from printed books.
4. At the beginning, i.e., in the third quarter of the fifteenth century, the number of printed texts available in the older libraries was relatively small, and such printed texts were listed together with the MSS, as curiosities.
5. Not always! There was sometimes great rivalry between printers and they hastened to publish some ancient texts, turning them out at great speed. The result is that some printed texts were inferior to good MSS. This has

been proved many times. In some cases, the printing caused the destruction of the original MS (we suspect that the MS was sometimes used by the very printers for the setting up of type) and then comparisons have become impossible, but the imperfections and obscurities of the printed text suggest overhasty work. In some cases, the MS was unduly abbreviated and the text mutilated. Lynn Thorndike: "Manuscript versus incunabulum," *Mélanges d'histoire du Moyen age, dédiés à Louis Halphen* (Paris: Presses Universitaires de France, 1951), pp. 693-99.

6. This is a reference to his book *De Plinii et aliorum in medicina erroribus* (Ferrara: Laurentius de Rubeis, de Valentia and Andreas de Grassis, de Castronovo, 1492). Klebs 598.1. 18 leaves, 202 x 143 mm. Leoniceno's work and personality will be discussed in my second lecture.

7. For Severinus, see John Ferguson: *Bibliotheca chemica 2,* 378 (Glasgow: Maclehose, 1906); V. Meisen: *Prominent Danish scientists* (Copenhagen: Levin & Munksgaard, 1932— *Isis 23,* 276-78), pp. 16-19. Severinus' views were popularized in Western Europe by William Davidson (fl. 1635-60), physician to the king of France and keeper of the Jardin des Plantes, in his *Commentariorum in Severini Ideam medicinae philosophicae prodromus* (The Hague, 1660).

8. We owe to Sten Lindroth an elaborate study of Paracelsism in Sweden down to the middle of the seventeenth century; unfortunately, it is in Swedish (Uppsala, 1943—*Isis 36,* 223). Such investigations should be carried through for the other countries of Europe and made available to the whole Republic of Letters.

LECTURE I

MEDICINE

9. For an example, see my account of the tradition of the *Aphorisms* in *History of science* (Cambridge, Mass.: Harvard University Press, 1952), vol. 1, pp. 379-83. The *Aphorisms* was the most popular of all the Hippocratic writings. There are some 483 MSS in the learned languages (140 in Greek, 232 in Latin, 70 in Arabic, 40 in Hebrew, 1 in Syriac) plus others in sundry vernaculars.

10. The first edition of *Liber Almansoris* was printed by Pachel and Scinzenzeler, Milano, 1481. The second and third were printed by Locatellus in 1497 and by Hamman in 1500, both in Venice (Klebs 826.1-3). For the *Articella,* see below, n. 53.

11. Joseph Archer Crowe and Giovanni Battista Cavalcaselle: *Raphael* (2 vols.; London: Murray, 1882-85), vol. 2, p. 437.

12. As the Arabs put it, *al-faḍl lilmutaqaddim*—honor to the forerunner.

13. This Andreas Brentius is probably Andreas Althamer (or Altheimer) born at the end of the fifteenth century at Brenz near Gundelfingen, Swabia; educated in Augsburg, Tübingen, Leipzig, Wittemberg. Historian and Lutheran priest. Died in 1540 or 1564 (*ADB 1,* 365).

14. *BL 2,* 102 (1930).

15. See my *History of science 1,* 353. Andrea Torresani (1451-1529) of Asola bought the typography of Nicolas Jenson, and his daughter Maria married Aldo Manuzio. Thus were the firms Aldus and Asulanus associated. Andrea's business was continued by his sons, Giovanni Francesco and Frederico, and later by the sons of the former, Andrea il Giovine, Gerolamo, and Bernardo (until 1575).

16. The text of that preface can be read in Littré's *Hippocrate* (Paris, 1839), vol. 1, p. 543.

17. See footnote 5.

18. The first Greek font used by Aldus the Elder is said to have contained, with its innumerable ligatures and contractions, over 1400 sorts. This preposterous number was soon reduced, but the sorts in the Greek case still remained high in the hundreds. Douglas C. McMurtrie: *The book* (New York: Covici Friede, 1937), p. 280.

19. Founded by Johann Froben, born in Franconia, 1460; died in Basel, 1527; Erasmus' friend and his publisher. He was succeeded by his sons, Hieronymus and Johann, and his son-in-law, Nicolas Bischoff (Episcopius); born in Alsace in 1501; died in Basel, 1563. Nicolas I was succeeded by his son, Nicolas II, who died in 1566.

20. These two terms, Physicus and Stadtphysicus, are used by Pagel in his notice, *BL 3,* 15 (1931). If we take them literally, it means that he was a private physician in the first city and a town physician in the second. I imagine that the distinction was not always clear. Many towns encouraged physicians to settle within their territory, offering them various advantages. For the history of town physicians, see *Introd. 3,* 1244, 1861.

21. Janus Cornarius: *Universae rei medicae epigraphe seu enumeratio* (Basel, 1529, 1534); *De peste libri duo* (Basel, 1551); *Medicina sive medicus, etc.* (Basel, 1556). In addition to those of Hippocrates, he edited works of Dioscorides (I-2), Galen (II-2), Artemidoros Daldianos (II-2), Adamantios Sophistes (IV-1), Aëtios of Amida (VI-1), Paulos of Aigina (VII-1), etc. He also translated a collection of mythical love stories in prose, the *De amatoriis affectionibus* of Parthenios of Nicaia. His translation appeared with the Greek princeps (Basel, 1531). Critical edition of the *Peri erōtikōn pathēmatōn* by Paulus Sakolowski: *Mythographi graeci* (Leipzig: Teubner, 1896), vol. 2, fasc. 1.

   Parthenios was a third-rate man of letters, but he was a friend of Virgil (I-2 B.C.) and of J. Cornelius Gallus (*c.* 66-26 B.C.), elegiac poet, the first Roman prefect of Egypt. It is said that Parthenios was Virgil's teacher of Greek; one of his verses was translated in *Georgica 1,* 437. Looking at it from another angle, Parthenios helped to transmit the romantic tendencies of the Alexandrian poets to Ovid (43 B.C.-A.D. 17).

22. The Junta family (Giunta, Zunta) was of Florentine origin. The founder, Luca Antonio, a Florentine bookseller, moved in 1480 to Venice, which was then the leading printing center. He established himself there and obtained fame as a printer of translations of the Aldine Greek texts. He died in 1538, was succeeded by his sons, chiefly Tommaso and the latter's nephews, Modesto and Bernardo. The firm Apud Juntas existed until 1791.

   Filippo, brother of Luca Antonio, had remained in Florence; in 1492 he had a shop near Santa Maria della Badia, at the "Red Lily," was protected by Pope Leo X, and published Greek and Latin classics. After his death in 1517, his sons, Benedetto and Bernardo, continued the business.

   Jacques François, nephew of Luca Antonio and Filippo, was sent from Venice to Lyon in 1520 to establish a new business; he published imitations of the Aldine Greek classics for export to Germany and Italy. When he died, he was succeeded by his daughters, Jacqueline and Jeanne (heredes Giunti). A red lily was the bookmark of all the Juntae of Italy and France.

23. Class 1: Authentic writings bearing the hallmark of Hippocratic style and

doctrine. Class II: Notes and memoranda edited by his son Thessalos, his son-in-law Polybos (IV-1 B.C.), or other immediate disciples. These writings are also authentic, yet may include interpolations. Class III: Works written not by the master but by his disciples. Class IV: Works which are completely apocryphal (Littré *1*, 170).

24. Hieronymus Mercurialis' treatise on gymnastics of 1569 was reprinted under a different title, *De arte gymnastica* (Venice: Juntae, 1573; 6th ed., 1602; other editions in Paris and Amsterdam). The *De puerorum morbis* was often reprinted in Venice, Frankfurt, and Basel; a German translation appeared in Frankfurt, 1605. It contains a chapter on stammering. For a longer bibliography see Haberling, *BL 4*, 171 (1932).

25. For Jean Fernel (1497-1558), French humanist and medical reformer, see Sir Charles Sherrington: *The endeavor of Jean Fernel* (234 pp.; Cambridge University, 1946—*Isis 37*, 199; *41*, 212).

26. *Oeconomia Hippocratis alphabeti serie distincta* (folio, viii + 694 pp.). It was reprinted by Samuel Chouët in Geneva, 1662, as *Operum omnium tomus secundus*, the first volume (1657) being a reprint of Foes' Greek-Latin edition of 1595 (reprinted 1621, 1624, 1645).

27. It will suffice to mention three: (1) The Greek-Latin edition of J. Antonides van der Linden (2 vols.; Leiden, 1665) about which see Sarton in Singer's *Festschrift* (vol. 2, 1953); (2) the Greek-French edition by Emile Littré (10 vols.; Paris, 1839-61), vol. 10 being an elaborate index; (3) the Greek-English selection by W. H. S. Jones and E. T. Withington in the Loeb Library (4 vols.; 1923-31). See *History of science 1*, 352-54.

28 *De medicina* is divided into 8 books which were Books VI to XIII of the whole (*Artium libri VI-XIII*). A few fragments of the agricultural and of the rhetorical parts remain, edited by Frederick Marx in *Corpus medicorum latinorum*, vol. 1. *A. Cornelii Celsi quae supersunt* (Leipzig: Teubner, 1915—*Isis 3*, 319).

29. In my *Introd. 1*, 240, I wrote mistakenly, "His work was lost during the Middle Ages." The early MSS now extant in Florence, Paris, and the Vatican were perhaps forgotten, yet their existence proves that some people were well acquainted with Celsus in the ninth and tenth centuries.

30. Giovanni Baptista Cipelli, called Egnazio (the Egnatii were members of an ancient family of Samnite origin; why did Cipelli resurrect their name?). He was born in Venice in 1473 (or 1478) and died there in 1553. He was a humanist, especially interested in Latin letters which he taught in Venice. He was a schoolmate of Leo X and remained his friend (*NBG 15, 735* [1868]).

31. It will suffice to mention those of Charles Daremberg (Leipzig: Teubner, 1859; reprinted, 1891), Frederick Marx (Leipzig: Teubner, 1915—*Isis 3*, 319), and the Latin-English edition by W. G. Spencer (3 vols.; Loeb Library, 1935-38).

32. Matyas Hollos, better known under his Latin name Matthias Corvinus (1443-90), King of Hungary from 1458 to his death.

33. A. de Hevesy: *La bibliothèque du roi Matthias Corvin* (103 pp., folio, 52 pls.; Paris: Pour les members de la Société française de reproduction des MSS à peintures, 1923). This includes a catalogue of the library: (A) 156 MSS now dispersed in many libraries, (B) 81 MSS known through descriptions or references but lost, (C) 3 printed books, (D) four printed books dedicated to Beatrice of Aragon, Matthias' queen. For Bartolommeo Fonti, see pp. 16-18, 51, 80, 84, 88.

34. The University of Buda had been founded by a previous king, Sigismund of Luxemburg, in 1389, but had hardly survived its founder, who died in 1437 (*Introd. 3*, 1400).

35. James Greive (or Grieve), M. D. Edinburgh, 1752; physician to St. Thomas', 1764, and the Charterhouse, 1765; FRS, 1769; died, 1773 (*DNB 23*, 223).

36. "Perhaps" must be added because of Soranos' contemporary, Rufus (II-1), whom many people would call the greatest physician of the Roman period, next to Galen. It is significant that both Rufus and Soranos were Ephesians. Ephesos was the capital of the Roman province of Asia and the greatest city of Asia Minor; it is natural that the greatest physicians were found in the greatest city. Pergamon (Galen's home) was less important, though it was also a metropolis and equally famous. It was because of their political importance that Ephesos and Pergamon were early centers of Christian activity.

37. I. E. Drabkin: *Caelius Aurelianus, On acute diseases and on chronic diseases* (1052 pp.; University of Chicago Press, 1950—*Isis 42*, 148-50), p. xvii.

38. *Ruffi Ephesii de vesicae renumque morbis, etc. Sorani de utero et muliebri pudendo* (Paris: Adr. Turnebus, 1554). A small book, 16 cm. high, 60 pp., in Greek italics, no Latin at all except the translation of the Greek title. The Soranos extract is at the end of the book, pp. 54 to 60. No editor is named; it was the printer himself, Adrien Tournebu, or Turnèbe, French Hellenist (born in the Andelys, Normandy, in 1512; died Paris, 1565), printer to the king, he published many Greek editions with the beautiful royal type ("grecs du Roi").

39. The Greek text was edited in Basel, 1566, by Kaspar Wolf (1525-1601), a Züricher, who obtained his M.D. in Montpellier, succeeded Conrad Gesner in 1565 as professor in his native city, and died there in 1601 (Pagel in *BL 5*, 979). The *Sorani gynaeciorum vetus translatio latina* was appended by Valentin Rose to his edition of Soranos (Leipzig, 1882); Rose edited it on the basis of three MSS dating from the ninth to the twelfth centuries; this proves that a Latin tradition of Soranos' gynecology continued during the Middle Ages; perhaps its Latinity was too poor to merit the attention of Renaissance scholars.

40. Contents in *Isis 11*, 161. The books on fractures had been edited before by Antonio Cocchi in his *Graecorum chirurgici libri* (Florence, 1754), pp. 45-51; and again by J. L. Ideler: *Physici et medici minores* (1841), vol. 1.

41. The perversion began early, because Caelius' book on acute diseases was plagiarized in the "Aurelius," the book on chronic ones in the "Aesculapius" —the date of these two treatises is unknown but not earlier than the sixth century and probably not much later (*Introd. 1*, 434).

42. See footnote 37.

43. There are no Arabic translations of Soranos, but Arabic physicians had some knowledge of Soranos through the translations of Byzantine authors quoting him.

44. The name is Sichardus in Latin; there are many variants of the German form: "Sichhart" (ending with *d, dt;* second *h* left out, etc.). Paul Lehmann: "Johannes Sichardus und die von ihm benutzten Bibliotheken und Handschriften," *Quellen und Untersuchungen zur lateinischen Philologie des Mittelalters 4*, 1 (247 pp.; München, 1911).

45. Andernach on left bank of Rhine, 10 m. NW of Koblenz. Other names: Guinterius (with *o*, 1 or 2 *i's*, and also with *th* instead of *t*). The French

named him Jean Gonthier, yet BN catalogues him under the name Winther. The date of his birth is 1505, not 1487. E. Turner: "Jean Guinter," *Gazette hebdomadaire de médecine 28,* 425-34, 441-48, 505-16 (1881). W. Haberling: "Die Wahrheit über den Namen, das Geburtsjahr und die Jugendzeit des Dr. Winther," *Scritti in onore del Prof. P. Capparoni* (Torino, 1941), pp. 90-95. Thanks to Dr. Ernest Wickersheimer for his kind help in this matter.

46. See article by Haberling in *BL 2,* 883-85 (1930) for a list of them. Let me mention one of them, L. A. P. Hérissant: *Eloge historique de Jean Gonthier, médecin ordinaire de François premier, avec un catalogue raisonné de ses ouvrages* (xx + 88 pp.; Paris: J. T. Hérissant, 1765). Not seen.

47. Some 120 treatises are included in the Greco-Latin edition of C. G. Kühn (22 vols.; Leipzig, 1821-33). Two volumes are divided into two, hence the last vol. indexing the whole collection is numbered 20. These 120 treatises can be classified as were those of Hippocrates (see note 23) in groups of decreasing authenticity.

48. For the differences between the Orthodox Christians and the Monophysites on the one hand, and between the Orthodox and the Nestorians on the other, see *History of science 1,* 380, n. 106.

49. It was edited in Arabic and translated into German by Gotthelf Bergsträsser (Leipzig, 1925). Elaborate English analysis by Max Meyerhof, *Isis 8,* 683-724. The text is preserved in a single MS, Aya Sofia 3631.

50. Toledo had been taken by the Muslims in 712 and reconquered by the Christians in 1085. In the twelfth century, it was a Christian city with a large Arabic-speaking population. For the background, see Angel González Palencia (1889-1949): *Los Mozárabes de Toledo en los siglos XII y XIII* (4 vols., folio; Madrid, 1926-30—*Isis 15,* 183-87). José Maria Millas Vallicrosa: *Las traducciones orientales en los manuscritos de la Biblioteca Catedral de Toledo* (372 pp.; Madrid, 1942—*Isis 34,* 518-19). Millas deals with Arabic and Hebrew MSS, not with Latin ones, yet his work throws much light upon Toledan scholarship in general.

51. There were other means of producing the needed copies, well explained by Jean Destrez: *La pecia dans les manuscrits universitaires du XIIIe et XIVe siècle* (2 vols.; Paris: Vautrain, 1935—*Isis 25,* 155-57). For the Montpellier documents of 1309 and 1340, see *Introd. 3,* 247.

52. For Niccolò Falcucci, who died in 1411, see *Introd 3,* 1194.

53. For details, see Klebs 116. 1-6. The *Articella* is a collection of medical treatises. The first edition printed by an anonymous printer in Padova before 1476 contained seven treatises, the five others printed by five printers in Venice (1483, 1487, 1491, 1493, 1500) contained those seven treatises plus four others, eleven in all, to wit, 6 by Hippocrates, 2 by Galen, 2 by Theophilos Protosphathario (VII-1), and 1 by Ḥunain ibn Isḥāq (IX-2). How did it happen that those five different printers published the selfsame collection within 18 years? Facsimile of first page of first edition of *De divisione librorum* (Venice, 1483) in *Osiris 5,* 137, 105.

54. With Pol's signature and date 1494. Facsimile of first page with marginalia in Pol's hand (*Osiris 5,* 136, 104). Max H. Fisch: *Nicolaus Pol Doctor 1494* (New York: Reichner, 1947—*Isis 40,* 56-58).

55. The Greek text was not known to the old editors. It was first printed in the Greek-Latin edition of René Chartier (1572-1654) of Vendôme (Paris: 1679). Chartier's Greek-Latin edition was first published together with Hippocrates (Paris, 1639).

56. Father of Joachim Camerarius junior of Nuremberg (1534-98), famous as a botanist, whose main work was the *Hortus medicus et philosophicus* (Frankfurt a.M., 1588). For philologists, the most illustrious Camerarius is Joachim Camerarius senior; for historians of botany, Rudolf Jacob Camerarius (1665-1721) of Tübingen.

57. C. Doris Hellman: *The comet of 1577* (New York: Columbia University Press, 1944), chiefly pp. 343-45.

58. Karl Sudhoff in *Archiv für Augenheilkunde 97*, 493-501 (1926—*Isis 10*, 149). The *Tabula oculorum morbos comprehendens* of L. Fuchs, with facsimile, *Dioptric Review 38*, 347-53 (London, 1936).

59. Some of Fuchs' illustrations are reproduced in Agnes Arber: *Herbals* (New edition; Cambridge University Press, 1938—*Isis 30*, 131-32), pp. 64-70. Felix Neumann: "Leonhard Fuchs, physician and botanist, 1501-66," *Smithsonian Report for 1917*, pp. 635-47, 7 pls.

60. The German Johann Günther of Andernach was also a great Galenic scholar, the first to publish a Latin translation of the *De anatomicis administrationibus* (1531), but we have already spoken of him.

61. Albertus von Haller: *Bibliotheca medicinae practicae* (Basel, 1776), vol. 1, p. 494.

62. Marignan in French. The Italian original name was Marignano, but is now Melegnano. The place is in Lombardy quite close to Milano.

63. According to Ronsard, Clément Jannequin was one of the immediate disciples of Josquin des Prés (*c.* 1445-1521). See article in Grove's *Dictionary of music and musicians*. An excellent record of *La bataille de Marignan* was made by the Chanterie de la Renaissance led by Henri Expert (Columbia DFX 19), 2 parts on one disk.

64. See any history of Renaissance music or a more general book like Paul Henry Láng: *Music in western civilization* (1123 pp; New York, 1941—*Isis 34*, 182-86). The *Isis* review reproduces Láng's map of the distribution of Flemish and Franco-Flemish composers in the period *c.* 1450-1550.

65. P. Allut: *Etude biographique et bibliographique sur S. Champier, suivie de divers opuscules français de Champier: L'ordre de chevalerie, le Dialogue de noblesse et les Antiquités de Lyon et de Vienne* (Lyon, 1859). F. F. A. Potton: "Etudes historiques et critiques sur la vie et les travaux de Champier et particulièrement sur ses oeuvres médicales," *Annales de la Société de médecine de Lyon*, XI (1863), 328-87; tiré à part 57 pp. (Lyon, 1864). E. Wickersheimer: *Dictionnaire biographique des médecins en France* (745 pp.; Paris, 1936—*Isis 26*, 187-89). Paule Dumaitre: "Un chevalier de Marignan," *Histoire de la médecine* (Paris, 1951), vol. 1, no. 3, pp. 7-14. John F. Fulton: *The great medical bibliographers* (Philadelphia, 1951—*Isis 43*, 90), pp. 4-10. Fulton gives facsimiles of title page and four identical woodcuts of *De medicinae claris scriptoribus* (his figs. 3-4).

66. For the bibliography of Guy de Chauliac see the edition of Edouard Nicaise: *La grande chirurgie* (Paris, 1890) and more briefly my *Introd. 3*, 1690-94. There are some 60 editions of the *Grande chirurgie* plus 9 lost ones and 60 editions of fragments and commentaries, all together some 129. Most of them in French, others in Latin, Italian, Dutch, Catalan, and English (*Isis 35*, 30).

67. The word *symphōnia* is used in the Greek sense of accord (not only of voices), agreement, compromise. It is much used in that sense by modern Greeks, but the Latin use is very unusual. I do not know another example of it than this title.

68. Aldus, that is Aldo (Teobaldo) Manuzio or Manuccio, Aldo il Vecchio (1459-1515). Sandys *2*, 98-100. See note 15.
69. This splendid folio volume of 376 leaves was printed by Manutius in Venice, 1499 (Klebs 405). It is sometimes designated as (*Scriptores*) *Astronomici veteres*, but that is not a title. It includes not only the *Sphaira* of Proclos (V-2) edited by Linacre and Grocyn but also the *Phainomena* of Aratos (III-1 B.C.) with the commentary of Theon of Alexandria (IV-2), the *Astronomicon* of Manilius (I-1), and the *De nativitatibus* of Firmicus (IV-1). New College, Oxford, keeps Linacre's own copy on vellum with his autograph.
70. Prince Arthur (1486-1502), the eldest son of Henry VII, was married to Catherine of Aragon in 1501. She married Henry VIII in 1509. Princess Mary (1516-58) was their third but only surviving child. Queen of England and Ireland from 1553 to 1558, known as Mary 1 or Mary Tudor ("Bloody Mary" to her Protestant enemies).
71. *Rudimenta grammatices*, printed (or reprinted) by Pynson in London about 1523. A more important grammatical work of his was published soon after his death, *De emendata structura latini sermonis* (London: Pynson, 1524), not reprinted in England but often on the continent. The aim was to illustrate good Latin (*le bon usage*) with classical quotations; "the king's Latin" you might call it.
72. English printers were very late in this. The finest use of Greek type was in the *Lactantius* printed by Sweynheim and Pannartz (Subiaco, 1465), the accents and spirits being added by hand. Nicholas Jenson of Venice was first to cut a beautiful Greek font (1471). The first book printed entirely in Greek was the grammatical *Erōtēmata* of Constantine Lascaris (1434-*c*. 1501), printed by Dionysius Paravisinus (Milano, 1476).
73. Sir John Cheke (1514-57) came too late to have known Linacre except as a child. He it was "who taught Cambridge and King Edward Greek." He defended the new Erasmian pronunciation of Greek against Stephen Gardiner, chancellor of the University of Cambridge, and told this Linacre anecdote in his treatise *De pronuntiatione graecae linguae* (Basel: Nic. Episcopius, Jr., 1555), p. 282. He was a Protestant and forced to abjure Protestantism in 1566. The statement referred to above is so bold that I feel it necessary to quote the very text, "In quo mihi perinde placere debet, atque in eo quod cum provecta admodum inclinataque aetate esset, homo studiis morbisque fractus et morti vicinus, cum sacerdos esset, jam tum novum Testamentum primo in manus caepisse, et ex eo aliquot Matthaei capita perlegisse: et cum quintum, sextum septimumque percucurrisset, abjecto iterum quantum potuit totis viribus libro, jurasse, aut hoc non fuisse Evangelium, aut nos non esse Christianos. . . ."
74. J. F. Payne, *DNB 33*, 266-71 (1893). William Osler: *Thomas Linacre* (64 pp., 11 pls.; Cambridge University, 1908). This was the first Linacre lecture of 1908, delivered in St. John's, Cambridge.
75. Each man taught to his own death, 1524, 1536. Leoniceno's sixty years' teaching in the same university was an extraordinary record. Yet, it was surpassed by my old friend, Sir D'Arcy Thompson (1860-1948), who was professor at St. Andrews for 64 years (*Isis 41*, 3-8).
76. Biographical facts given by Pagel (*BL 3*, 744) in a short note. Leoniceno's fame as a physician is proved by the publication of his *Opera omnia* soon after his death (Venice, 1530; also Basel, 1532, folio).
77. Sarton: "Hoefer and Chevreul," *Bulletin of the history of medicine 8*, 419-45 (Baltimore, 1940), pp. 440-41.

78. For the three incunabula editions of 1497, see Klebs 598-600. Facsimile reproduction of a few leaves of each in Karl Sudhoff, Charles Singer: *The earliest printed literature on syphilis* (Florence, 1925—*Isis 8*, 351-54).

79. Son of the more famous Ugo Benzi of Siena (*c.* 1370-1439). The elaborate study on Ugo Benzi by Dean Putnam Lockwood announced in *Introd. 3*, 1196, was finally published (University of Chicago, 1951—*Isis 43*, 60-62).

80. For the editions of Manardi's medical letters see note 96.

81. Very brief note by Pagel (*BL 4*, 50).

82 The Este family dating back to the tenth century and lasting until the end of the eighteenth century was one of the most illustrious families of Italy and one which did perhaps more than any other to foster the Renaissance. Its fortune reached a political climax with Niccolò III (1384-1441), who ruled Ferrara, Parma, Modena, Reggio. His eldest son, Lionello (1407-50), was tutored by Guarino of Verona; a younger son, Ercole I (1431-1505), had two daughters, Beatrice and Isabella, the two most accomplished princesses of the Italian Renaissance. Beatrice (1475-97), wife of Lodovico Sforza, Duke of Milano, was probably the model of *La belle ferronnière* (Louvre) painted by Leonardo da Vinci (?) at the end of her life. A few years later, in Dec. 1499, he made a very beautiful drawing of her sister Isabella (1474-1539), wife of Francesco Gonzaga, marquis of Mantova. That full-size drawing is also in the Louvre. Both princesses were great patrons of arts and letters, but Beatrice died prematurely at 22; Isabella's life was thrice as long; she patronized Leonardo, Raphael, Mantegna, Giulio Romano, Baldassare Castiglione. She is one of the most representative personalities of the Renaissance. Biographies of both sisters by Julia Cartwright (Mrs. Henry Ady, d. 1924): *Beatrice d'Este* (London: Dent, 1899), *Isabella d'Este* (2 vols.; London: Murray, 1903). For the University of Ferrara, see *Introd. 3*, 1400.

83. Guarino da Verona (1374-1460) had followed his Greek teacher, Manuel Chrysoloras (XIV-2), to Constantinople and brought back about 50 Greek MSS. He came to Ferrara in 1436 to tutor Lionello, eldest son of Niccolò d'Este. We have already mentioned him apropos of his discovery of a MS of Celsus in Bologna in 1426 (*Introd. 3*, 1292).

84. It was at Chinon in Touraine that Joan of Arc had been permitted to meet her King, Charles VII, in 1429.

85. The Cordeliers were Franciscans of the strict observance; they were so-called because they girdled themselves with a knotted cord, the cord which they used for self-discipline.

86. Guillaume Budé (1468-1540) of Paris was one of the greatest humanists of France and one of the leaders of the French Renaissance. He obtained some reputation because of his treatise on ancient coinage and metrology, *De asse et partibus eius* (Paris: Bade, 1514-15), often reprinted and discussed. More important was his leadership with Jean du Bellay in the foundation of the *Collegium trilingue* (Collège de France) and of the royal library of Fontainebleau (cradle of BN), and in the promotion of printing in France. His publications in many fields of classical philology are too many to be listed here. His memory is immortalized by them and by the *Association Guillaume Budé* (founded in 1917), main defender of the humanities in the French world.

> Eugène de Budé: *Vie de G. Budé* (301 pp.; Paris: Perrin, 1884). Louis Delaruelle: *G. Budé* (330 pp.; Paris: Champion 1907); *Répertoire de la correspondance de Budé* (272 pp.; Toulouse: Privat, 1907). Jean Plattard: *Budé* (48 pp.; Paris: Les belles lettres, 1923). Sandys 2, 170-73.

87. André Tiraqueau, born at Fontenay-le-Comte (Vendée), *c.* 1480; died in Paris, 1558. He defended his friend, Rabelais, against the Cordeliers. So vast was his learning that he was nicknamed "the Varro of his time."

88. According to my *Introd. 3,* 1321, the Sorbonne censured in 1530 the teaching of Greek (and Hebrew) at the Collège de France, but that special interdiction may have been preceded by others. Erasmus' edition of the New Testament was published with a new Latin translation, revising the Vulgate (Basel: Froben, 1516); for title page, see *Isis 27,* 429. The paraphrase of St. Luke was published in Hannover, 1517.

89. Sebastian Greiff (Gryphius). Born in Wurtemberg in 1493; died in Lyon, 1556. Editor of many Latin and French books. He was a good humanist, but his main glory was connected with French letters. He was the first to print *Gargantua* and *Pantagruel* (1532-52) and the complete works of Clément Marot (1538). Baudrier: *Bibliographie lyonnaise 8,* 11-286, 442 (Lyon, 1910).

90. Guillaume du Bellay (1491-1543) was an older brother of Rabelais' main protector, the cardinal Jean du Bellay (1493-1560). The most illustrious member of that family was their first cousin, Joachim du Bellay (1522-60), one of the heralds of the French Renaissance, the author of the *Deffense et illustration de la langue françoise* (Paris: Arnoul l'Angelier, 1549), manifesto of the Pléiade.

91. Marguerite d'Angoulême, duchesse d'Alençon, reine de Navarre (1492-1549), "la perle des Valois," patron of letters; poet, author of the *Heptaméron.* Very elaborate study of her life and works by Pierre Jourda (2 vols.; Paris: Champion, 1930).

92. *Sic. Gargantua,* which became the first book of the whole work, was published after *Pantagruel,* which became the second book.

93. I used the copy in the Harvard Library. It is an in-16, 105 mm. high. The Latin text covers 427 pp. To show the abundance of notes Hippocrates covers 77 pp. of text, 184 pp. of notes! In the translation of the *Aphorisms,* Book VII, Rabelais introduced two aphorisms omitted by Leoniceno but included in other editions anterior to his own.

94. A similar collection (the same treatises translated by the same scholars) was published in an anonymous edition of 1527 (s. 1.). It was a standard collection for medical teaching. Rabelais' little book was reprinted by Gryphe in 1543 with various modifications.

95. Montaigne (1533-92), who was equally great in a different way, if not greater, belongs to the following generation. And so does Ronsard (1524-85), though Ronsard was a little closer to him. If we assume that Rabelais was born *c.* 1494, Ronsard was 30 years and Montaigne 39 years younger.

96. Rabelais' edition was the third. Manardi's letters were first published in Ferrara, 1521; then in Strassburg, 1529. The fourth edition by Isingrinius (Basel, 1540) was the first to include Manardi's commentary on the *Grabadin* of Mesuë the Younger (XI-1). Later editions continued to include it; the last one was printed in Hannover, 1611.

97. Bartolommeo Marliani of Milano (dates unknown) was a classical archaeologist who collected Latin inscriptions and monuments. Rabelais' edition of his *Topographia* was the first; later editions: Rome, 1544; Basel, 1550; Venice, 1588.

98. The name is a Latinization of Kay or Kaye but so well established in English usage that we can use it even with an English first name. He is the Dr. Caius of the *Merry wives of Windsor. DNB 8,* 221-25 (1886). A more elaborate biography was written by John Venn, for the biographical

history of Gonville and Caius College (Cambridge University Press, 1901), vol. 3, pp. 30-63, and reprinted with additions in *The works of John Caius,* edited for the college by Ernest Stewart Roberts, a thick volume (Cambridge University Press, 1912), pp. 1-78. This is a reprint of the *Opera aliquot* (Louvain: Bergagne, 1556), plus the Annals of the Royal College of Physicians, 1518-72, not printed before, and Fleming's translation of the book on dogs (1576).

99. For Gonville, founded in 1349, reorganized by Caius in 1558, see *Introd. 3, 475.* The new letters patent were given to Caius by Philip and Mary on Sept. 1557.

100. He finally refused to accept their new pronunciation of Greek and explained his conclusions in *De pronunciatione Grecae et Latinae linguae* posthumously published by Day (London, 1574). His refusal to accept the reform advocated by Cheke is poorly expressed; it is simply a denunciation of change. The printer, John Day or Daye (1522-84), being an ardent Protestant was imprisoned by Mary, but released by Elizabeth. He printed the first book of church music in English (1560), the first edition of Foxe's *Martyrs* (1563), etc. Many typographical innovations are ascribed to him (*DNB 14, 233*).

101. Giovanni Battista da Monte (Verona, 1498—Padova, 1551). He wrote many commentaries on Galen and might have been discussed in this chapter, except that I had to restrict myself to a few specimens of three nations. Short note by Haberling (*BL 4,* 248).

102. *A boke or counseill against the disease commonly called the sweate or sweatyng sicknesse* (London: Grafton, 1552). Facsimile copy with introduction by Archibald Malloch (New York, 1937). *De ephemera britannica,* in his *Opera aliquot et versiones* (Louvain: Bergagne, 1556). The two texts were composed at about the same time, the first short and plain for the general public, the second for the doctors. According to Garrison, *History of medicine* (4th ed.; 1929), p. 243, "the epidemics of sweating sickness (*sudor anglicus*) which prevailed in 1528-29 were probably influenza. The epidemic of 1580 was the first to be recognized definitely as influenza. . . ."

103. *Galeni libri aliquot graeci, partim hactenus non visi, partim repurgati, annotationibusque illustrati* (Basel, 1544).

104. The printer, William Seres (Gul. Seresius), had been in partnership with John Day until the middle of the century. His patent for the printing of "primers" (forms of private prayers) was revoked by Mary but returned by Elizabeth (*DNB 51,* 251). He died *c.* 1579.

105. Brasàvola with one *s*; the second *s* was probably added by Frenchmen to indicate that the *s* must be hard, not soft like a *z*.

106. Antonius Musa (I-2 B.C.) was the most famous of Augustus' physicians. He cured Augustus by means of cold baths in 23 B.C.

107. The words *loch* and *suffuf* seem odd in this Latin title. They are Arabic words: *safūf* is a medical powder; the verb *lakhkha* may mean to anoint someone with perfume.

108. Dedicated "ad magnificam et illustrem Dianam Estensem." The book is not available to me, and I do not know who this Diana was. Could it be Isabella d'Este, marchioness of Mantova, who lived until 1539? See footnote 82.

109. That is the index forming vol. 20 of the Kühn Greek-Latin edition of Galen (Leipzig: Car. Cnobloch, 1833).

110. In the prologue to the *Canterbury Tales* (lines 411-49) Chaucer names

many ancient and medieval physicians. Rufus is named, but not Soranos (*Introd. 3,* 1204).

111. All the places mentioned apropos of those four doctors are relatively close together (Pergamon and Tralleis were both in the province of Asia; Aigina in Greece), except Amida which was far away in the East in Greater Armenia on the Upper Tigris (Arabic: Diyār Bakr or Āmid). In spite of the fact that Paulos witnessed the Muslim invasion of Egypt, he is (medically) pre-Islamic. Arabic medicine did not develop until the end of the eighth century, and we might even say until the ninth century.

112. We have only 1 to 15, 24-25, 43-49 and parts of 50-51, that is about 25 books out of a total of 70 (or 72?).

113. *Euporista* means the drugs which are easy to obtain (*remedia parabilia*). *Stricto sensu* the title applies only to Book 2. The whole work is a treatise of medicine written for the general reader rather than for the specialist.

114. Article on Rosario by Pagel (*BT, 4,* 724).

115. For bibliography of Greek editions of separate books, see *Introd 1, 431.*

116. The brothers Beringen, Godefroy and Marcellin, of German origin, began their printing activities in Lyon, 1544-45. Godefroy was a humanist whom other humanists like the martyr printer, Etienne Dolet (1509-46), were ready to befriend. Baudrier *3,* 31-55 (1897). For the Beringen edition of Aëtios, see p. 48.

117. It is listed but not numbered in Klebs (p. 34) who adds, "Copinger 378, n.p.d., Undated variant of the ed. Lyon, Fradin, 1504 (GW)." The book printed by François Fradin in 1504 was an incomplete and imperfect Latin translation. François Fradin, dit Poitevin (1470-1537), began printing as a companion in 1493, master printer in 1501. Baudrier *11,* 87-112 (1914), p. 98. I wrote "almost" because the *Liber urinarum* of Theophilos Protospatharios (VII-1) was included in the six editions of the *Articella* (Klebs 116).

118. The name Petrus or Petri is that of a distinguished family of printers in Basel. The ancestor, Hans Petri (1441-1512), originated from Franconia, established himself in Basel in 1460. He called his nephew Adam from the same village to come and help him. His son, Heinrich (1508-79), studied medicine but took over the printing business when the father died in 1525. After Heinrich's retirement, the business was continued by the oldest and youngest of his many sons, especially by the latter, Sebastian Petri, who died in 1629 (*ADB 25,* 520).

119. Edited by J. L. Heiberg: *Pauli Aeginetae libri tertii interpretatio antiqua* (256 pp.; Leipzig, 1912).

120. Simon de Colines (*c.* 1475-1546), printer and bookseller in Paris. He worked with Henri Estienne and married his widow, *c.* 1521. It was in that year that the first book bearing his own imprint was published, the first of many hundreds. He was one of the creators of small-sized classbooks and of many forms of type (italics, grec accentué, grec royal). He was not only a printer but a humanist.

121. Guillaume Rouillé l'ancien, better known under the name Rouville, Rovillius (b. *c.* 1518 near Loches, Touraine; d. Lyon, 1589). He was one of the great printers of Lyon and the bibliography of himself and followers fills vol. 9 of the *Bibliographie lyonnaise* (Lyon, 1912).

122. *Biographie universelle 41,* 642.

123. Joseph Boulmier: *Estienne Dolet, sa vie, ses oeuvres, son martyre* (316 pp.; Paris, 1857); Richard Copley Christie: *Dolet, the martyr printer of the Renaissance* (579 pp.; London, 1880. Rev. ed., 1899); Octave Galtier:

Dolet (Paris: Flammarion, 1908); Marc Chassaigne: *Dolet, portraits et documents inédits* (350 pp.; Paris: Michel, 1930).

124. In my *Introd.*, I placed him in the ninth century and even called IX(2) the Time of al-Rāzī. It would have been better, I now realize, to place him in the tenth century. It is always difficult to deal with men bestraddling almost equally two periods.

125. For al-Rāzī see Klebs 825 to 827, for 'Alī ibn 'Abbās, no. 498. Title pages of the *Continens* (first ed.; Brescia, 1486) in *Osiris 5*, 143, and of the *Regalis dispositio* (first ed.; Venice, 1492) in *Osiris 5*, 145. For details concerning these first editions see *Osiris 5*, 107-8 (1938). The *Continens* was an enormous work and its first ed. a folio volume of 1180 pages.

126. The dates are quoted in both styles, Hegira and Christian, to illustrate the difficulties which arose when one tried to celebrate his millenary on an international basis. The Muslim millenary of his birth occurred in 1370 (= 1950/51); the Christian ninth centenary in 1880/81; as to the ninth centenary of his death, the Muslim date is 1328 (= 1910/11) and the Christian date 1936/37. The difficulties are multiplied by discrepancies in the original Muslim dates (*Isis 42, 314*).

127. Aydin M. Sayili: "Was Ibni Sina an Iranian or a Turk?" *Isis 31*, 8-24. The main cultural influences to which Avicenna was exposed were Islamic, Persian and Arabic, and his writings are imperishable monuments of the Arabic language.

128. Consider the indexes of my *Introduction, s.v.* Ibn Sīnā, in vol. 1, p. 810, 2 lines; in vol. 2, p. 1232, 11 lines; in vol. 3, p. 2065, 17 lines. It is a pity that I was too lazy to analyze these innumerable references and to add explanatory words to each.

129. To give the reader an idea of the size of the *Qānūn* and of its architecture, let us say that it is divided into five books or *kutub*. Each *kitāb* is divided into sections or *funūn*. Each *fann* into treatises or *ta'alīmāt*. Each *ta'alīm* into sums or *jumal*. Each *jumla* into chapters or *fuṣūl*. The *faṣl* was the smallest unit. MSS in Arabic or other languages might contain only one or more of each of these subdivisions. The possibilities of choice and combination are endless.

130. For Toledo, see footnote 50.

131. There are no Arabic incunabula *stricto sensu*, but a couple of incunabula included Arabic letters or words printed from woodcuts. The first book printed in Arabic characters was the *Horologium* produced by Gregorio de' Gregorii (Fano, 1514). Many Arabic books were published in the sixteenth century, but all of them in the West, particularly in Rome. There was no Arabic printing in the East before the eighteenth century. The Psalter printed at Quzḥaya, Lebanon, 1610, contained Arabic, but in Garshūni character (*Introd. 3, 360*). Joseph Nasrallah: *L'imprimerie au Liban* (Harrisa, 1949—*Isis 44*, 161).

132. Both works are described by Christian Friedrich de Schnurrer in his *Bibliotheca arabica* (Halle a.S., 1811), pp. 449-51, 457-62.

133. For Alpago, see Sarton: "Arabic achievements of the fifteenth century" in Millás Festschrift (Barcelona, 1955).

134. That biography was written by Ibn Sīnā's favorite disciple 'Abd al-Wāhib ibn Muḥammad al-Jūzjānī (*Introd. 3, 700, 1530*).

135. Cannot identify him, except that he was a physician of the second half of the sixteenth century. Palamedes seems to be a pseudonym. The adjective Adriensis added to his name may refer to various Italian localities (Adria); I do not know which is meant. The original Palamedes was a Greek hero of

the Trojan age, traditionally credited with many useful inventions (light-houses, measures, scales, dice, alphabet, etc.).

136. Vopiscus Fortunatus Plempius (Amsterdam, 1601—Louvain, 1671). His original Flemish name was Plemp. Leader of the anti-Cartesian party in Louvain. He was highly respected for his great learning, but we can hardly understand today the fame which he enjoyed. *Biographie nationale de Belgique 17,* 803-6 (1903). His almost exact contemporary, the old gossip Guy Patin (1601-72), wrote from Paris, 22 Jan. 1672, "Je viens d'apprendre . . . que Monsieur Plempius célèbre Professeur en Médecine est mort le 12. de Décembre dernier. Adieu la bonne doctrine en ce pais-là. Descartes et les Chymistes ignorans tâchent de tout gâter tant en Philosophie qu'en bonne Médecine. Ce Mr. Plempius était un savant homme Hollandois de nation et Huguenot, qui se fit Catholique pour être Professeur à Louvain. Il dit un jour à Monsieur Riolan qui me le redit, Si Messieurs les Etats me veulent donner une de leurs Charges de Professeur en Médecine à Leyden, je me reterai Huguenot, et irai domeurer lira cum. Que ne feroit-on pas aujourdui pour gagner sa vie." This is the very last letter (no. 545) published in the *Lettres choisies de feu Mr. Guy Patin* (3 vols.; Cologne: Pierre du Laurens, 1691). Tricot-Royer: "La bibliothèque de Plempius," *Recueil des mémoires couronnés de l' Académie royale de médecine* 22 (112 pp.; Bruxelles, 1925—*Isis 25,* 213).

137. Peter Kirsten (1577-1640) was born in Breslau, and after long studies abroad and extensive travels he practised medicine in his native city. He was rector of the Elisabetshaus and inspector of schools but resigned in 1616. He learned Arabic for the sake of his medical studies and became one of the leading orientalists of his day. He spent the last few years of his life in Sweden, having been appointed royal physician and professor of medicine in Uppsala. He died there in 1640 (*ADB 16,* 34).

138. Santorio Santorio (1561-1636), of Capo d'Istria, studied and taught in Padova. Physician to the king of Poland for 14 years. He became in 1611 professor of theoretical physics in Padova. He invented various instruments, e.g., a fever thermometer. He wrote commentaries on Galen as well on Avicenna. *Opera omnia* (4 vols.; Venice, 1660); *BL 5,* 21 (1934).

139. Pierre Vattier (1623-67), born near Lisieux in Normandy, studied medicine and became physician to Gaston, duke of Orléans. He was professor of Arabic at the Collège de France from 1658 until his death in Paris, 1667 (*NBG*).

140. Pietro Salio Diverso practised medicine in the second half of the sixteenth century first in Naples, then in his native city, Faenza. He wrote a treatise on pestilential fever (Bologna, 1584, etc.) and commentaries on Hippocrates and Avicenna, *BL 2,* 279 (1930).

141. Giovanni Arcolani (Herculanus), born at Verona, date unknown; professor of medicine in Bologna, 1412-27, then in Padova and Ferrara, where he died in 1460 or 1484. He wrote commentaries on Avicenna and Rhazes which are said to contain original observations. His *Practica medica seu expositio vel commentarii in nonum Rhazis ad regem Almansorem* was very popular (Klebs 79): Verona or Padova, 1480; Venice, 1493, 1497, 1504, 1542, 1557, 1560; Basel, 1540.

142. This is not a book title but a traditional description. The same remark applies to many other collections listed below; they are generally designated not by the title which may be awkward but by a description, say, *Collectio de balneis,* or *Balneorum scriptores.* The title of that particular collection begins *De balneis omnia quae extant apud Graecos, Latinos et Arabos.*

143. All the collections listed here are in Latin except when otherwise stated.
144. Johann Caesarius, born in Jülich in 1460, studied in Paris and flourished in Cologne where he died in 1551 in very old age. He was a philosopher, physician, and philologist. Short note in *BL 1*, 796 (1929).
145. These woodcuts of 1544 are a great contrast with the more scientific ones available in the *Fasciculus medicinae* (1491, etc.). For SS. Cosmas and Damian see *Introd. 3*, 863, 1247.
146. Jean de Gorris (1505-77). Born in Paris and professor in its Faculty of medicine. In spite of being a Calvinist, he survived the St. Bartholomew purge of 1572; he died in 1577, presumably in Paris. He edited works of Hippocrates and of Nicandros of Colophon (III-1 B. C.). His *Definitiones* was first printed by Andr. Wechel (Paris, 1564); it was reprinted in Frankfurt a.M., 1578, 1601; Paris, 1622.
147. The story is told by John Maxson Stillman: *Paracelsus* (Chicago: Open Court, 1920—*Isis 4*, 146), p. 65, no source being quoted. It is repeated, without source, in Henry M. Pachter: *Paracelsus* (New York: Schuman, 1951—*Isis 42*, 244-46), p. 7.
148. Gianmatteo Ferrari da Gradi of Milanese origin obtained his M.D. at Milano in 1436, was professor of medicine at Pavia, died in 1472. Henri Maxime Ferrari: *Une chaire de médecine au XVe siècle, Un professeur à l'Université de Pavie de 1432 à 1472* (334 pp., 6 fig.; Paris: Alcan, 1899).
149. The *Practica* was the first commentary to appear in print; it was issued by an anonymous printer in Pavia before 1480, perhaps as early as 1471-72 (Klebs 393.1; *Isis 7*, 198). The *Liber Almansoris* of Rhazes was printed only in 1481 in Milano (Klebs 826.1-3).

LECTURE II

NATURAL HISTORY

1. For the Aristotelian incunabula, see Klebs 82 to 96. Pages of the Latin princeps (1472) and Greek princeps (1495) of the *Opera* are reproduced in *Osiris 5*, 128-29; other pages, in my *History of Science 1*, 482-83 (1952).
2. Simon Grynaeus of Heidelberg (1493-1541). German Hellenist, who taught Greek in Vienna and Buda and finally settled in Basel (1529) where he spent the end of his life. His main discovery was that of five lost books of Livy (I-2 B.C.) in the abbey of Lorch (on the Rhine, below Bingen).
3. Friedrich Sylburg (1536-96) of Marburg was one of the most distinguished Hellenists of his century. He was befriended by Henri Estienne and worked for the latter's *Thesaurus*. He edited many Greek and Latin texts with great care, adding to each elaborate indexes. His indexes to the 11 vols. of his Aristotle were reprinted by the Clarendon Press with Bekker's Greek text, but without the latter's pagination! (11 vols.; Oxford, 1837).
4. More Greek (or Greco-Latin) editions appeared in the seventeenth and eighteenth centuries. They are all superseded by the Greek-Latin edition prepared under the auspices of the Prussian Academy by Immanuel Bekker (1785-1871) (4 vols.; Berlin, 1831-46). Vols. 1-2, containing the Greek text, appeared in 1831; an index volume was published in 1870. The best way of referring to an Aristotelian text is to quote the Bekker pagination. English translation edited by W. D. Ross (11 vols.; Oxford: Clarendon Press, 1908-31), referring to the Bekker pagination.

NOTES

5. Klebs 85.1. Theodoros Gaza was born in Thessalonica *c.* 1400; he studied Latin under Vittorino da Feltre at Mantova; he lived in many Italian cities and finally in Calabria, where he died *c.* 1475. He translated many books from Greek into Latin, and two treatises of Cicero from Latin into Greek. He wrote in Greek a Greek grammar, which enjoyed a long popularity; Erasmus translated it into Latin and Budé used it in his teaching.

6. I have examined in Harvard Library these incunabula, except the third. The editions of 1476, 1492, 1498 contain Theodoros Gaza's translation of *De historia animalium, De partibus* and the *De generatione,* together with Theodoros' dedicatory preface to Sixtus IV, pope 1471-84. The contents of the third edition (1495), which I have not seen, are very probably the same. Note that the printers of the four Venetian editions are different; I imagine that the first printer used the original MS and that the three others copied one of the preceding printed editions.

7. Julius Caesar Scaliger (1484-1558), one of the greatest classical scholars of France in the first half of the sixteenth century. Born in Italy (on the Lago di Garda), he was educated in Germany, but his early marriage with Andiette de la Roque of Agen (on the Garonne) fixed him in that city until the end of his life. He was one of the champions of Ciceronianism against Erasmus; a botanist and physician as well as an outstanding Latinist. Vernon Hall, Jr.: "Life of J. C. Scaliger," *Transactions American Philosophical Society 40,* 85-170 (1950)— *Isis 42,* 321.

8. Michael of Ephesos was a pupil of Michael Psellos (XI-2). See *Introd 2,* 494, 584.

9. Vittore Trincavella of Venice (1496-1568). Hellenist and physician who obtained medical fame during a plague in Murano. The Venetian senate gave him a chair of medicine in Padova; he taught there from 1551 until 1568, then accepted a position of consulting physician in Carinthia, but he died the same year. He did much to promote Hippocratism and wrote *Consilia medica* (Basel, 1586) and many other books on medicine and philosophy.

10. Jacques Lefèvre d'Etaples, Jacobus Faber Stapulensis (1455-1537). See my third lecture.

11. There had been exceptions of the same kind also in the Middle Ages, the outstanding one being that of Albert the Great (XIII-2). St. Albert had observed many animals with his own eyes (*Introd. 2,* 938-40); he was the foremost naturalist of the Middle Ages.

12. For William Turner, see Charles E. Raven: *English naturalists* (Cambridge University Press, 1947—*Isis 39,* 196), chiefly pp. 48-137.

13. The *Avium historia* was reprinted by George Thackeray (Cambridge, 1823), but that reprint is almost as rare as the original edition. English translation by A. H. Evans: *Turner on birds* (244 pp.; Cambridge University Press, 1903), with Latin text on opposite pages, notes pointing out Turner's original observations, and list of birds dealt with. Evans' is the third edition of the Latin text.

14. Facsimile reprint of the *Book of wines* with modern English version and introduction by Sanford V. Larkey (New York: Scholars' facsimiles, 1941— *Isis 35,* 231).

15. François de Tournon, born at Tournon, Ardèche (Vivarais), in 1489; cardinal in 1530; died in Paris, 1562. He was a famous minister, a diplomat serving under four kings, from François I to Charles IX, a humanist, a protector of arts and letters. Among his protégés were the three naturalists with whom we are now dealing, Rondelet, Belon, Salviani, also Champier.

He founded the Collège de Tournon (Paris), which he intrusted to the Jesuits, and was buried there. Michel François: "Correspondance du cardinal François de Tournon," *Bibliothèque de l'Ecole des hautes études,* fasc. 290 (468 pp.; Paris: Champion, 1946). François summarized or edited 760 letters written by the cardinal from 1521 to 1562. The collection is disappointing to the historian of science, for he finds no reference to the naturalists; and there are none to Budé, Ronsard, etc. The cardinal was a grand seigneur, willing to patronize men of genius but having himself more important things to bother about. On Cardinal de Tournon, see also Abel Lefranc: *La vie quotidienne au temps de la Renaissance* (Paris: Hachette, 1938), pp. 39-42.

16. Lobelius (1538-1616) for whom see the botanical section below.

17. For Mathieu or Macé Bonhomme, printer in Lyon, Vienne, and Avignon from 1535 to 1569, see Baudrier: *Bibliographie lyonnaise 10,* 185-270 (1913), specifically pp. 239, 259.

18. Detailed investigations concerning him and his works were made by Paul Delaunay: "L'aventureuse existence de Pierre Belon du Mans," and published by him in the *Revue du seizième siècle,* vols. 9 to 12 (Paris, 1922-25) and reprinted in a separate volume with illustrations, a new preface, addenda, and index (200 pp., 11 fig.; Paris: Champion, 1926—*Isis 9,* 515). See also P. Delaunay: "Un adversaire de la Réforme. Les idées religieuses de Belon," *Bull. de la Commission historique de la Mayenne 38,* fasc. 134, 97-117 (Laval, 1922). The notice by Hoefer in the *Nouvelle biographie générale 5,* 295-99 (1866) is full of errors, which have been copied in other books.

19. His portrait in *De aquatilibus,* 1553, is stated to represent him *aet.* 36.

20. La Soultière is a very small hamlet, now a part of Cerans (Sarthe). It was in the province of Maine of which the capital was Le Mans; therefore he called himself "Pierre Belon du Mans." In spite of its smallness, La Soultière has been the cradle of two great men, Belon in 1517 and Marin Mersenne in 1588.

21. Gabriel de Luetz, baron d'Aramon, born at Nîmes in Gascony at the end of the fifteenth century; died after 1553; Ambassador of France to Turkey from 1546 to 1553; credited for having gained the support of Sulaimān II and obtained his alliance with François I against Charles Quint. He followed Sulaimān in Persia, and traveled also in Egypt and Palestine. The account of his travels was written by one of his secretaries, Jean Chesneau: *Le voyage de Monsieur d'Aramon, ambassadeur pour le Roy en Levant, escript par Jean Chesneau,* edited by Charles Schefer, vol. 8 of *Recueil de voyages et documents pour servir à l'histoire de la géographie* (358 pp.; Paris, 1887). Belon is referred to six times in the footnotes.

22. The conclave which elected Julius III, pope from 1550 to 1555. The abbey of St. Germain des Prés has now disappeared; the Boulevard St. Germain crosses its site.

23. I do not know whether Belon and the illustrious poet Pierre de Ronsard (1524-85) knew one another well. Ronsard's references to Belon are curious. Two poems of his were originally dedicated to André Thévet. You will find them in the *Oeuvres de Ronsard,* edited by Paul Laumonier, vol. 2, pp. 19, 443 (Paris: Lemerre, 1914-19). In the posthumous editions of Ronsard's work, Thévet's name was replaced by Belon's! Ronsard honored Belon in order to punish Thévet. What had the latter done to him?

André Thévet (1502-90) of Angoulême, a Cordelier (later secularized), traveled extensively in the Near East and sailed to Brazil. Upon his return, he was appointed historiographer and cosmographer to Marie de Médicis. He was a prolific writer and his royal connections gave him power to help his friends (if he wished to help them).

24. This colloque, which took place in Poissy (Seine-et-Oise) in Sept.-Oct. 1561, was a reunion of Catholic and Protestant theologians brought together by that noble magistrate, Michel de l'Hospital (1507-73), chancellor of France, with the vain hope of establishing religious peace. The Protestants were led by Théodore de Bèze (1,519-1605), the Catholics by Cardinals of Tournon and of Lorraine, both of whom were Belon's patrons. For the first, see note 15. The second, Charles de Lorraine (1525-74), was a member of the illustrious family of the dukes of Lorraine (and Guise). He was a great bibliophile, immoral but orthodox, for a time very influential in the royal council. But for the opposition of the chancelier de l'Hospital, he would have organized the Holy Inquisition in France instead of peace. H. Outram Evennett; *The cardinal of Lorraine and the Council of Trent* (564 pp.; Cambridge University Press, 1930).

25. This restriction (Western) must be added, because there are a few Chinese treatises devoted to botanical groups, e.g., a treatise on litchi written in 1059 (*Introd. 1,* 776-77); another on oranges in 1178; treatises on chrysanthemums, on mushrooms, on bamboo, etc. (*Introd. 2,* 57).

26. The history of acclimatization of plants and animals is a vast subject which has not yet been dealt with properly. A full account of it should include Roman and Chinese efforts; all the great nations and many of the smaller ones have taken part in such attempts, more or less successfully. Gardens of acclimatization are different from the ordinary botanical or zoölogical gardens, but the line between them is not always easy to draw.

27. The only work of his which is more in the humanistic tradition of his time is an isolated one which I left out of his bibliography. Let me mention it here for the sake of completeness. *De admirabili operum antiquorum et rerum suspiciendarum praestantia liber primus; De medicato funere seu cadavere condito et lugubri defunctorum ejulatione liber secundus; De medicamentis nonnullis servandi cadaveris vim obtinentibus liber tertius* (58 leaves; Paris: B. Prévost, 1553). Also published with a new colophon (Paris: Guillaume Cavellat, 1553). The interest which this book offered to philologists is proved by its inclusion in the *Thesaurus graecarum antiquitatum* of Jacobus Gronovius (13 vols., folio; Leiden: Van der Aa, 1697-1702), vol. 8 (1699), col. 2541-2640.

28. For more details, see my *History of science 1,* 541-42. Charles Singer: "The placental shark," *Studies in the history and method of science* (Oxford: Clarendon Press, 1921), vol. 2, pp. 29-37 (ill.).

29. Not to be confused with his contemporary and namesake, Pierre Gilles of Antwerp, friend of Erasmus, who published the first edition of the *Utopia* (Louvain, 1516). Thomas More loved him and included in the *Utopia* a dedicatory letter and many kind references to him.

The two names, Pierre (Petrus) and Gilles or Giles (Aegidius), were fairly common in Christian lands; hence, it is not surprising to come across two distinguished contemporaries called Pierre, whose fathers were probably called Gilles (the French spelling is generally with two *l*'s; the English with one). For the Pierre Gilles with whom we are now concerned, see *NBG* (*20,* 542) and Miall (*57,* 1912). For some mysterious reason, the printer, Sébastien Gryphe of Lyon, wrote Gilles' name with a *y* (Gyllius). Baudrier *9,* 70 (1910).

30. Georges d'Armagnac (*c.* 1501-85), a protégé of the duke and duchess of

Alençon (sister of François I), was made bishop of Rodez (Aveyron; Rouergue); later, he was sent as an ambassador to Venice and Rome and finally established as a cardinal in Rome. He deserves to be remembered because of his patronage of men of science and men of letters.

31. Reprinted by the same printer in 1535. See Baudrier 8, 70, 85 (1910). There is a copy of the reprint in the Harvard Library. Reprinted a third time by another Lyon printer, Guillaume Rouillé I, in 1565 (Baudrier 9, 300).

32. Berrhoea (Beroia) is the old name of Aleppo. The *Descriptio nova elephanti* was reprinted separately in *Bibliophilo heringiano* (Hamburg, 1614).

33. The Latin name of Città di Castello is Tiferni Tiberini; hence the author called himself Hippolytus Salvianus Tiphernas.

34. P. 2 of his preface "tribus herbulis, ac potius tribus verbulis. . . ."

35. For the defense of J. C. Scaliger as botanist, see the biography by Vernon Hall, Jr., *Trans. American Philosophical Society (40, 87-170 [1950]— Isis 42, 321)*, p. 141.

36. The translator from Latin into Greek was possibly Maximos Planudes (XIII-2).

37. For the contents of the *De plantis*, see my *History of science 1, 546*.

38. One might add the Italian, Rufinus, who was still unknown when I published my survey of XIII-2. He compiled at the end of the thirteenth century a herbal which was edited by Lynn Thorndike: *The herbal of Rufinus* (520 pp.; University of Chicago, 1945—*Isis 36*, 256-57, 1 pl.; *Introd. 3*, 1834). Albert the Great died in 1280; Rufinus, writing his herbal not long after 1287, ignored completely Albert's work (*Isis 36*, 257).

39. Facsimile pages of the Greek princeps (1497) and of the Latin one (1483) may be seen in my *History of science 1, 552-53*.

40. The main biographer of Cesalpino is Ugo Viviani, *Vita ed opere di Andrea Cesalpino* (2d ed., 254 pp.; Arezzo, 1922—*Isis 6*, 158); *Tre medizi aretini, A. Cesalpino, F. Redi e F. Folli* (250 pp.; Arezzo, 1936—*Isis 26*, 518). Viviani died in Arezzo in 1948 (*Isis 40*, 118).

41. The expression which I am using is perhaps misleading. At any rate, the following interpretation is necessary. These earliest chairs of botany were really devoted to "simples" (lectura de simplicibus), that is, to the botanical basis of materia medica. Such lectures might become almost exclusively botanical if the teacher was so inclined.

42. For Luca Ghini di Croara d'Imola (*c.* 1490-1556), see Giovanni Battista de Toni, *Gli scienziati italiani 1*, 1-4 (Roma, 1921).

43. There may be ambiguities concerning the dates, for the foundation of a garden may be given different dates according to different interpretations, but it is certain that the Renaissance gardens began in N. Italy in the forties of the sixteenth century. As to ancient and medieval botanic gardens, see *History of science 1*, 556; *Introd. 3*, 224, 816.

44. A. Arber. *Herbals* (Cambridge University Press, 1938—*Isis 30*, 131-32), p. 140.

45. *De plantis libri XVI* (quarto, 20 leaves, 621 pp., index; Florence: Georgius Marescottus, 1583). Linnaeus' copy of it bears marginal notes in his own hand; he added his own generic names.

46. Meaning Adam of Zalužan near Pisek, about 70 miles south of Prague. His family came from Zalužan, but he was born in 1558 in another place in the same region.

47. Thanks to my friend, S. Harrison Thomson of the University of Colorado, who has kindly excerpted Czech accounts for me, I am able to give more

biographical information than is available in Western books. His sources are quoted by him as follows. Excellent article in the *Ottův Slovník Naučny*. There is another article on him by J. V. Šimak in the same *Časopis* above mentioned in 1915, p. 77ff. For further bibliography, see J. Jakubec: *Dějiny literatury české* (Prague, 1929), I, 774.

48. Agnes Arber: *Herbals* (Cambridge University Press, 1938—*Isis 30*, 131-32), p. 144.

49. Sarton: "Brave Busbecq," *Isis 33*, 557-75 (1942).

50. This MS, Vindobonensis Med. Gr. 1, is readily available because it was completely reproduced in facsimile (2 vols., elephant folio; Leyden, 1906). The introduction by Karl Wessely was also printed separately (490 pp.; Leyden, 1906). *Introd. 1*, 259. The plant illustrations were reproduced by Robert T. Gunther: *The Greek herbal of Dioscorides illustrated by a Byzantine in 512 and Englished by John Goodyer in 1655* (Oxford University Press, 1934—*Isis 23, 461-62*) A few may be seen in *Isis 33*, 568.

51. In the following bibliography all editions refer to Dioscorides' materia medica (*Peri hylēs iatricēs*), though some of the editions may include one or more of his lesser works.

52. This edition is entitled *Dioscoridis libri octo graece et latine. Castigationes in eosdem libros*. This includes the five books on materia medica plus three books on poisons. The Greek and Latin texts are beautifully printed in parallel columns. The translation of the materia medica is Jean Ruel's.

53. Editions marked with a star are the Greco-Latin ones already mentioned. One of them at least (Frankfurt, 1598) was printed separately; that is, the same printer (Wechel's heirs) published a Greco-Latin edition and a Latin edition at the same time.

54. Juan de Jarava was a Spaniard established in Louvain. Dates and places of birth and death unknown to me. He translated into Spanish Biblical and classical texts, the apophthegmata of Erasmus. Many of his books were published in Antwerp and Louvain. In spite of the deceptive title, his Dioscorides is really a very abbreviated translation of the *Historia stirpium* of Leonhart Fuchs (Basel, 1542).

55. This was done many times during the Renaissance, printers using the woodcuts of an illustrated treatise to form an album for the sake of people who prefer to look at pictures than to read. Our tabloid newspapers cater to similar needs. It is interesting to notice that their gratification began so early.

56. Andreas a Lacuna: *Anatomica methodus, seu de sectione humani corporis contemplatio* (Paris: J. Kerver, 1535).

57. Elaborate biography by Joaquín Olmedilla y Puig: *Estudio histórico de la vida y escritos del sabio español Andrés Laguna medico de Carlos I y Felipe II y célebre escritor y botánico* (200 pp.; Madrid: El Correo, 1887).

58. Harry Friedenwald: *The Jews and medicine* (Baltimore, 1944—*Isis 35*, 346), vol. 2, pp. 419-29. The passage concerning witchcraft is reproduced in facsimile from a later edition of the Spanish Dioscorides (Salamanca, 1566), p. 421, under Stramonium, and translated into English. Dr. Friedenwald suggests that Laguna was perhaps of Marrano descent. As to Wierus (Johann Weyer, 1515-88) see Gregory Zilboorg: *The medical man and the witch during the Renaissance* (225 pp.; Baltimore, 1935—*Isis 25*, 147-52). Zilboorg's book illustrates an aspect of the scientific Renaissance upon which I have no space to dwell, but which should be taken into account in every general study of it.

59. Elaborate information concerning him is given by Harry Friedenwald:

The Jews and medicine (Baltimore: Johns Hopkins, 1944—*Isis 35*, 346), *passim; Jewish luminaries in medical history (ibid.*, 1946—*Isis 37*, 239), p. 35-37.

60. Castelo Branco (Latin, Castellum Album), a small city in the Beira Baixa province, C. E. Portugal.

61. This subject has been discussed in my *Introd. 3*, 56, 1059-61. The Spaniards obliged Jews to be converted, and when the Jews had been converted under duress, their sincerity was doubted. It was a vicious circle caused by intolerance and persecution.

62. Antonio Brasàvola (not Brassavola). See note 105 of Lecture I.

63. John Falconer, an English merchant, who was in Ferrara *c.* 1541-47. He learned from Luca Ghini the art of keeping dried plants and his herbarium, *Maister Falkonner's Boke,* is one of the earliest herbaria, if not the very earliest, mentioned in botanical literature. William Turner often referred to him (B. D. Jackson in *DNB 18,* 161 [1889]). Amatus Lusitanus also spoke of Falconer's herbarium in his commentary on Dioscorides (1553).

64. Gian Battista Canano (1515-79) of Ferrara. Author of the *Musculorum humani corporis picturata dissectio* (Ferrara, 1541?); facsimile reprint (Florence, 1925—*Isis 9,* 433). He was the real discoverer (*c.* 1541) of the valves of the veins (the discovery is generally ascribed to Fabricius ab Acquapendente, 1574). Canano's work was interrupted and overshadowed by Vesalius' *Fabrica*, 1543.

65. The last century was first printed in the first collected edition of the seven centuries (Venice: Vincentius Valgrisius, 1566). Facsimile title pages in Friedenwald (1944), pp. 341, 343, 344.

66. For Euricius and Valerius Cordus, see Edward Lee Greene (1843-1915): *Landmarks of botanical history* (Washington: Smithsonian Institution, 1909), pp. 263-314, and any history of botany.

The father and son originated in Simshausen and their German name was Eberwein. The genus *Cordia* of tropical shrubs (family *Ehretiaceae*) was established in their honor by Plumier.

67. For Pierre Coudenberg or Koudenbergh (1520-94), see *Biographie nationale de Belgique 4,* 417-19 (1873). For the *Guidon des apotiquaires,* Baudrier *4,* 52 (1899).

68. The *Botanologicon* of Euricius Cordus was first printed alone in 1534 (183 pp., index; Cologne: J. Gymnicus, 1534).

69. Caspar Wolf (Wolff or Wolphius), born in Zürich in 1525, studied in Montpellier, succeeded Conrad Gesner as professor of physics and later of Greek, died in 1601. Author of many medical books, chiefly on gynecology.

70. The sack of Rome by the imperialists in May 1527 was a terrible blow for the Eternal City. How deeply did it affect its intellectual life? Many libraries and archives were wantonly destroyed; the Vatican library escaped destruction because it was the headquarters of Philibert, prince of Orange. But how were the men of science and learning affected? The matter deserves investigation. For the political history, see Ludwig Pastor: *History of the Popes* (London: Kegan Paul, 1910), vol. 9, pp. 388-467. The sack was ordered by Charles Quint, emperor and king of Spain, and it was perpetrated with equal cruelty by Germans and Spaniards. The war cry was "Empire! Spain! Victory!" Pope Clement VII was imprisoned. The sack was followed by famine and pestilence. Spaniards claimed that the worst iniquities had been committed by Lutheran Landknechte, and Cardinal Quiñones went so far as to accuse Charles Quint of being an agent of Luther! The Spaniards were as greedy and as merciless as the Germans.

There were two sacks of Rome, which began respectively on May 7 and on Sept. 25, 1527. The whole story is incredibly sordid. Think of the Christian King Charles Quint destroying the Christian center of the world and holding the Pope under duress at the very time when the Church was jeopardized by the Reformation.

According to Edward Gibbon (*Decline and fall*, ch. 31) the sack of Rome by the Catholic King, Charles Quint, was far more destructive than the sack by Alaric in 410.

71. Sarton: "Brave Busbecq" (1522-92), *Isis 33*, 557-75 (1942), specifically p. 570.

72. Mrs. Arber writes (*Herbals*, 94), "The success of the *Commentarii* was phenomenal; it is said that 32,000 copies of the earlier editions were sold." That saying combines precision with imprecision, but we may remember that Mattioli was the botanical best seller of his age.

73. The *Bauhinia* are named after the brothers Jean and Caspar Bauhin. It is a genus of tropical shrubs (e.g., maloo climber, mountain ebony) member of the *senna* family (*Caesalpiniaceae*).

74. Antoine du Pinet, or Dupinet, sieur de Noroy, was born *c.* 1510; he spent a good part of his life in Lyon but died in Paris *c.* 1584. He was Protestant. He translated into French not only Mattioli, but also Pliny (1542), the *De occultis naturae miraculis* (Antwerp, 1559) of the Dutch physician Levinus Lemnius of Zierikzee (1505-68), and *alii*. For the very curious personality of Lemnius, see *NNBW 8*, 1028-31 (1930).

75. As all his books were published in Latin, he is better known under his Latin name Fabius Columna.

76. To *phu* or *agria nardos* (*Sylvestris nardus*) is now identified with *Valeriana Dioscoridis*, not *V. officinalis*. Robert T. Gunther: *The Greek herbal of Dioscoridis* (Oxford, 1934—*Isis 23*, 261-62) p. 13.

77. Glossopetra are fossil shark teeth, and objects resembling them or resembling a tongue. Purpura are the marine snails (*murex*) which the Phoenicians used to produce a purple dye (*History of science 1*, 109).

78. For a description of Hernandez's publications see Bashford Dean and Eugene Willis Gudger: *Bibliography of fishes* (3 vols.; New York: American Museum of Natural History, 1916-23—*Isis 6*, 456-59), vol. 3, p. 258.

79. It is said to be the first botanical book in which copper engravings were used. The frames surrounding each figure are not part of the engravings.

80. On fossil ivory, see *Introd. 2*, 412; *3*, 1186.

81. With regard to botany (Book XII), Pliny quotes 16 Latin authorities and 42 Greek. His main authority was Theophrastos (IV-2 B.C.), though he mentioned him only in his preliminary index. Whether he read Dioscorides or not, is a moot question; his latest editor, Alfred Ernout (Paris: Collection Budé, 1949—*Isis 44*, 104) inclines to believe that Pliny used Dioscorides' books. Then why did he not mention him in his index? Pliny the Elder (23-79) and Dioscorides flourished at about the same time; the dates of birth and death of the latter are unknown.

82. Klebs 786.1-15, 787.1-3. For the success of the *Historia naturalis* in later times, see Eugene Willis Gudger: Pliny's *Historia naturalis*. The most popular natural history ever published (*Isis 6*, 269-81 [1924]). Gudger inflated the number of incunabula, as bibliographers often do who fail to identify the editions by autoscopy. Misleading descriptions and wrong datings introduce "ghost" editions, which it is almost impossible to drive out.

83. One might write an essay entitled "The sack of Mainz and the diffusion

of typography." It is true enough that progress has often been accelerated by calamities and infamous deeds.

84. Cristoforo was a grandnephew of the famous musician, Francesco Landino (XIV-2), *Introd. 2*, 1567.

85. The vicissitudes of the patriarchate of Aquileia are of great political and ecclesiastical interest. The city founded in 181 B.C. at the head of the Adriatic (not far from Trieste) was of great importance in the Roman empire, being second only to Rome. It was destroyed by the Huns in 452. The title of Patriarch was assumed in 557 by a seceding bishop. During the later Middle Ages, the political authority of Venice increased gradually; it was completed in 1438 when the city was destroyed by an earthquake. The patriarchate was abolished in 1748 by Benedict XIV, the last patriarch being the 109th one. Good article by Thomas J. Shahan in *CE 1*, 661-62 (1907).

86. The podestà was somewhat like the "city manager" of American cities but in a more violent and truculent style. He was always chosen outside of the city which he was expected to govern.

87. Giovanni Sforza (1466-1510) was the lord of Pesaro; he had been driven out by Cesare Borgia in 1500 but had come back in 1503. Collenuccio was accused of connivance or "collaboration" with Borgia.

88. Juan Hurtado y Angel González Palencia: *Historia de la literatura española* (3rd ed.; Madrid, 1932—*Isis 19*, 606), p. 444-45. *Algunas obras del doctor F. Lopez de Villalobos* (Madrid, 1886). G. Gaskoin: *The medical works of F. Lopez de Villalobos, now first translated* (320 pp.; London, 1870), not seen. Pagel, *BL 5*, 759 (1934).

89. For the first time in Basel. Camers' index was first published in Venice, 1526, by Melchior Sessa and Petrus Serenae. It was also published separately by the same printers.

90. Renaissance publishers often introduced into their books supplements (indices, notes, etc.) with a different pagination or none; sometimes these supplements were sold separately; occasionally, they were bound with other editions. This causes bibliographical difficulties which I am not competent to deal with.

91. Dalechamps' Latin version of the *Deipnosophistai* (Lyon: A. de Harsy, 1583). Greek edition by Isaac Casaubon published together with Dalechamps' Latin version (Heidelberg, 1597; reprinted Lyon, 1598, 1612, 1657). *Introd. 1*, 326.

92. For example, see Gisela M. Richter: *Animals in Greek sculpture* (New York: Metropolitan Museum, 1930—*Isis 29*, 138).

93. For botanical iconography, see Herrmann Fischer: *Mittelalterliche Pflanzenkunde* (München: Münchner Drucke, 1929—*Isis 15*, 367-70). Agnes Arber: *Herbals* (Cambridge University Press, 1938—*Isis 30*, 131-32). *Introd. 2*, 54-55; *3*, 225, 1163, 1177, 1633, 1835. Wilfrid Blunt: *The art of botanical illustration* (335 pp.; London: Collins, 1951—*Isis 43*, 295-96). Claus Nissen: *Die botanische Illustration, ihre Geschichte und Bibliographie* (2 vols.; Stuttgart: Hiersemann, 1951—*Isis 43*, 295-96). See also the excellent book by Joan Evans: *Nature in design. A study of naturalism in decorative art from the Bronze Age to the Renaissance* (133 pp., 82 fig.; Oxford University Press, 1933).

94. See Pliny's *Historie of the world*, as translated by Philemon Holland (2 vols., folio; London: Adam Islip, 1601), vol. 2, p. 210 (chapter 2 = 4 of Book 25). Referring to Cratevas, Dionysios, and Metrodoros, Pliny says "they painted every hearbe in their colours, and under the pourtraicts they

couched and subscribed their several natures and effects. But what certeintie could there be therein? pictures (you know) are deceitfull; also in representing such a number of colours, and especially expressing the lively hew of Hearbs according to their nature as they grow, no marveile if they that limned and drew them out, did faile and degenerat from the first pattern and originall." Etc. Read the whole chapter either in Holland's delightful prose or in the translation by John Bostock and H. T. Riley (London: Bohn Library, 1856). The ancients had herbals which were collections of colored illustrations of plants with relatively short text.

95. A religious purpose animated naturalists like Jan Swammerdam (1637-80) and Maria Sibylla Merian (1647-1717); it is quite probable that Cybo's inspiration was of the same kind (*Isis 39,* 184).

96. This observation was made by the Dutch botanist, Hugo De Vries (1848-1935), one of the rediscoverers of Mendelism (*Isis 1,* 24).

97. The German herbal first printed by Peter Schöffer (Mainz, 1485) was better illustrated than the Latin herbals, and some illustrations were realistic The text was probably written by Johann von Cube, town physician in Frankfurt, who may be called the greatest herbalist of his time, the forerunner of Otto Brunfels (1530). According to the preface of the *Ortus sanitatis* or *Gart der Gesundheyt,* the author, whoever he was, had traveled considerably in Southern Europe and the Near East, taking a cunning painter with him. He realized that different plants flourished in different countries. He described 435 of them. A facsimile edition of that book was published by the Verlag der münchner Drucke (München, 1924), together with a study by W. L. Schreiber: *Die Kraüterbücher des XV. und XVI Jahrhunderts* (64 pp.).

98. For bibliography of the incunabula, see Klebs 505 to 509, 637. For more detailed study, see the books of Agnes Arber (1938), Wilfrid Blunt (1951), and Claus Nissen (1951) mentioned in a previous note.

99. For the sake of accuracy, it must be added that the early printers did sometimes correct a text in the course of its impression, and the results of their tamperings are those "variants" which give so much pleasure to some bibliographers. The same mistakes have sometimes been repeated by later printers (*Isis 2,* 133). Such "variants," however, are accidental and their existence does not invalidate the general rule: the copies of the same edition of a definite book may be assumed to be identical.

100. In spite of these obvious improvements, such is human inertia that scholars may have continued to prefer the old ways, compact writing and printing, etc. For example, when one is much used to an abbreviation the abbreviated word is easier to read; it is for that very reason that initials are introduced in our own writings. "UNESCO" is certainly clearer than the six words which it replaces.

It is told that Louis XIV, "le Roy Soleil" (d. 1715), did not like the reading of print. When it was necessary for him to read a book, he had it copied in longhand by an amanuensis. We may be sure that those copies were written in a clear and beautiful hand, with proper spacing, but how could the king be certain that the copy was absolutely faithful?

101. In what follows I shall give this word *engraving* a more general meaning than the usual one. In order to avoid the use of two words, *woodcuts* and *engravings,* I shall assume that engraving may be on wood as well as on metal. The word *engraving* refers to the act or art, and to the impressions themselves. Hence, we shall say "this book contains many engravings . . ."

meaning illustrations obtained by means of engraved wood blocks or engraved copperplates.

102. For further discussion, see Sarton: "Iconographic honesty," *Isis 30*, 222-35 (1939); "Portraits of ancient men of science," *Lychnos*, 249-56, 1 fig. (Uppsala, 1945); *Horus*, 42-43.

103. That proverb is known to me from the Elias Modern dictionary Arabic-English (Cairo, 1950), wherein it is quoted in Arabic translation (p. 835)!

104. The great Umbrian painter, Piero della Francesca (1420?-92), who wrote a mathematical book, *De corporibus regularibus*, plagiarized by Luca Paccioli (see Gerolamo Mancini, Roma, 1916—*Isis 3*, 102; *37*, 197). It is believed that he painted his own portrait in the fresco of the "Resurrection" (Borgo San Sepolcro, Galleria communale) and also in the "Madonna della Misericordia" (same Galleria).

105. Jean Babelon: "Gianello della Torre," *Revue de l'art ancien et moderne 34*, 369-78, ill. (1913).

106. Paul Gandz: "Les portraits d' Erasme," *Revue de l'art ancien et moderne 67*, 3-24, ill. (1935). Emil Major: "Erasmus von Rotterdam," *Virorum illustrium reliquiae 1* (90 pp., 32 pls.; Basel: Frobenius, 1926?).

107. The book was reprinted by Plantin's son-in-law, Frans van Ravelingen or Raphelengien (Leiden, 1603), then by Willem Janssonius (Amsterdam, 1612). Facsimile edition of the original book (1574) with French-Dutch introduction by Max Rooses (Antwerpen: Nederlandsche boekhandel, 1901). There are 61 portraits, each one being etched within a frame. The persons represented include Chiron, Aesculapius, Machaon, Homer, Pythagoras, Plato, Aristotle, etc. The portraits of some of the contemporaries are probably genuine, e.g., Fernel, Gesner, Andernacus (Johann Günther), Mattioli, but the author did not seem to realize that a portrait of Mattioli and one of Pythagoras are absolutely different things.

108. A large collection of plant drawings in water color (1856 of them) is (or was) preserved in the National Library of Berlin. These drawings had been made by Pieter Van der Borcht and others to illustrate Clusius: *Rariorum aliquot stirpium per Hispanias observatarum historia* (Antwerp: Christopher Plantin, 1576).

109. They were destroyed during World War II. Another block used for the title page of the second edition of the *Fabrica* (Basel: Oporinus, 1555) was also used for the New York reprint of 1934. That particular wood block preserved in the library of the University of Louvain was also destroyed during World War II.

110. Andreas Vesalius: *Icones anatomicae* (folio; New York: New York Academy of Medicine, 1934—*Isis 28*, 467-69). Samuel Lambert, Willy Wiegand, and William M. Ivins, Jr.: *Three Vesalian essays* (New York: Macmillan, 1952—*Isis 44*, 119).

111. We should not decide a priori that a non-illustrated herbal was reactionary. The new botany implied the careful observation of plants. A botanist might be able to observe them carefully and yet not be able to draw them, or he might make drawings (or have them made for him) and fail to obtain their publication.

112. For Valerius Cordus, see above and Chauncey D. Leake: "Valerius Cordus and the discovery of ether," *Isis 17*, 14-24,3 pls. (1925). The portrait of Cordus reproduced by Leake with the legend "source unknown" is taken from the *Icones medicorum* of Sambucus (1574).

113. C. Doris Hellman: *The comet of 1577* (New York: Columbia University, 1944), pp. 428-29.

114. John Ferguson: *Bibliotheca chemica* (2 vols.; Glasgow: James Maclehose, 1906), vol. 2, pp. 450-55.
115. Arras is in the Pas-de-Calais dept., NW France. Its history is very complicated. It was originally in the county of Flanders. Lille in the Dept. du Nord was also originally a Flemish city. The Flemish names of those two cities are Atrecht and Ryssel, the Latin names Nemetocerna or Atrebatum and Insula.
116. The remarks which might be made about the books of these men are innumerable. Each introduced some new plants. For example, the first description of the potato occurred in Clusius' *Rariorum plantarum historia* (Antwerp: Johann Moretus, 1601). We select this example among thousands because of the enormous importance of the potato. Redcliff N. Salaman: *The history and social influence of the potato* (710 pp.; Cambridge University Press, 1949—*Isis 42*, 85).
117. In that strange lottery, Lobelius won the best prize, for the *Lobelia* are a large family better known than the others. However, the *Clusia* include the waxflower of Guiana and the wild fig of the West Indies.
118. Sarton: "Brave Busbecq," *Isis 33*, 557-75 (1942).
119. *Il viaggio di monte Baldo della magnifica città di Verona* (16 pp., 4to.; Venice: Valgrisio, 1566). It was translated into Latin and that translation was often published (Venice, 1571; Frankfurt a.M., 1586, etc.). His Latin name was Calceolarius. Who remembers Calzolari and yet who does not know the graceful *Calceolaria?*
120. It was the third book, but the first new one. The first two were a Catechism by St. Francis Xavier (1557) and a *Compendio espiritual* by Dr. Pereira, first archbishop of Goa (1561).
121. Not to be confused with his contemporary the Spanish Jesuit José de Acosta (b. Medina del Campo, 1539; d. Salamanca, 1599), missionary in America, author of the *Historia natural y moral de las Indias* (Sevilla: J. de Léon, 1590), often reprinted and translated into Latin, French, English. The "Indias" of Father José, Monardes, and Hernandez was America; the "Indias" of Orta and Acosta, India. Spain and Portugal had divided the world between them, and the division applied to natural history.
122. Francisco Javier, born in Pamplona, was not a Portuguese but a Basque. In 1541, he was sent as a missionary to Goa by João III, and spent the rest of his life in India and Eastern Asia in the service of Portuguese Christianity.
123. English translation of Garcia da Orta by Sir Clements Markham: *Colloquies on the simples and drugs of India* (London: Sotheran, 1913—*Isis 2*, 415-18). This is illustrated with the Acosta drawings, and contains a list of 68 plants giving references for each of them to Orta and to Acosta.
124. *Isis 34*, 34.
125. Abundant information concerning the early Lincei and Federico Cesi is available in Giuseppe Gabrieli: *Il carteggio Linceo* (3 parts, 1446 pp.; Roma: Giovanni Bardi, 1938-42—*Isis 39*, 87; *41*, 113).
126. For Father Schreck, S.J., see *Isis 41*, 221. See also Gabrieli's book mentioned in preceding footnote.
127. The *Hernandiaceae*, a small family of tropical plants, of the order *Ranales*, are named after him.
128. There is a considerable literature on Olivier de Serres. As the reformer of French husbandry and the organizer of sericulture, he is a figure of first importance in French history. With agriculture, we leave botany and enter the larger field of political economy. The best studies are by Henry Vaschalde: *Olivier de Serres* (232 pp.; Paris: Plon, 1886) and by Mlle A.

104—117

Lavondès (Carrières-sous-Poissy: La Cause, 1936—*Isis 35,* 61). The Bibliothèque Nationale organized a special exhibition to celebrate the fourth century of Olivier's birth, *Les travaux et les jours dans l'ancienne France* (100 pp., 15 pls.; Paris: BN, 1939).

129. The identity of the author of the *Boke of husbandry* is uncertain. He was formerly identified with Sir Anthony Fitzherbert (1470-1538), judge, author of *La graunde abbregement de le ley* (3 pts., folio; London: Restell, 1516), a legal compendium (*DNB 19,* 168-70 [1889]). Other scholars ascribe the book to Sir Anthony's brother John. In the book itself the author is called "Mayster Fitzherbarde." The text was reprinted from the edition of 1534 (the third?) by Walter W. Skeat for the English Dialect Society (Series D, 168 pp.; London, 1882), with notes and glossary.

130. Thomas Moffett is an Elizabethan, but his scientific work *Insectorum sive minimorum animalium theatrum olim ab E. Wottono, C. Gesnero, Thomaque Pennio inchoatum . . .* was published in 1634 (London: T. Cotes). A poem of his, *The silkewormes and their flies,* had been published in London, 1599.

131. For a better acquaintance with them read Charles E. Raven: *English naturalists from Neckham to Ray* (Cambridge University Press, 1947—*Isis 39,* 196). Raven's book covers not only the Middle Ages and the Renaissance but also two-thirds of the seventeenth century; it covers almost five centuries.

132. Discussed in Lecture I. Such as the works of Galen (II-2), the *kunnāsh or pandectae* of Serapion the Elder (IX-2), the *Ḥāwī* of al-Rāzī (IX-2), the *Malikī* of 'Alī ibn 'Abbās (X-2), the *Qānūn* of Ibn Sīnā (XI-1).

133. In spite of its immense size, the *Speculum naturale* of Vincent of Beauvais was printed thrice in the fifteenth century, the first time in Strassburg *c.* 1475-78; the second time in Nuremberg, 1486 (the first two printers are not known); the third time by H. Liechtenstein in Venice, 1494 (Klebs 1036.1-3). The first edition is a folio of 698 leaves printed in two columns. The first edition of the *Buch der Natur* of Conrad von Megenberg (Augsburg: Johann Bämler, 1475) contains printed drawings of animals (*Osiris 5,* 111-12, fig. 32-34); it was reprinted 5 times before the end of the century (Klebs 300.1-6).

134. Röslin's book, *Der schwangeren Frauen und Hebammen Rosengarten,* is the oldest German book on midwifery to be printed. No incunabulum. First edition by Martin Flach (Strassburg, 1513). Facsimile reprint with introduction by Gustav Klein (München, 1910).

135. The part dealing with insects was reprinted by Thomas Moffett in his *Insectorum theatrum* (London, 1634).

136. After writing this, I discovered in Ibn Jubair (XII-2) a reference to Muslim pilgrims and Christians climbing Mount Lebanon. Arabic edition by William Wright, revised by M. J. De Goeje (Gibb Series, vol. 5; Leyden, 1907), p. 287. English translation by R. J. C. Broadhurst (London: J. Cape, 1952), p. 300.

137. We are well informed on early Alpinism because of the enthusiasm and zeal of the Rev. William August Brevoort Coolidge (1850-1926), a New Yorker and Anglican divine, who flourished in Switzerland (from 1885) and became famous as a practical and theoretical alpinist. His heavy tome, *Josias Simler et les origines de l'Alpinisme jusqu' en 1600* (950 pp.; Grenoble: Allier, 1904), is not well organized, but very rich in information. *Introd. 3,* 189, 1878.

138. The *epistola* was printed at the beginning of Gesner's *Libellus de lacte et*

operibus lactariis (Zürich: Chr. Froschauer, 1541). It can be read in Latin and French in Coolidge's book (pp. v-xvii).

139. To say "the first" is always a challenge. In 1480 the Dominican Felix Fabri of Ulm had written about the sublimity of the Alpine world, a kind of terrestrial paradise. Franz Struntz (1875-1953): *Die Vergangenheit der Naturforschung* (Jena: Diederichs, 1913), pp. 192-93.

140. *Descriptio Montis Fracti, sive Montis Pilati,* printed by Gesner in his *Commentariolus de raris et admirandis herbis quae Lunariae nominantur* (Zürich, 1555), pp. 44-54. Reprinted with French translation in Coolidge's book, pp. 196*-221.*

141. *Vallesiae descriptio; De Alpibus commentarius* (Zürich: Christopher Froschauer, 1574). Reprinted by the Elzeviers (Leiden, 1633), by Conrad Orelli (Zürich, 1735), by Coolidge (1904), pp. 1-307. The Valais or Wallis (SW Switzerland), capital Sion (Sitten), is a member of the Swiss federation since 1815. The author's name is Simler not Simmler.

142. Douglas W. Freshfield: *The life of Horace Bénédict de Saussure, 1740-99* (London: Arnold, 1920—*Isis 6,* 64-71).

143. These two items are no. 3 and 14 in Ley's list. The list includes 66 items.

144. For more details on Gesner as bibliographer, consult J. Christian Bay: "Gesner, the father of bibliography," *Papers of the Bibliographical Society of America* (Chicago, 1916), vol. 10, pp. 53-88. John F. Fulton: *The great medical bibliographers* (Philadelphia: University of Pennsylvania, 1951— *Isis 43,* 90), pp. 17-25.

145. *Dictionarium Germanicolatinum novum. Die teütsch Spraach* (544 leaves; Zürich: Froschauer, 1561). An excellent book praised by Jacob Grimm. The author's name is spelled in its title Josua Maaler; his Latin name was Pictorius. He was born in the Black Forest in 1529 but flourished in Zürich, where he died in 1599.

146. For a new survey, see Antoine Meillet and Marcel Cohen: *Les langues du monde* (828 pp., 18 maps; Paris: Champion, 1924—*Isis 10,* 298). The index of language names covers 176 columns! A new edition of this work is in the course of preparation.

147. A list of well over 200 plants discovered by Gesner is given by W. Ley in his book of 1929 (pp. 402-4).

148. Pilgrimages afforded the best means of eschewing disagreeable obligations and penalties. A man's distant pilgrimage enabled him to disappear for a sufficiently long time until the clouds had drifted away and the sky was clear. A good example is Vesalius' pilgrimage in 1564. This does not imply that pilgrims were necessarily insincere, far from it. *Introd. 2,* 34.

149. Facsimile copy of the first pharmacopoeia (Nürnberg, 1546), edited by Ludwig Winkler (Mittenwald, Bayern: Gesellschaft für Geschichte der Pharmazie, 1934—*Isis 24,* 215). Facsimile copy of the third (Augsburg, 1564), edited by Theodor Husemann (Madison: State Historical Society of Wisconsin, 1927—*Isis 10,* 69-71, 4 fig.).

150. Aldrovandi was then 77. I do not know of another example of a work, the author's masterpiece, the publication of which began so late in life. Aldrovandi was so old (83 years), when he died in 1605, that one forgets he was a contemporary of Belon, Gesner, Rondelet, who were considerably younger when they died in 1564, 1565, 1566.

151. Saliceto in French, Italian, Latin (Klebs 484-87), Lanfranchi in French, Latin, Dutch, Spanish (Klebs 585-87), Mondino in Latin and Italian (Klebs 688), Chauliac in French, Italian, Latin, Spanish, Dutch (Klebs 491-97). Mondeville was first edited by Julius Pagel in 1889 (*Introd. 3,*

872) and Vigevano by Ernest Wickershcimer in 1913 (*Introd. 3*, 846).

152. Critical edition of Vicary's book by Fredr. J. Furnivall and Percy Furnivall (Early English Text Society, extra series no. 53, London, 1888), with many documents.

153. Gabriele de Zerbi (or Zerbus, de Zerbis), born in Cuorgnè, Aosta, Torino; obtained his M.D. in Pavia and practised in Padova, Rome, finally in Turkey where he was murdered in 1505. He wrote the first treatise on gerontology, at any rate the first to be printed, *Gerontocomia scilicet de senum cura atque victu* (Rome: Silber, 1489). Another treatise of his was printed a few years later, *De cautelis medicorum* (Venice: unknown printer, 1495). Often reprinted. Klebs 1056-58. His *Liber anathomie corporis humani et singulorum membrorum illius* was first printed by Locatelli in Venice, 1502.

154. Charles Singer: *Evolution of anatomy* (New York: Knopf, 1926—*Isis 10*, 521-24), p. 97.

155. *Musculorum humani corporis picturata dissectio* (Ferrara: Bart. Nigrisoli, 1541?). Facsimile edition by Harvey Cushing and Edward C. Streeter, *Monumenta medica 4* (Florence, 1925—*Isis 9*, 433).

156. *De dissectione partium corporis humani libri tres a Carolo Stephano editi, una cum figuris et incisionum declarationibus a Stephano Riverio* (folio, 375 pp.; Paris: S. Colinaeus, 1545). French edition by the same printer in 1546. The artist was Estienne de La Rivière.

157. *In Hippocratis et Galeni physiologiae partem anatomicam isagoge a Jacobo Sylvio conscripta et in tres libros distributa* (folio, 66 leaves; Paris: Hulpeau, 1555). Often reprinted: Basel, 1556; Paris, 1561, 1587, etc.

158. *Introd. 3*, 1195, 1440.

159. A startling exception is the crucified Christ whose body was admirably shaped after a nude model for the abbey of Meaux (Yorkshire) in 1339-49 (*Introd. 3*, 1256).

160. J. Playfair McMurrich: *Leonardo the anatomist* (285 pp., 89 fig.; Washington: Carnegie Institution, 1930—*Isis 15*, 342-44). K. D. Keele: *Leonardo on movement of the heart and blood* (160 pp., 68 pls.; Philadelphia: Lippincott, 1952—*Isis 43*, 270). Charles D. O'Malley and J. B. de C. M. Saunders: *Leonardo on the human body* (quarto, 506 pp., 215 pls.; New York: Schuman, 1952—*Isis 44*, 65).

161. *Introd. 3*, 1659.

162. A few recent publications on Vesalius. *Vesalii Icones anatomicae* (folio; New York Academy of Medicine, 1935—*Isis 28*, 407-69). Harvey Cushing: *A bio-bibliography of Vesalius* (268 pp., ill.; New York: Schuman, 1943—*Isis 35*, 338-41). Charles Singer and C. Rabin: *A prelude to modern science. The tabulae sex*, 1538, with facsimile of them (London: Wellcome Historical Medical Museum, 1946—*Isis 38*, 109-11). L. R. Lind: *The Epitome of Vesalius translated with facsimile of the Latin text*, 1543 (New York: Macmillan, 1949—*Isis 41*, 210). J. B. de C. M. Saunders and Charles D. O'Malley: *The illustrations . . . of Vesalius* (252 pp.; Cleveland: World Publishing Co., 1950—*Isis 42*, 53). Samuel W. Lambert, Willy Wiegand, William M. Ivins, Jr.: *Three Vesalian essays* (140 pp., New York: Macmillan, 1952—*Isis 43*, 119).

The latest full biography of Vesalius was by Moritz Roth (508 pp., 30 pls.; Berlin: Reimer, 1892). We need a new one, more elaborate and brought up to date; C. D. O'Malley is preparing it.

162a. It is not certain that Vesalius reached the Holy Land. When he died in Zante, was he on his way to Jerusalem or on his way back? Sarton: "The death and burial of Vesalius and, incidentally, of Cicero," *Isis 45*, 131-37

(1954). C. Donald O'Malley argues (*ibidem*, 138-44) that although "there seems to be definite evidence of Vesalius' visit [in Jerusalem], at least temporarily the evidence has vanished." It is a good rule of life to abandon "vanished evidence" to gossips; it has no place in courts of law or scholarship.

163. Eustachi's great work remained almost unknown because it was lost. The splendid copperplates which he had prepared to illustrate it were discovered by another Roman anatomist, Gian Maria Lancisi (1654-1720), who published them with his own commentary (Rome, 1714).

164. Botallo was Piemontese but often counted a Frenchman and called Botal ("trou de Botal") because he was a royal physician in France. He was physician to Henri III (ruled 1574-89).

165. The date of Coiter's death is definitely 1600. *NNBW 2*, 717 (1912). A biography of Coiter by a young doctor, Robert Herrlinger, has just been published, but I have not yet seen it. *Isis 44*, 283.

166. Geminus was an engraver who abridged Vesalius' work in 1545 (*DNB 21*, 118). As to Caius he had sat at Vesalius' feet in Padova and lived in his very house.

167. These drawings occur in his *Histoire de la nature des oyseaux* (folio; Paris: Benoist Prévost, 1555), pp. 40, 41.

168. There was a contemporary Carlo Ruini of Reggio nell' Emilia whose enormous law books were published in Lyon, 1546, and in Bologna, 1575. The anatomist was a jurist but he did not write on legal topics; he was a member of the council of elders in Bologna in 1578, then senator; he died in Bologna on 3 Feb. 1598. His book appeared only at the end of 1598. E. Leclainche: *Histoire de la médecine vétérinaire* (Toulouse: Office du livre, 1936—*Isis 27*, 360-63), pp. 154-61.

169. For medieval treatises on veterinary medicine see my *Introd. 2*, 1091; *3*, 284, 1238, 1837. Many of these MSS were illustrated (*Introd. 3*, 284).

170. There are medical incunabula bearing his name (Klebs 171-73) but the *Historia corporis humani, sive Anatomice* was not printed before 1502 (Venice: B. Guerraldus. Reprinted 1527, 1528).

171. Karl Sudhoff: "Graphische und typographische Erstlinge der Syphilisliteratur," *Alte Meister der Medizin 4* (folio, 38 pp., 24 pls.; München: Kuhn, 1912—*Isis 1*, 272); "The earliest printed literature on syphilis, 1495-98," *Monumenta medica 3* (Florence, 1925—*Isis 8*, 351-54).

172. Girolamo Fracastoro: *Syphilis*. Edition of the Latin text with English version by Heneage Wynne-Finch (254 pp.; London: Heinemann, 1935). Leona Baumgartner and John F. Fulton: *Bibliography of the poem Syphilis* (158 pp., ill.; New Haven: Yale University Press, 1935—*Isis 24*, 437-39).

173. Johann Weyer: *De praestigiis daemonum et incantationibus ac veneficiis* (Basel: Joannes Oporinus, 1563). Gregory Zilboorg: *The medical man and the witch during the Renaissance* (225 pp.; Baltimore: Johns Hopkins, 1935 —*Isis 25*, 147-52, 2 ill.). Weyer was preceded by Andreas a Laguna (see footnote 58), except that Andreas' views were not published in a special treatise but incidentally in his commentary on Dioscorides (Antwerp, 1555).

174. The main leaders in the perpetuation of the demoniac atmosphere were the Frenchman, Jean Bodin (1530-96), and the Hispano-Belgian Jesuit, Martin Delrio (1551-1608), whose *Disquisitiones magicae* were first printed in Louvain by Gerard Rivius (3 vols.; 1599-1600), often reprinted and translated into French (*Isis 39*, 209).

175. On spices, see my *Introd. 3*, 229, 1182.

176. The priority of Pisa or Padova has been discussed by local archaeologists. See the article of Giovanni Battista de Toni on Luca Ghini, *Gli scienziati*

italiani 1, 1-4 (Roma, 1921). It suffices for our purpose to put them *ex aequo c.* 1545.

177. For the garden of Theophrastos (IV-2 B. C.) see my *History of science 1*, 556. For medieval gardens, *Introd.* 2, 55; *3*, 224, 816, 895, 1170, 1177, 1645.

178. The earliest example of acclimatization of a single plant is that of the ginkgo (*Gingko biloba*), a kind of living fossil (close to the cycads) which was considered sacred and grown around Chinese temples. What are the Chinese traditions about that?

179. Tea was introduced from China by the Dutch in 1610, coffee by the Venetians from Arabia in 1615. Both beverages did not obtain their present popularity until at least a century later. Other sources of xanthines are maté, much used in S. America, the kola nuts, Paullinia. Cocoa contains theobromine; tea, theophylline; coffee, tea, kola, and Paullinia include various proportions of caffeine.

180. For ancient menageries, see my *History of science 1*, 157, 460. For medieval ones, *Introd.* 2, 576-78; *3*, 1189, 1470, 1859. For Busbecq, *Isis 33*, 568. For menageries in general, Gustave Loisel: *Histoire des ménageries* (3 vols.; Paris, 1912).

181. Or guaiac. *Guaiacán* is a Spanish word of Caribbean origin. The Latin word was *guaiacum* or *lignum vitae*. G. Sarton: "The strange fame of Demetrio Canevari," *Journal of the history of medicine 1*, 398-418 (1946). Max H. Fisch: *Nicolaus Pol* (New York: Reichner, 1947—*Isis 40*, 56-58), p. 41-45.

182. I know the text from Ulrich von Hutten's *Schriften*, hrg. von Eduard Böcking (Leipzig, 1861), vol. 5, pp. 396-497, Latin and old German.

183. *Andreae Vesalii . . . epistola rationem modumque propinandi racinis Chynae decocti . . . pertractans* (Basel, 1546). Six sixteenth-century editions are listed by Harvey Cushing: *Bio-bibliography of Andreas Vesalius* (New York: Schuman, 1943—*Isis 35*, 398-41), pp. 154-70, 3 fig.

184. *Introd. 3*, 289.

185. This was already clear by the middle of the century, witness the book of Thierry de Héry: *La méthode curatoire de la maladie vénérienne* (273 pp.; Paris: M. David, 1552). Thierry de Héry was a friend of Paré who survived him; they were both military and royal surgeons; they had made public dissections together in the medical school of Paris. Paré incorporated a good part of Héry's *Méthode curatoire* in his *Chirurgie* without sufficient acknowledgment. Janet Doe: *Bibliography of Paré* (University of Chicago, 1937—*Isis 29*, 220).

186. *Alchemia Andreae Libavii . . . opera e dispersis passim autorum veterum et recentium exemplis . . . collecta . . . explicata et in integrum corpus redacta* (2 vols., 4to; Frankfurt a.M.: J. Saurius, 1597). Reprinted by same firm, 1606 (wrongly dated 1506!) and 1607. The date of the *Alchemia* is often given as 1595, but that is probably a confusion with another Libavius work, the first part of his *Rerum chymicarum epistolica forma . . . liber primus* (same printer, 1595). A fully annotated German translation of the *Alchemia* has been completed and the Gmelin Institut hopes to be able to publish it together with a facsimile edition of the Latin text (letter from Prof. Pietsch, Clausthal-Zellerfeld, 3 March 1953).

187. For development of these views on the artificiality of Latin, see *Introd. 3*, 333-35.

188. For early Spanish translations of Arabic agricultural treatises, see J. M. Millás Vallicrosa: *Las traducciones orientales en los manuscritos de la Biblioteca Catedral de Toledo* (371 pp., 17 facs.; Madrid, 1942—*Isis 34*,

518-19). For the survival of Arabic in Christian Spain, see Angel González Palencia: *Los Mozárabes de Toledo* (3 vols., folio; Madrid, 1926-30— *Isis 15*, 183-87). For medieval traditions on husbandry, see *Introd. 2, 55; 3,* 227-28, 1180-82.

189. The ideas of revulsion and derivation were not understood in the same way by all the disputants. The differentiation was peculiarly difficult in the case of a central inflammation like pleurisy. Pierre Brissot: *Apologetica disceptatio qua docetur per quae loca sanguis mitti debeat in viscerum inflammationibus, praesertim in pleuritide* (4° a-k; Paris: S. Colinaeus, 1525). This was Brissot's first and last publication, but it was reprinted in 1529 and reëdited in 1622. Long article on Brissot by Max Salomon in *BL 1,* 703-4.

LECTURE III

MATHEMATICS AND ASTRONOMY

1. Aristotle did not devote a single treatise to mathematics, except a small one (apocryphal?), *On indivisible lines.* A posthumous work of Sir Thomas Heath puts together all the mathematical texts found in Aristotle's works, *Mathematics in Aristotle* (305 pp.; Oxford: Clarendon Press, 1949— *Isis 41,* 329).

2. His original name was Pierre de la Ramée (1515-72), but he was always called Ramus. For example, the Harvard Library has original copies of the four royal sentences of condemnation dated 1543-44 (in all 20 pp.). I have examined one of them; though written in French the name of the delinquent given on the title page is Ramus.

3. Elaborate bibliography of Euclid by Pietro Riccardi: *Saggio di una bibliografia Euclidea* (5 parts; Bologna, 1887-93). For the editions anterior to 1600 this is superseded by Charles Thomas-Stanford: *Early editions of Euclid's Elements* (68 pp., 12 pls; London: Bibliographical Society, 1926—*Isis 10,* 59-60).

4. For example, the English translator of the *Elements,* Billingsley (1570), calls the author "the most auncient Philosopher Euclide of Megara."

5. Robert Recorde repeats it in his *Pathway to knowledge* (London: R. Wolfe, 1551).

6. That translation was printed as early as 1491/92 in the *Opera varia Boethii* (Venice: Gregoriis), reprinted by the same printers in 1498/99 (Klebs 192.1-2), and by Heinrich Petri in Basel (1546, 1570). It was also reprinted nine times together with the *Sphaera mundi* of Johannes de Sacrobosco (XIII-1); the first time by Hopyl (Paris, 1500; Klebs 874.29). There are thus three incunabula editions of it.

7. Erhard Ratdolt (*c.* 1443-1528) was a famous printer in Venice (1476-86), then in Augsburg. During his Venetian career, he published a trade list of his books (1484), which is reproduced in *Osiris 5,* 168. The list includes his Euclid and other mathematical and astronomical books.

8. There were only two incunabula (Klebs 383.1-2). The edition of Ulm, 1486, is a ghost. I apologize for having helped to perpetuate that error in my Campani article (*Introd. 2,* 986). The same pages of both incunabula editions (1482, 1491) are reproduced in *Osiris 5,* 130-31, and described *ibidem,* pp. 102-3. One can see that the second edition reproduces the first, page for page, but in Roman instead of Gothic type.

137—144

9. Unless the *Prospectiva communis* of John Peckham (XIII-2) is earlier. Its edition by Petrus of Corneno, Pavia, is undated but probably 1482 (Klebs 738.1). It contains 77 diagrams.

10. Jacobus Faber Stapulensis, born at Etaples, Pas-de-Calais, in 1455, studied in Paris and Italy, returned to France *c.* 1492 and died at the court of Marguerite de Valois at Nérac, near Agen, in 1537. Philosopher, theologian, humanist, as well as mathematician and astronomer. Some of his Aristotelian and other commentaries were printed early (Klebs 591, 592, etc.), also his *Epitome* of the *Arithmetica* of Jordanus Nemorarius (XIII-1) (Paris: Higman and Hopyl, 1496; Klebs 563.1). His French translation of the NT was the basis of the version adopted by the French Reformed Church. He had Calvinist inclinations but was not a reformer; he is one of the many humanists who helped to prepare the Reformation.

11. Cuthbert Tunstall (1474-1559), educated in Oxford, Cambridge, Padova; master of the rolls and bishop of London, later of Durham; diplomat. He remained a Catholic but lost his office in 1553, again in the year of his death. His works are theological or religious, except the *De arte supputandi* (London: Richard Pynson, 1522), first arithmetic published in England. His name is Tunstall but the Latin form had to be changed to Tonstallius because if the *u* had been kept it would have been pronounced like *ou* in French. Later the name was changed back from Latin to English, Tonstall.

12. According to the elaborate Jesuit bibliography, his original name was Clau or Klau, not Schlüssel.

13. Pasquale M. d'Elia: *Galileo in Cina* (Rome, 1947—*Isis 41*, 220-22).

14. Sarton in *Isis 23*, 177.

15. Rodrigo Zamorano (or Çamorano) was born in 1542; date of death unknown. His name is listed in the *Catálogo de autoridades de la lengua*, published by the Spanish Academy.

16. It contains Books I to XIII, 454 pp., with a great many diagrams. There are two copies of it in the Harvard Library: the one in my own collection, the other in Houghton. This second copy is bound in a superb Italian binding of the period.

17. For the sake of curiosity let me mention a new Arabic translation of Books I-VI made upon the English text of John Playfair, *Elements of geometry* (1795, often reprinted) by the American Cornelius Van Alen Van Dyck (1818-95) and published in Beirūt, 1857. For Van Dyck see *Isis 27*, 20-45, fig. 4 (1937).

18. *Tusculanae quaestiones* (liber V, cap. 23). "When I was quaestor in Sicily, I found, hedged in and overgrown with briers and brambles, his tomb, unknown to the Syracusans, who did not believe in its existence. I retained in my memory certain verses which I had heard were inscribed on his monument, in which it was said that a sphere with a cylinder was placed on the top of his tomb. After making thorough search . . . I noticed a column very little higher than the surrounding shrubbery, with the figures of a sphere and a cylinder on it" (Andrew P. Peabody's translation; Boston, 1886). The Archimedean discovery referred to is the theorem "that the cylinder whose base is the greatest circle in any sphere and whose height is equal to the diameter of the sphere is itself in magnitude half as large again as the sphere, while its surface [including the two bases] is half as large again as the surface of the sphere" (*On the sphere and cylinder*, beginning of Book II; Heath's translation).

19. For example, Gianello della Torre, clockmaker to Charles Quint and Philip II mentioned above. A much later example is Christopher Polhem (1661-1751),

nicknamed the Swedish Archimedes (*Isis 43*, 65). This was as ludicrous and irrelevant as if Edison had been styled by his admirers "the American Archimedes."

20. The treatise on the regular heptagon was translated from Arabic into German by Carl Schoy many centuries later (*Isis 8*, 21-40 [1926]).

21. Jacopo da S. Sassiano Cremonese, regular canon. He was a pupil of Vittorino da Feltre and his successor as tutor (*c.* 1435-49) to the sons of Luigi III Gonzaga in Mantova. Later he flourished in Rome and was employed by Nicholas V.

22. The Campanus mentioned in the title is Giovanni Campani (XIII-2), immortalized by his translation of Euclid printed in 1482. Boetius was one of the most famous men throughout the Middle Ages and the Renaissance because of his *De consolatione philosophiae*. The grouping of Archimedes (III-2 B. C.), Boetius (VI-I), and Campani (XIII-2) is curious.

23. Luca Gaurico, born at Giffoni (Salerno) in 1476, died at Rome in 1558. He was a mathematician and astronomer; and was astrological adviser to many popes and to Henri II of France. What is more to his credit, he was one of the promoters of the calendar reform in his *Calendarium ecclesiasticum novum* (Venice: Juntae, 1552).

24. It was an error to call Tartaglia's book the first Archimedean print in any language (*Horus*, 19), but it was a venial error. Tartaglia it was, who revealed the mathematician Archimedes to the Western world.

25. French, Pasquier Duhamel (d. 1565).

26. French, Jean Borrel.

27. According to Henri Bosmans' excellent article on Romanus in *Biographie nationale de Belgique 19*, 848-88 (1907), p. 866, this book was not printed in Würzburg (as the title says), but in Geneva. Adriaan van Roomen (Adrianus Romanus)—born Louvain, 1561; died Mainz, 1615—was one of the most distinguished mathematicians of his age. He would deserve a full-sized biography. Romanus' book on Archimedes was primarily an attack against the unsound arguments of the "quadraturists," chiefly Joseph Scaliger to whom it was dedicated. It includes the Greek text of Archimedes with Latin translation.

28. Maurolico (Latin, Maurolycus) was one of those fortunate scholars who had a native knowledge of Greek; his father was a Byzantine physician who had fled to Sicily and established himself in Messina. For biographical details, see M. Cantor; *Vorlesungen 2*, 558 (1913) and Maurolycus: *The Photismi in lumine*. A chapter in late medieval optics, Englished by Henry Crew (1859-1953) (154 pp.; New York: Macmillan, 1940—*Isis 33*, 251-53).

29. *Promotus Archimedis, seu de variis corporum generibus gravitate et magnitudine comparatis* (Rome: Aloysius Zanettus, 1603).

30. I have devoted to him two long memoirs: *Simon Stevin of Bruges* (*Isis 21*, 241-303, 30 ill. [1934]); *The first explanation of decimal fractions and measures (1585) together with a history of the decimal idea and a facsimile of Stevin's* Disme (*Isis 23*, 153-244, 52 ill. [1935]).

31. According to Heiberg a Latin translation of the *Cōnica* had already been made by Gerard of Cremona (XII-2) or a member of his school. The matter is uncertain.

32. The evolute of a curve (called its involute) is the locus of the center of curvature or the envelope of the normals. This is enough to refresh a mathematician's memory, but even much more would not be helpful to others.

33. *Francisci Vietae Apollonius Gallus, seu exsuscitata Apollonii Pergaei peri epaphōn geometria* (Paris: D. Le Clerc, 1600). *Problema Apolloniacum quo,*

datis tribus circulis, quaeritus quartus eos contingens, antea ab F. Vieta propositum, jam vero per Belgam Adrianum Romanum constructum (20 pp.; Würzburg: G. Fleischmann, 1596).

34. Marino Ghetaldi . . . *Apollonius redivivus, seu restituta Apollonii Pergaei inclinationum geometria* (Venice, 1607), *idem, Liber secundus* (Venice, 1613).

35. *Libellus J. Verneri . . . super vigintiduobus elementis conicis . . .* (Nürnberg: F. Peypus, 1522).

36. Published long after Maurolico's death, *Emendatio et restitutio Conicorum Apollonii* (Messina, 1654).

37. *Essay pour les coniques.* Englished by Frances Marguerite Clarke (*Isis 10,* 16-20 [1928]) with facsimile of the French original.

38. The word *almagest* is derived from the Greek original title with the Arabic article *al.* The original title was *Mathēmaticē syntaxis* or *Megalē syntaxis tēs astronomias* (the great astronomical treatise); in the course of time it was called *Megistē syntaxis* (the greatest) and one of the first Arabic translators al-Ḥajjāj ibn Yūsuf (IX-1) called it *Kitāb al mijistī* (hence *almagest*).

39. Anatoli's Hebrew version was retranslated into Latin by Jacob Christmann (Frankfurt, 1590). Christmann's book was thus the end of a long chain of translations—Greek into Arabic, Latin, Hebrew, Latin!

40. Gerard's translation was printed again by Joh. Petreius (Nürnberg, 1537) and by Christ. Wechel (Paris, 1546). A new translation was published with the Arabic text and notes by Jacobus Golius (3 parts; Amsterdam, 1669). Golius' edition was the Arabic princeps.

41. The Latin translation by George of Trebizond was reprinted in the collected works of Ptolemy (the Geography excepted) edited by Hieronymus Gemusaeus (Basel: H. Petrus, 1541) and by Erasmus Osvaldus Schreckenfuchs (Basel: same printer, 1551).

42. His Greek name reads Bēssariōn, but he was so occidentalized that it is better to call him Bessarion, or in the Italian way, Bessarione. He came to Italy in 1439 with Joannes VIII Palaiologos, the last but one emperor of Byzantium from 1425 to 1448. He is immortalized by the journal bearing his name, *Bessarione,* pubblicazione periodica di studi orientali, diretta a facilitare l'unione delle chiese (39 vols.; Roma, 1896-1923).

43. He was called by his younger contemporary, the famous humanist Lorenzo Valla (1407-57), "Latinorum graecissimus, Graecorum latinissimus." An abundance of materials concerning Bessarion has been published by Ludwig Mohler: *Kardinal Bessarion als Theologe, Humanist und Staatsman* (3 vols.; Paderborn, 1923-42).

44. See in *Osiris 5,* 162-63, facsimile of his *Epitoma* and of his trade list (Nürnberg, 1474). For explanation of the trade list see *ibidem,* p. 115. Klebs 834 to 839. Only a very few of Regiomontanus' books were printed in his own shop; his trade list included many titles which his untimely death kept from publication.

45. Sixtus IV was pope from 1471 to 1484. The reform of the calendar was not realized until a century later, in 1582, by Gregory XIII, pope from 1572 to 1585. The Franciscan Sixtus IV was a great patron of learning; he has justly been called the second founder of the Vatican library.

46. The circumstances of his death are mysterious. It was whispered that he had been poisoned by the sons of George of Trebizond; the plague was decimating Rome at that time and he may have been one of its many victims. Ernst Zinner: *Leben und Wirken des Regiomontanus* (306 pp., 46 pls.; München: Beck, 1938—*Isis 30,* 109-11).

NOTES

47. Adolphe Rome: *Commentaires de Pappus et de Théon d'Alexandrie sur l'Almageste* (3 vols.; Vaticano, 1931-43—*Isis 36*, 255-56), to be continued.
48. Klebs 812.1-7, 813.1. The Latin princeps without maps was issued by H. Liechtenstein (Vicenza, 1475). The Latin princeps with maps by Lapis (Bologna, probably 1477). This second edition bears the wrong date, 1462, and was therefore believed to be the first. Sarton: "Incunabula wrongly dated," *Isis 40*, 227-40 (1949).
49. Plato of Tivoli (XII-1) translated the *Quadripartitum* from Arabic in 1138; the *Centiloquium* had been translated in 1136 by John of Seville (XII-1). Both works appealed so much to medieval minds that there were many other translations from Arabic into Latin, Hebrew, etc. (*Introd. 2*, 178).
50. For details and commentaries, see *Isis 35*, 181. See *Isis 44*, 278-78, however.
51. I do not know whether the term kitāb al-mutawassiṭāt was coined by Nāsir al-din or whether it is of earlier origin. A chapter of the Nafā'is al-funūn fi 'arā'is al-'uyūn deals with the 'ilm al-mutawassiṭāt. The Nafā'is al-funūn is a large encyclopedia (in Persian) of all the sciences, compiled about the middle of the fourteenth century by the Persian philosopher Maḥmūd al-Āmilī (XIV-1).
52. Klebs 1012.1. For complete title and contents see BMC, V, 523. Joseph Mogenet: *Autolycus* (Louvain, 1950), pp. 23-30. The *Nicephori logica* mentioned in Valla's title is the treatise on logic by Nicēphoros Grēgoras (XIV-1).
53. Valla's encyclopedia is an enormous folio, which I examined in the Houghton Library. It is beautifully printed, the lines stretching across the whole page. The text is divided into 49 books and not paginated or foliated; the whole work covers perhaps as much as 1,000 pages. Book XVI is entitled *Liber sextus decimus et astrologiae primus;* it covers 32½ pages. The lack of pagination or foliation is remarkable in a book printed in Venice as late as 1501.
54. Abū Naṣr (X-2) was the teacher of the famous al-Bīrūnī (XI-1). The Dā'irat al-ma'ārif al-'uthmāniya has published recently a collection of 15 mathematical and astronomical treatises written by Abū Naṣr for al-Bīrūnī (Hyderabad: Deccan, 1948—*Isis 44*, 110).
55. The book was printed in Oxford, Sumptibus Academicis, in 1758. It includes Halley's translation (112 pp.; printed *c.* 1706-10), plus 10 pp. of title and preface printed on different paper, added by Costard. For other books printed yet unpublished see *Isis 29*, 422.
56. Max Krause: *Die Sphaerik von Menelaos aus Alexandrien in der Verbesserung von Abū Naṣr* (370 pp., 7 pls.; Göttingen, 1936—*Isis 29*, 417-22). The *Isis* review contains many details in which we have no space to enter and 3 facsimile pages of the Halley edition (Oxford, 1758).
57. We owe an excellent instrument for the study of Renaissance arithmetic to David Eugene Smith (1860-1944): *Rara arithmetica* (Boston: Ginn, 1908); *Addenda* (62 pp.; *ibidem*, 1939—*Isis 32*, 468). For Smith's bibliography see *Osiris 1*. The best general account of Renaissance mathematics is still Moritz Cantor: *Vorlesungen zur Geschichte der Mathematik* (Leipzig, 1899-1900), vol. 2, pp. 213-648; unchanged reprint in 1913.
58. The Arabic writers called them more correctly Hindu numerals. The history of those numerals is too complicated to be told here; see my *Introduction* (3 vols. *passim*).
59. Paper read at the Metropolitan Museum of New York in February 1952.
60. In Arabic the terms warrāq (paperseller) and kutubī (bookseller) were almost equivalent (*Introd. 2*, 870), because the two trades were combined. The situation was very probably the same in the Christian West.

61. Georges Barraud: "La naissance de l'humanisme en Espagne ou l'osmose italo-ibérique de la Renaissance," *Bull. de l'Association G. Budé,* Mars 1953, pp. 89-94. Salamanca was then already an old university—about three centuries old—for it had been founded before 1230 (*Introd. 2,* 573).

62. These two arithmetics have been fully described by David Eugene Smith ir *Isis 6,* 311-31, 2 fig. (1924); *8,* 41-49 (1926). The Klebs nos. are 115.1 and 205.1-3. Indeed, the second is represented by three incunabula editions, all in Venice: Ratdolt, 1484; Leoviler, 1488; Ferrariis, 1491.

63. Klebs 419.1. Description by L. C. Karpinski: "The first printed arithmetic of Spain," *Osiris 1,* 411-20 (1936).

64. Klebs 277.1. D. E. Smith: *Rara arithmetica* (1908), p. 58. Describing the second edition (Paris, 1505); the book was reprinted in 1509 and 1513. Ciruelo was born at Daroca, Aragon, *c.* 1470, was professor of philosophy at Alcalá de Henares, and died at Salmanaca in 1560.

65. Klebs 604.1. Licht's book was reprinted in 1505, 1509, 1513, 1515. D. E. Smith: *Rara arithmetica* (1908), p. 70.

66. *Algorithmus* (Klebs 52 to 58). *Ars numerandi* (Klebs 112.1-2). *Regula falsi* (Klebs 843).

67. *Rara arithmetica* (1908), p. 278.

68. Frances Marguerite Clarke: "New light on Robert Recorde," *Isis 8,* 50-70 (1926).

69. More exactly Finé was succeeded by Jean Pena (de la Pêne; Latin, Penna) of Aix, who taught at the Collège Royal from 1555 to his death in Paris, 1558. Thanks to Ramus' intercession, Forcadel was appointed in 1560.

70. The full title reads *"L'arithmétique par les gects* de P. Forcadel de Béziers divisée en trois livres de l'invention dudict Forcadel." This puzzled me because, if *gects* meant *getons* (counters), there was really no invention. Prof. René Taton very kindly examined for me the copy in the Bibliothèque Nationale, Paris. Forcadel explains how to make various computations (including rule of three, problems of partnership, extraction of square and cubic roots). His account lacks novelty as well as clearness. It includes a curious remark (p. 8 v): "nonante cinq qui se doit nommer par quatre vings [*sic*] quinze." The simpler phrase "nonante cinq" is still used in Belgium.

71. See facsimile in *Isis 21,* 207-9; see also *Isis 24,* 113; *35,* 331.

72. As quoted by D. E. Smith: *History of mathematics* (Boston: Ginn, 1923), p. 338. The statement was made by Luther in his *Schrift an die Ratsherren aller Städte Deutschlands.* Happy days when music and the other branches of low mathematics were deemed sufficient for education.

73. One said in German, "To count like Adam Riese"! Simple people would even give the name Riese to a mathematician. The same thing happened at the end of the seventeenth century in France apropos of Barrême and in England apropos of Cocker. Bertrand François Barrême (1640-1703) of Lyon wrote a *Livre des comptes faits* (1682), hence the common word *barrême* or rather *barème* for such a book or for a good accountant. As to Edward Cocker (1631-75), he was a teacher of penmanship and arithmetic in London. *Cocker's arithmetic, being a plain and easy method* (1678) was reprinted more than a hundred times. One would say "according to Cocker" to mean good arithmetic. The same man published *Cocker's decimal arithmetic, His artificial arithmetic or logarithms, His algebraical arithmetic or equations* (in 3 parts; 1684-85). Article in *DNB 11,* 193-95 (1887).

74. This Portuguese text was one of the few arithmetical texts overlooked by D. E. Smith. Bertha M. Frick: "The first Portuguese arithmetic," *Scripta Mathematica 11,* 327-39 (1945; i.e., 1946), with full bibliography.

NOTES

NOTES

NOTES

NOTES

NOTES

NOTES

NOTES

151—159

75. Pedro Nuñez (1492-1577) is famous for his investigations of a curve of double curvature, the *linea rhombica*, which cuts all the meridians under the same angle. Later Willebrord Snel (1591-1626) called it loxodrome; Jacob Bernoulli (1654-1705) applied the integral calculus to its study (1691). The organ of Portuguese historians of science is entitled *Petrus Nonius* in his honor; it began to appear in 1937 (*Horus,* 231).

76. The book was printed twice in Antwerp in the same year 1567: (1) by the heirs of Arnoldo Birckman, (2) by the widow and heirs of Juan Steelsius. J. F. Peeters-Fontainas: *Livres espagnols imprimés aux Pays Bas* (Louvain, 1939), nos. 419, 419bis. A great many books were printed in Spanish in the Netherlands, mainly in Antwerp (Amberes), but also in Amsterdam, Bruxelles (Bruselas), Cambrai, Douay (Douai), Flessingue, Gand (Gante), La Haye (La Haya), Leyde, Liége (Lieja), Louvain (Lovaina), Malines (Malinas), Middelburg, Rotterdam, Ruremonde. Portuguese books were occasionally printed in Amsterdam, not in the other Netherlandish cities.

77. C. M. Waller Zeper: *De oudste interesttafels in Italie, Frankrijk en Nederland* (Amsterdam, 1937—*Isis 36,* 185). This includes a facsimile reprint (92 pp.) of Stevin's Tables. G. Sarton: "S. Stevin," *Isis 21,* 241-303, 30 fig. (1934).

78. Books I-IV out of thirteen (the last seven having been lost very early). This was the first Diophantos text in any vernacular, with the exception of problems translated into Italian by Rafaele Bombelli in his *Algebra* (Bologna: Gio. Rossi, 1572). It was made freely from the Latin text given by Xylander (Basel: E. Episcopius, 1575). I have not dealt with Diophantos (III-2) in this book because that would have sidetracked me. The Greek princeps of Diophantos was published only in Paris, 1621, by Bachet de Méziriac.

79. The facsimile of the French *Disme* is included in Sarton: "The first explanation of decimal fractions and measures," *Isis 23,* 153-244, 30 fig. (1935).

80. His classification was not like our own. To put it in our own language, he classified the equations according to the numbers of different terms which they contained; thus he recognized 13 kinds of cubic equations. The modern classification of equations based upon the top degree of the unknown quantity was invented by Stevin (1585) and completed by Descartes (1637).

81. Also called Abraham Savasorda, for whom see Martin Levey, *Isis 43,* 257-64 (1952); *Osiris 11,* 50-64 (1954).

82. Stevin was already 35 when he matriculated at the University of Leiden. His early education was probably insufficient; he was an autodidact of genius. His best language was Flemish (Dutch), then French; it is probable that his knowledge of Latin remained inadequate; he knew no Greek.

83. When one studies the history of Greek mathematics, one reference to Stevin suffices, while references to Viète obtrude repeatedly.

84. Viète: *Deschiffrement d'une lettre écriste par le commandeur Morco au roy d'Espaigne du 25 octobre 1589* (14 pp.; Tours: Jamet-Métayer, 1590). His *Traité pour déchiffrer les écritures secrètes* was also printed by Mettayer, but is lost. The art of writing messages in cipher and the art of decoding such messages are both very ancient. Their progress was parallel as was (and is) the progress of arms and armor, means of attack and means of defense. Many diplomats and soldiers of the Renaissance used ciphers, and various treatises were devoted to the subject. The first to be printed was the *Polygraphia* of Joannes Trithemius (Oppenheim, 1518), who died in 1516. A more elaborate book of his, the *Steganographia,* appeared in Lyon, 1531. Both works were often reprinted; the *Polygraphia* was translated into French by Gabriel de Collange (Paris, 1561). Other treatises were published by the

160—174

Italians, Girolamo Cardano and Giov. Batt. della Porta, and by the Frenchman, Blaise de Vigenère. Viète must have known some of these treatises, if not all of them.

85. James Hume was a Scot established in France, author of many mathematical books in Latin and (like this one) in French. He was the son of the historian, David Hume (1560?-1630?).

86. The original Sanskrit name of the sine was *jīva* or *jyā* (bowstring); in Arabic this was changed to *jaib* (there is no *v* sound in Arabic), meaning any kind of opening, as a pocket in one's outside garment, a cleft or hollow. *Jaib* was translated into Latin *sinus*, a word which has the same variety of meanings. For the Sūrya-Siddhānta see *Introd. 1*, 386-88.

87. Modern edition by Axel Anthon Björnbo (Leipzig: Teubner, 1907). For the continuation of the edition of Werner's works see *Isis 2*, 205.

88. It was printed together with the *Sphaerica* of Abraham Scultetus (1566-1625).

89. Vesalius' *Fabrica* was published in Basel in the same year, 1543, which is thus the birthyear of the new anatomy as well as of the heliocentric astronomy. Copernicus' book was the first to appear. It was printed by Joh. Petreius in Nürnberg during the winter 1542/43, and Copernicus received a copy of it on the day of his death (May 24, 1543). The *Fabrica* was published by Joh. Oporinus in Basel in June 1543. The two dates are very close.

90. The works of Tycho Brahe (1546-1601) can be consulted in the best manner in the exemplary edition by John Louis Emil Dreyer (1852-1926) in 15 vols. (Copenhagen, 1913-29). For Dreyer, see *Isis 21*, 131-44 (1934).

91. Klebs 718.1. *Osiris 5*, 114, 161. Page 161 reproduces the title page which is a long table of contents. The early printers often did that and hence the contents of many books can be known before opening them; or they printed on the title a general statement comparable to the statements which modern printers put on the jacket. A good example of that is the statement on the cover of Copernicus' book (1543) ending with an invitation to buy and read it and avail oneself of it: "Igitur eme, lege, fruere."

92. First printed by Dino in Florence, 1481, then by Pacini in the same city in 1497, and by Ugoletus in Parma, 1497? (Klebs 271.1-3) There are thus *four* incunabula editions.

93. Klebs, p. 282, not numbered by him. *Osiris 5*, 188, 193, 223. Correction of the error by Bertha Frick in *Isis 30*, 510. In the second edition of the *Margarita* (Johann Schott: Strasbourg, 1504) the author's name is revealed in a poem dated 1496. This caused the belief in the existence of an incunabula edition, "Heidelberg, 3 kal. Jan. 1496."

94. Giovanni Paolo Gallucci of Salo (Lago di Garda) (1538-1621?). Author of many mathematical and astronomical books.

95. Guido Zaccagnini: *B. Baldi nella vita e nelle opere* (2da ediz., 373 pp.; Pistoia, 1908). The mathematical writings are very poorly dealt with.

96. *The Bullettino di bibliografia e di storia delle scienze mathematiche e fisiche* edited and published by Baldassare Boncompagni (1821-94) was the first great journal on the history of science (20 vols., folio; Roma, 1868-87; *Horus, 208*). Long extracts of Baldi's *Vite* were published with copious annotations in the *Bullettino 5*, 427; *7*, 337; *12*, 420; *19*, 335, 437, 521; *20*, 197.

97. *Isis 1*, 256; *4*, 39.

EPILOGUE

1. Quoted from my *Introd. 3*, 1204, where more details may be found.
2. For the Collège de Saint Côme, see *Introd. 3*, 863-65. The guild was the medieval form of a trade union; it united men engaged in the same pursuits (in this case, surgery) for mutual aid and for protection against outsiders. For medieval guilds in general, see *Introd 3*, 152, 325; those guilds continued during the Renaissance and later; there are still vestigial remains of them today, e.g., the livery companies of London.
3. Religious wars between Christians, mind you. Different kinds of Christians hated each other so much that it was impossible to unite them against the common enemy, the Muslim Turks, who were frightening Europe. The naval victory of Lepanto (1571) won by the Christian League (Papacy, Venice, Spain, Genoa) could not be fully exploited because of jealousy between the Catholic nations. Religious fanaticism bred unbelief. See Lucien Febvre: *Le problème de l'incroyance au XVIe siècle. La religion de Rabelais* (Paris: Michel, 1942).
4. This, in spite of the facts that many Arabic, Persian, and Turkish scholars flourished in the West, that such a collection as the *Bibliothèque orientale* of Barthélemy d'Herbelot was published (first ed.; Paris, 1697; four larger ones in the eighteenth century), and that Chinese reports began to arrive. All these things were considered interesting but exotic and somewhat irrelevant. When one spoke of culture, classical culture was meant, no other.
5. For the *Vulgate*, and its importance in the Latin humanities, see *Introd. 1*, 363, 486; *2*, 554; *3*, 330, 1321.
6. For a good, if prolix, account of this, see Raymond Schwab: *La renaissance orientale* (Paris: Payot, 1950). The same has written *La vie d'Anquetil-Duperron* (Paris: Leroux, 1934). See also Sarton: "Anquetil-Duperron, 1731-1805," *Osiris 3*, 193-223, 11 fig.
7. A deep knowledge of Latin and if possible of Greek was an essential qualification for high offices of state or church and for diplomatic preferment. When people applied for such positions, one did not investigate the purity of their manners so much as the purity of their Latin.

GENERAL BIBLIOGRAPHY AND
KEY TO ABBREVIATIONS

Indications such as (III-2 B.C.) or (II-1) after a name mean two things: (1) the man flourished in the second half of the third century before Christ or in the first half of the second century; (2) he is dealt with in my *Introduction*.

Baudrier   Baudrier, Henri Louis B. (1815-84), and Julien Baudrier (d. 1915). *Bibliographie lyonnaise*. 12 vols. Lyon, 1895-1921. Tables by Georges Tricou (Genève: Droz, 1950).

BL   *Biographisches Lexikon der hervorragenden Aerzte.* 2nd ed. 5 vols. and suppl. Berlin und Wien: Urban und Schwarzenberg, 1929-35.

Choulant   Choulant, Johann Ludwig. *Handbuch der Bücherkunde für die ältere Medizin.* 2nd ed. 456 pp. Leipzig: Leopold Voss, 1841. Anastatic reprint, 1911.

Fulton   Fulton, John Farquhar. *The great medical bibliographers.* 122 pp. Philadelphia: University of Pennsylvania Press, 1951.

Isis   *Isis. International review devoted to the history of science and civilization.* Founded and edited by George Sarton. 43 vols., 1913-52. Now published by the History of Science Society, Cambridge, Mass. (Vol. 46 in 1955).

Klebs   Klebs, Arnold Carl. "Incunabula scientifica et medica," *Osiris 4,* 1-359. Bruges, 1938.

Osiris   *Osiris. Commentationes de scientiarum et eruditionis historia rationeque.* Edidit Georgius Sarton. 11 vols. Bruges: The Saint Catherine Press, 1936-54.

Sandys   Sandys, Sir John Edwin (1844-1922). *History of classical scholarship*. Vol. 1, 3rd ed., Cambridge University Press, 1921. Vol. 2, Cambridge University Press, 1908.

History of science   Sarton, George. *A history of science*. Vol. 1, 646 pp. Cambridge, Mass.: Harvard University Press, 1952. This volume deals with ancient science down to the end of the fourth century B.C.

Horus   ———. *A guide to the history of science*. 334 pp. Waltham, Mass.: Chronica Botanica Co., 1952.

Introd.   ———. *Introduction to the history of science*. 3 vols. in 5. Baltimore: Williams and Wilkins, 1927-48.

———. "Simon Stevin of Bruges," *Isis 21*, 241-303 (1934); and "The first explanation of decimal fractions and measures (1585). Together with a history of the decimal idea," *Isis 23*, 153-244 (1935). 52 fig., 30 pp. facs.

———. "The scientific literature transmitted through the incunabula," *Osiris 5*, 41-245. 60 facs. Bruges, 1938.

STC   *Short-title catalogue of books printed in England, Scotland, and Ireland, and of English books printed abroad, 1475-1640*. Compiled by A. W. Pollard and G. R. Redgrave. 625 pp., quarto. London: Bibliographic Society, 1926.

A new edition, which will include a large number of new items, is being prepared by William Alexander Jackson of the Houghton Library, Harvard University. Thanks to his courtesy, I was able to consult the MS.

Smith, David Eugene. *Rara arithmetica; a catalogue of the arithmetics written before the year MDCI*. 523 pp. Boston: Ginn and Co., 1908. *Addenda*. 62 pp. Boston: Ginn and Co., 1939.

INDEX

The names of Renaissance printers have been indexed only when some information was given about them, other than the printing of a definite book. A list of sixteenth-century printers was given by Lynn Thorndike: *History of Magic* (New York: Columbia University Press, 1941), Vol. 6, pp. 603-12.

Design by Guenther K. Wehrhan—Composition and printing by the Kutztown Publishing Company, Kutztown, Pa.—Binding by Arnold Bindery, Reading, Pa.

This book was set in Baskerville with Bodoni Modern display type and printed letterpress on basis 45 Warren's "1854" supplied by the Schuylkill Paper Co., Philadelphia. The binding is a basis 70 Blue Kilmory Text printed by offset in black ink over 80 point binder's board. The line illustrations and type ornaments were drawn by Guenther K. Wehrhan.

The binding design is taken from a black and white marble mosaic of the fifteenth century from a mosque in Cairo. It is now in the University Museum of the University of Pennsylvania.